FIFTY YEARS OF **FARM TRACTORS**

The 8–16hp International Junior with a mid-mounted radiator and chain-driven rear wheels was built in America between 1917 and 1922. The sloping bonnet would not look out of place on tractors made in 1999.

FIFTY YEARS OF **FARM TRACTORS**

Brian Bell MBE

FARMING PRESS

First published 1999

Copyright Brian Bell 1999
1 3 5 7 9 10 8 6 4 2

ISBN 0 85236 525 X

A catalogue record for this book is available from the British Library

Published by Farming Press,
Miller Freeman UK Ltd,
2 Wharfedale Road, Ipswich IP1 4LG, United Kingdom

Distributed in North America by Diamond Farm Enterprises,
Box 537, Bailey Settlement Road, Alexandria Bay, NY 13607, USA

Cover Design by Mark Ruggles
Printed and bound in Great Britain by Bath Press

CONTENTS

ACKNOWLEDGEMENTS

My thanks are due to many people and companies who have provided information and illustrations for this book. Particular thanks are due to Arthur Batelle, Toon Boer and family, John Briscoe (AGCO), Alan Clark, Ivan Clarke, Mike Clarke and Alun Scott (Renault Agriculture), Richard Clarke, Dick Davidson (Motokov UK), Gordon Day (John Deere), Graham Edwards (HST), Bert Niks, Bruce Dawson and Peter Wheeler (Lely), Steve Mitchell, Frank Moore, Doug Potts, Martin Richards (IMT Southern), Laurence Rooke (Claas UK), Andrew Scarlett, Mervyn Spokes (UMO Belarus) and Dennis Watson.

INTRODUCTION

'Fifty Years of Farm Tractors' traces the changes in farm tractor design since the end of World War Two when Harry Ferguson's tractor hydraulic system sparked off a revolution in power farming. However, many tractors made in the 1930s gave sterling service during the immediate post-war years and they are also included in this book.

The second half of the twentieth century has seen a revolution in farm power. Even 50 years ago it was not unusual to see a threshing contractor with his steam traction engine hauling a drum and elevator from farm to farm during the winter months. Horses were still a major source of power and the farm tractor was little more than a mechanical horse. It had a drawbar to pull many different trailed implements, probably a belt pulley for driving a hammer mill, a baler or chaff cutter and perhaps a power take-off shaft to drive a self-binder or potato digger.

In the early 1930s there were approximately 30,000 tractors working on British farms but the number had risen to just over 261,000 tractors by 1948. Although there are fewer farms and farm workers in 1999 compared with 50 years ago, the tractor population in Britain is now well in excess of 500,000 with more tractors than drivers on many farms.

The average power output of farm tractors in the late 1940s when there were many holdings with fewer than 20 acres was 25hp. Small ride-on tractors were beginning to replace the only horse on these smallholdings and in recognition of their contribution to the mechanisation of small farms they have been included in this book.

The UK tractor population had reached the 360,000 mark in 1960 and although most of the big names in the tractor world were still in business some were destined to disappear within the next 20 years. Average tractor power in the late 1970s was approaching 65hp with 45–95hp models accounting for more than 90 per cent of total sales. Four-wheel drive tractors were gaining popularity and the major manufacturers, who were building their own four-wheel drive models by the late 1970s, curtailed the activities of County and Roadless Traction.

More than half of the new tractors sold to British farmers in 1985 had four-wheel drive and a similar proportion were in the 80–100hp bracket. The change to four-wheel drive increased rapidly and 85 per cent of new tractors over 40hp sold in the early 1990s had four-wheel drive. There were 19,784 new tractors registered in 1996 and figures for 1997 indicated an average tractor power close to 110hp. The major tractor companies produced two or three different models in the early 1950s which generally met the farmer's needs but within a few years the decline in the number of farm workers led to a demand for a much wider choice of tractor size and power. In-cab computers gradually took control of many of the operational functions which had previously been the driver's responsibility. Massey Ferguson, SAME and Fendt were among the first to introduce wheelslip control systems in 1990. The early 1990s also saw the arrival of computerised monitoring systems to pre-set tractor performance levels and record the results.

Some famous names in the tractor world have disappeared since the mid-1970s while others have merged to form worldwide organisations. By 1997 there were five major manufacturing groups: the AGCO organisation which includes Fendt, Massey Ferguson and White, the Case IH/Steyr organisation and John Deere were the big three in America and SAME Lamborghini Deutz-Fahr group and New Holland-Ford-Fiat were the major producers in Western Europe.

Where possible engine horse power relates to Din brake hp but in earlier days manufacturers' literature often quoted SAE or gross brake hp and that will always be higher than the Din rating for the same engine.

Where registered trade names are given they have only been used to identify the particular system or machine. Dates and periods of production are mainly taken from manufacturers' literature and even here conflicting information can be found. In some circumstances stockpiled tractors were sold for considerable periods after production ceased and in other cases new models were introduced to the farming public many months before they went into quantity production.

EARLY DAYS

The first petrol-engined motor car was built in America in 1885 and it is generally accepted that an internal combustion-engined tractor was made there in 1889 – the British made Hornsby-Ackroyd oil-engined tractor did not appear until 1897. Early oil-engined tractors, especially those made in North America, looked like and weighed almost as much as a steam engine. They were well suited to belt work but were rather too heavy for many field operations.

Several British engineers, including Dan Albone and H.P. Saunderson, were developing smaller and more manoeuvrable oil-engined tractors at the turn of the century. Dan Albone, who owned a bicycle repair business at Biggleswade, decided to build a lighter and more compact tractor which could take over from horses. The first tricycle-wheeled Ivel, named after a Bedfordshire river, was demonstrated to farmers in 1902 and Albone formed a new company called Ivel Agricultural Motors to build his new tractor. It had a forward and reverse gear and the driver's seat was conveniently placed, at least in the winter, by the side of a 30 gallon water tank which cooled the 22hp twin-cylinder horizontally-opposed engine. The 1908 Saunderson Model F also made at Bedford had a 2 cylinder paraffin engine, a 3 forward and reverse gearbox and a top speed of 6mph.

1. The Mogul 8-16 was made at the International Tractor works at Chicago between 1915 and 1917.

Marshalls of Gainsborough, Albone with his Ivel, and Saunderson were some of the more important tractor makers in the early years of the twentieth century when Britain was the world's leading tractor exporter. The history of Case, John Deere, International Harvester, Massey-Harris and others who were making tractors in America and Canada can be traced back to the pioneering days of the 1890s.

International Harvester, formed by the merger of several harvest machinery manufacturers in 1902, made their first tractor in 1906. The steam engine lookalike 20hp Mogul launched in 1909 and the Titan which followed in 1910 had chain-driven rear wheels. About 3,000 Moguls and Titans were among a large number of tractors imported from America during World War One by the British Ministry of Munitions in order to boost food production.

The farm tractors of the time were little more than mechanical horses used to pull implements and their steel wheels limited the top speed to a few miles per hour. A belt pulley, inherited from the steam engine to drive threshing machines and other stationary farmyard equipment, was usually a standard item. The period between the two world wars saw the introduction of the power take-off shaft on the International Harvester 8-16 in 1918, a mechanical power lift in 1928, and the the first tractor with a full diesel engine, the Caterpillar 65 Crawler, introduced in 1931. An Allis Chalmers Model U sold in 1932 was the first tractor with low-pressure pneumatic tyres and the Minneapolis Moline UDLX Comfort Tractor of 1938 was the first to have an enclosed cab with a radio, heater and windscreen wiper.

The Fordson Model F was the world's first mass-produced tractor. It was made in America from 1917 and within a couple of years about 7,000 were in use on British farms but they were still hopelessly outnumbered by working horses. Fordson tractors date back to 1907 when Henry Ford made his first tractor with a

2. The Fordson Model F was built in America from 1917 to 1929 and at Cork in Ireland between 1919 and 1922.

collection of car and farm implement components. Several experimental models were built over a ten-year period; some had Henry Ford & Son name plates but later versions were Fordsons. The Model F made at Dearborn in America had a 4 cylinder side valve engine with trembler coil ignition and a water bath air cleaner. It developed 23hp when running on petrol and 20hp on paraffin. Trembler coil ignition was also used for early Ford cars but it was not very reliable in cold weather. The electric current was generated by a system of magnets on the flywheel which rotated close to a series of fixed primary coils. The current was passed to the trembler coils which increased the voltage and delivered it to the sparking plugs. The moving parts splashed oil around the engine cylinder block and the big end bearings were lubricated by small scoops on the bearing caps. Failure to maintain the correct oil level in the sump was asking for trouble and standing the tractor on a slope with the engine running could starve the front or back big end and main bearings of oil. The white metal bearings would then run dry and overheat or even melt if the engine was left running for any length of time. The multi-plate clutch immersed in oil also served as a brake and the 3 forward and reverse gears transmitted power through worm and wheel reduction gears to the steel wheels.

The Model F was made until 1929 when it was replaced by the Fordson N. It was made in Ireland until production moved to the new Fordson factory at Dagenham in 1932. The Model N, still with a water bath air cleaner, was painted blue. In 1937 the colour changed to orange and from 1939 the tractors were green, probably in an attempt to provide camouflage during the war years. There were four versions of the model N. The standard tractor had steel wheels, the land utility had pneumatic tyres and the range was completed by an industrial version and the tricycle-wheeled rowcrop model. The N was probably better known as the Fordson Standard which originated from the standard version on steel wheels. The model N cost £156 in 1931

3. The tricycle-wheeled rowcrop Fordson Model N was popular in America but very few were sold in Britain.

but this was reduced by £21 in 1936 to encourage sales during the years of depression. The lower priced Model N with cleated steel rear wheels was cheaper than a team of three horses and with a ploughing rate of half an acre in an hour it could do the work of eight horses.

Jerome Increase Case made a crude threshing machine in 1842 and by 1886 Case were the largest manufacturer of steam engines worldwide. J.I. Case of Racine, Wisconsin, made their first tractor in 1892 and an improved model appeared in 1895 but little more was heard of Case tractors until 1913. Early models included the 2 cylinder Case 12-25 and the 4 cylinder 10-20; the 12-20 was one of four transverse-engined tractors. The J.I. Case Co introduced the Model L in 1929 and later the Model C and the rowcrop Model CC.

4. The Massey-Harris General Purpose tractor introduced in 1930 was one of the first practical designs of a four-wheel drive tractor.

Tractor makers were already experimenting with four-wheel drive and tracklayers in the early 1900s. The Moline Universal of 1914 was the first rear-wheel steered articulated tractor. Massey-Harris introduced the 25hp four-wheel drive General Purpose tractor in 1930. It was made for six years and had 2 forward gears and reverse and a pivoting rear axle to give improved traction on uneven ground.

5. The Case 12-20 had a transverse engine. This one caused its owner a few problems during the grand parade of vintage tractors in the show

Crawler tractor development owed much to the military tank. Holt and Best, who eventually merged to form the Caterpillar Tractor Co, were two of the leading tracklayer makers in America by 1910. Clayton and Shuttleworth, who already held a similar position in Britain, introduced a crawler with clutch and brake steering in 1918 and ten years later International Harvester Co entered the American crawler market with the 10-20 TracTracTor.

Although diesel engines were in limited use by the early 1900s they were not used for farm tractors until the mid-1920s. Garretts of Leiston, famed for their steam engines, were making diesel-engined tractors by 1930 but the most progress in this field was made by Lanz in Germany who produced their single-cylinder two-stroke Bulldog tractors with a semi-diesel or hot bulb engine.

6. Lanz made the Bulldog at Mannheim in Germany from 1921. This tractor was used to pull a 1936 Case Model Q peg drum harvest thresher.

Farmers were giving serious thought to buying a tractor by the mid-1930s when an expert of the day suggested that other than in exceptional circumstances it should not exceed 15hp at the drawbar. For those who probably did not understand the significance of drawbar horse power they were advised that a 20 drawbar hp tractor should be able to plough about an acre per hour on stiff land when pulling four 12 inch wide furrows 5 to 6 inches deep at 3mph. This was quite a feat but in those days the only compaction suffered by farm land was that caused by horses' hooves and the farmer's boots.

Petrol/paraffin (or kerosene)-engined tractors were being made in the early 1900s but two-stroke diesel or four-stroke petrol engine tractors were generally preferred until the relatively inexpensive tractor vaporising oil (tvo) became widely available in the 1930s. Tvo-engined tractors were then used on most farms until the four-stroke diesel engine took over in the early 1950s.

Charles Anthony Vanderville founded an engineering business in Britain in the early 1890s. The company, which became CAV, was making diesel fuel injection equipment in 1932. Perkins at Peterborough were using CAV fuel pumps and injectors for diesel engines from the mid-1930s. Some forward-looking farmers bought these engines to convert their Fordson Model N tractors to diesel power. Simms Motor Units Ltd of Finchley, London, (who also made

7. The Howard DH 22 was made in Australia from 1922. Originally designed for use with the Howard Rotavator it was equally suitable for other field work.

8. Steering brakes, operated by a system of cables linked to the steering mechanism, were a feature of McCormick Deering Farmall tractors made in the late 1920s.

fuel injection equipment) were CAV's main British competitor for many years but they joined CAV in 1968 and the new company operated from the CAV factory at Acton in London.

The 1928 Howard DH 22 had a 22hp 4 cylinder water-cooled overhead valve petrol/paraffin engine, 5 forward gears and reverse, and a power take-off shaft mainly used to drive the Howard Rotavator. Pneumatic tyres and power lift were optional extras on later models of the tractor.

International Harvester were making rowcrop, ploughing, orchard, industrial and fairway tractors in the 1930s. All five variants of some International Harvester models were made. The same 4 cylinder 15–17hp petrol/vaporising oil engine and similar transmissions were used on the Farmall F 14 rowcrop version, the McCormick Deering W-14 plow tractor, the I-14 industrial, the O-14 orchard and the F-14 Fairway (turf) models.

Cultivating between rowcrops was much easier when using a tractor with independent steering brakes. Standard on most tractors made from 1946, this luxury was already in use on some Farmall tractors by the late 1920s. The McCormick Deering independent brakes were operated by a cable system from the steering linkage. When the steering wheel was turned the cable applied one of the brakes which enabled the driver to make sharp turns on the headland.

The WD-40, introduced in 1934, was the first International Harvester diesel tractor but it was started on petrol with a cranking handle and only switched to diesel mode when warm. There were separate inlet valves for petrol and diesel operation and a hand lever was used to reduce the compression ratio to 6:1 for starting. When the engine was warm, the lever was used to isolate the inlet valve on the petrol side of the engine and this increased the compression ratio to 14:1 for diesel operation. The engine had a carburettor and magneto on one side of the cylinder block while the diesel injection pump and injectors were on the opposite side.

Although John Deere made a tractor in 1892 they did little else in the tractor field until 1918 when they bought the Waterloo Gasoline Tractor Co and manufactured the Waterloo Boy Model N until 1923. Two-cylinder air-cooled petrol engines provided the power for John Deere wheeled tractors until the late 1950s after the first diesel tractor with the leaping deer badge appeared in 1949.

9. The first John Deere with tricycle front wheels arrived in East Anglia under the American lease-lend scheme at the end of World War Two.

There were approximately 30,000 tractors at work on British farms in the early 1930s. Annual production of farm tractors in Britain had reached the 18,000 mark by 1937 when at least one third were exported. Most tractor manufacturers turned to armament production during the war years but Fordsons were produced in considerable numbers throughout this period. Roadless Traction's war effort included the conversion of the Fordson Model N for the Air Ministry. The tractor was supplied with rubber-jointed full tracks and an extended fore-carriage which not only turned it into a half-track but also added stability on tractors fitted with a front-mounted crane or winch.

A number of new manufacturers appeared in the immediate post-war period and 58,000 farm tractors and 27,600 market garden machines were made in 1947. The 1948 Agricultural Machinery Census recorded that a total of 261,180 tractors, including 14,800 tracklayers, were being used on British farms and the working horse population had dropped from 724,000 in 1939 to 517,000 in 1948. The influence of American tractors was still strong in Britain but David Brown, Ferguson, Fordson Marshall and Nuffield were gaining ground in a market where demand still exceeded supply.

Running costs of farm tractors have always been of interest to those who have to pay the bills. Figures covering the period 1919–1928 indicated that the average cost of running a tractor was £85.5s.5d per year or 2s.7d (12½p) per hour of use. Another set of statistics on the full operating costs of a tractor, written off over a ten-year period, gave an hourly figure of 3s. 3½d (16½p) per hour. This was made up from depreciation costs of 7¾d (3p), repairs and overhauls of 5¼d (2½p), fuel at 1s.6d (7½p) and 8.5d (3½p) for labour.

ALLIS-CHALMERS

The Allis-Chalmers Manufacturing Co was formed in 1901 when the American company Fraser and Chalmers went into business with a steam engine manufacturer named Edwin Allis. The steel wheeled 10-18 made at Milwaukee, Wisconsin, in 1914 with an opposed twin-cylinder engine which developed 10 drawbar hp and 18hp at the belt pulley was the first Allis-Chalmers farm tractor. Other medium-powered models, including the United tractor first made in 1929 for the United Tractor & Equipment Co of Chicago, were introduced in the 1920s. When this company went out of business in 1932 the United tractor with Continental side-valve engine became the Model U, which remained in production until 1950. Allis-Chalmers used their own overhead-valve 4 cylinder petrol/paraffin engine for the 28–34hp Model U which had the distinction of being the first tractor to have pneumatic tyres. It had a 4 forward speed and reverse gearbox and a hand-lever operated band brake. Electric starting and lights were available at extra cost from the mid-1940s. Variants included the tricycle front wheel Allis-Chalmers Allcrop, later known as the Model UC rowcrop tractor. 'Hot-rod' versions of the Model U were used in America for speed trials and tractor races.

The 50hp four-plow capacity Model A was made between 1936 and 1941 and the popular Allis-Chalmers Model B was introduced to American farmers in 1937. By the mid-1940s the Allis-Chalmers tractor range included the Model B, C, U, WF and the tricycle-wheeled rowcrop WC. The first Model Bs had a Waukesha petrol/paraffin engine and a fixed front axle but this was soon changed to an Allis-Chalmers over-head valve engine and an adjustable front axle.

The Model B was not available in the UK between 1942 and 1947 when the first British-built Allis-Chalmers tractors were made at Totton near Southampton. Production peaked at about 1,000 tractors per year when

This streamlined Tractor has everything to make it complete for every kind of job. Rear wheel centres from 53 in. to 74 in. in steps of 3 in., making it particularly suitable for all row-crop cultivations—tool-bar frame beneath the tractor, fitted with ridging bodies, enabling it to draw out and split potato rows—the same tool-bar frame can be fitted with grubbing tines or hoe blades. Hydraulic lift for implements—easy steering—three forward speeds—a gear for every purpose and many other advantages.

10. Introduced in 1940, the 16hp Allis-Chalmers Model C on steel wheels and advertised as a 'two-row rowcrop tractor' was produced for ten years.

manufacture moved to Essendine in Lincolnshire. The Model B had a 22hp 4 cylinder, overhead valve vaporising oil engine, 3 forward gears and reverse, independent brakes and adjustable wheel track. High ground clearance and narrow transmission housing made the Allis-Chalmers B with a hand-lever operated mid- or rear-mounted tool bar an ideal tractor for rowcrop work. Advertised as 'the tractor with a two-minute tool bar' it was claimed that the tool bar could be wheeled into position and attached or removed very quickly by one person without the need for spanners.

Lawrence Edwards & Co of Kidderminster introduced the Hingley three-point linkage conversion kit with an adjustable top link for the Model B tool bar in 1949. The £25 kit may well have prompted Allis-Chalmers

11

to produce their own three-point linkage –
an optional extra in 1951 when the
basic tractor without an electric starter,
power take-off or belt pulley cost £335.
Some Model B tractors made from
1954 had a Perkins P3 diesel engine
and 4 forward gears.

The Model B vaporising oil engine
and four-speed transmission were
retained on the D 270 which superseded
the B in 1955. With a vaporising oil
engine the D 270 cost £440, while the
same tractor with a Perkins P3 diesel
engine was £570.

A 30hp petrol engine, 26hp
vaporising oil engine or a 31hp Perkins
P3 diesel were the options for the
Allis-Chalmers D272 made at Essendine
from 1957 to 1960. The basic price
excluded electric starting, belt pulley,
live hydraulic linkage and power
take-off but an electric starter was

*11. Sales literature for the American Allis-Chalmers Model G rowcrop
tractor made between 1948 and 1955 explained that its 4 cylinder
engine produced enough power 'to operate a 12 inch moldboard
plow at speeds of up to 3mph in average soils at customary plowing
depths'.*

included in the standard price of £514 for the diesel model. Power-adjusted rear wheels, full road lights, a
factory-installed radiator shutter and wheel weights were included in an extensive list of optional extras.

The ED 40 announced in 1960 was described in sales literature as 'Today's finest all-duty tractor ...
Handsome! ... Versatile! ... and Economical!' But this 37hp diesel-engined tractor made until 1968 was the last

12. The 19¹/₂ belt hp and 16 drawbar hp Allis-Chalmers Model B had a top speed of 8mph.

Allis-Chalmers model manufactured in Britain. The live category I hydraulic system, with an optional category II conversion kit, was supplied with oil from an engine-mounted pump. The new selective weight transfer system was claimed to minimise wheelslip even in the worst possible conditions. Engine power was increased to 41hp in 1963 when the improved Depthomatic hydraulic system replaced the earlier weight transfer system.

Production of Allis-Chalmers wheeled tractors continued in America. The 100hp barrier was breached in 1963 with the launch of the 107hp two-wheel drive D21 and a turbocharged model put it past the 130hp mark in 1965. Ten years later Allis-Chalmers were still making a range of 40hp-plus wheeled tractors in America but the flagship 200hp four-wheel drive with a Cummins V8 engine was made for them by the Steiger Tractor Co of Fargo, North Dakota.

Allis-Chalmers' interest in crawler tractors began in 1928 with the purchase of the Monarch Tractor Co of Illinois. The 31 drawbar hp Allis-Chalmers Model M tracklayer, based on the Model U wheeled tractor and made between 1933 and 1942, had a steering wheel instead of the more conventional levers to control the steering clutches. The HD series crawlers launched in 1940 and made for about ten years included the HD 7, HD

13. The Allis-Chalmers D 270 and succeeding models had an unusual live power take-off. A hand lever, which controlled a clutch on the right-hand half-shaft, was used to disconnect the drive to the rear wheel. This stopped forward travel without disengaging the drive to the power shaft.

10 and HD 14 with super-charged General Motors 3, 4 and 6 cylinder two-stroke diesel engines. A number of Allis-Chalmers HD crawlers were imported by the British War Agricultural Committee under the wartime lease-lend programme. In performance tests held in Nebraska the HD7, described as a 6–8 14 inch plow (furrow) tractor, recorded 57 drawbar hp while the 8–12 plow HD 10 developed 82 drawbar hp. The HD 14, mainly used by the construction industry, recorded 127 drawbar hp.

The HD 5, HD 9 and HD 15, also with two-stroke engines and maximum drawbar hp rated at 40, 72½ and 109 respectively, replaced the previous models in 1951. The HD 5 was a 5 or 6 plow tractor but most HD 9s and HD 15s were more suited to civil engineering and construction work. New crawlers introduced in the late 1950s with four-stroke diesel engines and clutch and brake steering, including the

14. A twin-range gearbox with 8 forward and 2 reverse gears gave the Allis-Chalmers ED40 a top speed of 13mph.

66½hp HD 6, were sold in Britain. The HD 6 cost £3,900 in 1959. The construction equipment division of Allis-Chalmers in America became Fiat-Allis, when K-H-D acquired the farm machinery business in 1985. Fiat-Allis was sold again when the Allis Gleaner Corporation (AGCO) was formed in the early 1990s.

15. The model numbers of the Allis-Chalmers HD 7, HD 10 and HD 14 crawlers were said to indicate how many furrows the tractor could pull. This may have been so in America but didn't necessarily apply to the heavier soils in the UK.

AVELING-MARSHALL

British Leyland Special Products Group adopted the Aveling-Marshall name when they bought the Marshall-Fowler business in 1975 and continued production of Aveling-Marshall crawlers at the Marshall Britannia Works in Gainsborough in Lincolnshire. The Aveling side of the company had started as Aveling & Porter, steam engine manufacturers in the mid-1800s. The road roller manufacturer Aveling-Barford established in 1933 was acquired by Leyland in 1968.

The Track Marshall 56, 75C and 90, now painted buttercup yellow, were all of similar weight and size with 56 inch track centres. The model number indicated engine horse power. The Track Marshall 56 had 6 forward gears and 2 reverse compared with 5 forward and 3 reverse on the Track Marshall 75C and 90. Optional equipment included hydraulic linkage, power take-off and a weather cab. The 125hp 6 cylinder Fowler Challenger 33, which had 6 forward and 4 reverse gears, and was later re-named the AM 140, completed the 1975 crawler range.

Buttercup yellow paint and the Aveling horse symbol were used for the Aveling-Marshall AM100 and AM105 launched in 1975 with a 6 cylinder 100hp Perkins and a 105hp Ford engine respectively. The AM 120

16. The Track Marshall 90 was in production when British Leyland bought Marshall, Sons & Co of Gainsborough in 1975.

with a 6 cylinder Ford engine, a 5 forward and reverse speed gearbox and a single-lever hydraulic steering system was added in 1976. The new tractors had a twin-plate clutch, power take-off, three-point linkage and a quiet cab with optional air conditioning. When Charles Nickerson bought the Aveling-Marshall crawler business from Leyland in 1979 he revived the Track Marshall name and production continued at Gainsborough.

BEAN

Mr Bean designed a self-propelled tool bar for use on his smallholding and a small number of them were made at Blackburn in 1946 before production was transferred to Humberside Agricultural Products at Brough in Yorkshire. This company also manufactured Bean seeder units for drilling root and vegetable crops and other tool bar equipment.

The Bean tool bar had an 8hp Ford industrial engine with electric starting, a Ford 10cwt van rear axle and independent brakes. The four-wheel model cost £295 in 1950, a four-row hoe attachment was £45 and a five-row drill unit cost £68. A

17. Early versions of the Bean self-propelled toolbar had a single front wheel steered with a tiller handle. A four-wheel model, also with tiller steering, was added in 1950.

1950 sales brochure was generous in its praise of Mr Bean's tool bar, claiming that it would 'drill, hoe, top dress or spray six 12 inch rows with a greater degree of accuracy and uniformity than had ever before been attained'. Furthermore it 'would enable a man or a girl to work through four or five acres of rowcrops in a day'. In the 1950s Thomas Green & Sons at Leeds took over the manufacture of the Bean tractor but only until 1959. A new version of the Bean rowcrop tractor with a 3 forward speed and reverse gearbox, inboard hydraulic brakes and tiller arm steering was made in Scotland by Strathallan Engineering in the early 1960s. Various attachments including hoes, seeder units and crop sprayer were made for the underslung tool bar raised and lowered with hydraulic rams.

18. A Petter 16hp twin-cylinder diesel engine was used on Strathallan Engineering's early 1960s version of the Bean tractor.

BELARUS

The Russian Traktoroexport organisation adopted the Belarus name for products made at the Minsk Tractor factory built in 1946 in order to manufacture crawler tractors. The factory workers were given an ambitious output target of 50 tractors per day. The first Belarus MTZ-2 wheeled tractors were introduced in 1953 and within seven years four models of tractor were in production at Minsk.

The 55hp diesel-engined Belarus MTZ-50 and MTZ-52 launched in 1961 were identical apart from the front-wheel drive on the MTZ-52. The MTZ-50X designed for cotton field cultivations and the T-54V narrow gauge crawler for vineyard work were variants of the MTZ-50. The initials MTZ were derived from the Minsk Tractor Zavod (Zavod is Russian for factory) and a figure 2 in the model number denoted four-wheel drive.

The MTZ-50 Super and MTZ-52 Super with a 70hp long stroke diesel engine launched in 1969 were the first Belarus tractors sold in Britain when Satra Motors at Byfleet in Surrey became the Belarus importer in the UK in 1970. Drive to the front axle on the MTZ-52 was engaged automatically when the rear wheels started to slip. Both tractors had 9 forward and 2 reverse gears, power-assisted steering, disc brakes, independent and ground speed power take-off, independent front suspension and 'an extremely comprehensive tool kit'.

Independent front axle suspension was a feature of the Belarus T40 Super and the four-wheel drive T 40A Super with a 50hp air-cooled direct injection diesel engine introduced in 1971 were made at the LTZ Lipetsk Tractor Zavod. Advertisements suggested that the British countryside would make a nice rest for tractors more used to Russian winters and they would ease their way through even the toughest farm work. The claim had apparently been proved by a group of British farmers who accepted a challenge to 'bash the T 40 to destruction' but failed to do so.

Engine output on the MTZ-50 and 52 was increased to 75hp in 1973 and although an extremely thorough pre-delivery inspection was necessary the tractor was sold for the very low price of £1,427.34 plus delivery. A magazine advertisement for the Belarus MTZ-52 which carried the slogan 'More ploughing miles per hour than any other comparable 75hp tractor' asked readers if they could think of another 75hp model available for such a low price.

19. The safety cab with a removable roof was not included in the £1,199 price tag for the Belarus MTZ-52 Super, nor for the even cheaper MTZ-50 two-wheel drive version of the tractor.

16

Tractors were becoming more powerful by the mid-1970s and Belarus followed this trend with the launch of the 90 SAE hp MTZ 80 and MTZ 82 in 1974. The 29hp 2 cylinder air-cooled, two-wheel drive Belarus T25 from the Vladimir Tractor Zavod introduced at the 1974 Smithfield Show was a bi-directional tractor with an unusual 8 forward and 6 reverse speed gearbox. The tractor could be driven equally well in reverse for rowcrop work, harvesting or mechanical handling after re-locating the seat above the battery box, reversing the steering mechanism with a small bevel gearbox and re-arranging the foot pedals. The T25 with Category II linkage, ground speed power take-off and two-door Lambourn quiet cab on rubber mountings cost £2,295 when UMO Belarus, a British subsidiary of the Russian United Machinery Organisation, replaced Satra Belarus in 1976 as the UK distributor of Belarus tractors and machinery.

The Russian-built 300hp Belaz K-710 heavy duty tractor also sold by UMO in the UK during the mid-1970s was a giant tractor with a 12 cylinder diesel engine, a 16 speed gearbox and hydraulic linkage which could pull a 12 furrow plough or a 60 ton load at the drawbar.

A donkey petrol engine with an electric starter was used to start the 4 cylinder diesel engine on the 85hp Belarus DT 75 crawler tractor launched in the early 1970s with track equipment similar to that used on an army tank. Engine power was increased to 90hp in 1975 when the DT75M with clutch and brake steering, hydraulic linkage and a weather cab cost £7,008.

New models were introduced in 1978 and existing tractors were re-designated to bring UK model numbers into line with those used in other countries. The D75M crawler became the 750 and a new wide-tracked version was known as the 750B. A touch of luxury was added in 1980 when an optional Lucas radio was on offer for an extra £74.50. The re-numbering exercise turned the T25 into the Belarus 250 and the MTZ-50, 52, 80 and 82 became the 500, 520, 800 and 820 respectively.

The new 400 and four-wheel drive 420 tractors had a 58hp air-cooled diesel engine, 6 forward speeds and reverse, independent power take-off and quiet cab. The Belarus 420 front-wheel drive engaged automatically when wheelslip exceeded 4 per cent.

20. The Belarus DT 75 M crawler was introduced to British farmers in 1973.

21. A donkey engine with an electric starter motor was used to bring the turbocharged 165 SAE hp V6 engine on the Belarus 1500 into life.

UMO Belarus were aware that tractor drivers had come to expect in-cab entertainment in the late 1970s when they advertised the new V-6 engined Belarus 1500 with a banner headline reading, 'If at £19,978 the 165hp Belarus looks to give you all you will ever need in an articulated tractor ... then for a further £63 (the cost of a Lucas radio) we can make the price sound positively sweet music.' The 1500 gearbox had 3 forward ratios and reverse in each of four hydraulically selected ranges, power steering, category III hydraulics and an air compressor which could be used to inflate the tractor's tyres. A two-seat air-conditioned quiet cab completed the package. The Lucas radio was the only optional extra.

The 400 and 420 were discontinued in 1981 to leave a range of Belarus wheeled tractors from 29 to 165 SAE hp and two models of the 750 crawler on the UK market. Sales competition was intense in the early 1980s and some companies offered free gifts to help sell new tractors. A complimentary seven-day holiday in Russia was on offer to farmers who bought a 50hp-plus Belarus tractor in 1981. Improved 70hp and 90hp D series tractors appeared in 1983. The 560/562D and 860/862D had a similar specification which included live hydraulics, hydrostatic steering, disc brakes, engine and ground speed power take-off and a luxury quiet cab. Farmers wanted a wider gear range on medium-powered tractors and this demand was met with 9 forward and 2 reverse speeds on the 560D/562D and an 18 forward and 4 reverse gearbox with a top speed of 21mph for the 860D/862D.

Belarus launched the 100hp MTZ-100 and made their two millionth tractor in 1984. The 110 SAE hp Belarus 1060 and 1062 were introduced in 1985, and apart from a more powerful turbocharged 110hp engine, they were much the same as the 90hp 860 and 862. The articulated Belarus 1507 was very similar to the 1500 which it replaced in 1986. The six turbocharged cylinders developed 185hp and a 24 volt electric starter replaced the very dated donkey engine starting system used for the Belarus 1500.

The 70hp Belarus 570 and 572 launched in 1988 were direct injection versions of the earlier 560 and 562 but to confuse the issue some late 560/562 models also had this type of engine. The new 60 SAE hp 540/542 with 12 forward and 2 reverse gears was added in 1989 to fill a power gap in the Belarus range. Tractors with the letter H after the model number were equipped with the Scandinavian-designed Belarus Hydrotronic hydraulic linkage control system used for a year or two on some of the 560/562, 860/862 and 1060/1062 tractors sold to British farmers. Apart from the improved 570SB/572SB with 18 forward and 4 reverse speeds the Belarus range was little changed in 1991.

The break-up of the Soviet Union resulted in the UMO name appearing on some Russian-built tractors. Those made at the Minsk factory in the state of Belarus retained the Belarus badge but tractors built at Lipetsk and Vladimir had a new black, red and silver livery and the UMO brand name.

The 1993 Smithfield Show was a busy one for UMO Belarus. The UMO 250/252 and the first of the new Belarus 900 series still with the old orange paintwork were launched alongside improved versions of the 540/542 and the 115hp 1082 in the new colour scheme. The Belarus 1082 had a 24 forward and 8 reverse synchromesh gearbox instead of the earlier powershift transmission, a draft, position and intermix hydraulic system and a flat floor cab. Features of the 34hp UMO 250/252 included an air-cooled 2 cylinder engine, 8 forward and 6 reverse gears and hydrostatic steering.

A revised colour scheme was used for the 130hp Belarus 1221 launched in 1994 with a 6 cylinder

22. The Belarus 862D introduced in 1983 had a standard specification equal to many of its more expensive competitors.

23. The 1025 which replaced the 1082 in 1994 was one of the first tractors made at Minsk with the new Belarus styling and colour scheme.

24. Peter the Great, made in Russia's oldest tractor factory at Kirov near St Petersburg, weighed 16 tons and had a 175 gallon fuel tank.

turbocharged engine, a 16 forward and 8 reverse speed synchronised transmission and electro-hydraulic front-wheel drive engagement.

The 81hp 900/920 and the 93hp 950/952 tractors styled to match the Belarus 1025 were launched in 1995 and the three millionth tractor was made at Minsk in the same year. Features of the 900 series tractors included a synchromesh 14 forward and 4 reverse gearbox, dry disc brakes and a 540/1000rpm power take-off with ground speed.

'Peter the Great' was the largest Russian-built tractor available in the UK when it was introduced to British farmers in 1996. The 184hp articulated tractor and its 257hp big brother had a 16 forward and 8 reverse power shift transmission, category III and IV hydraulic linkage and a 25ft radius turning circle.

The 1997 UMO catalogue listed 24 models, including a 14hp four-wheel drive articulated mini-tractor with a Briggs & Stratton engine, two- and four-wheel drive models in the 60–130hp bracket, articulated four-wheel drive models and the VT 100 crawler. The VT100, from the Volgograd factory. where the DT 75 was made in the late 1960s, had a 4 cylinder turbo-charged diesel engine with two horse power ranges. The injection pump could be adjusted to give a maximum of 150 power take-off hp and 120hp at the drawbar. Other features of the VT 100 included 10 forward and 5 reverse gears and air-assisted brakes and steering.

25. The VT100, with optional rubber, steel-reinforced rubber or steel tracks is the late 1990s version of a long line of Belarus crawlers made at Volgograd.

B.M.B PRESIDENT

Brockhouse Engineering manufactured the B.M.B President at Southport between 1950 and 1956. The specification included a Morris 8/10hp 4 cylinder petrol/paraffin engine, a 3 forward speed and reverse gearbox and spur gear final drive. Brockhouse Engineering were already well known for the two-wheeled B.M.B Hoe-Mate, Cult-Mate and Plow-Mate garden tractors originally made in the 1930s by British Motor Boats of London and later at Banbury. Independent brakes, an adjustable 40–72 inch wheel track, swinging drawbar and a 6 volt electrical system (later changed to 12 volts) were included in the 1951 basic price of £239.10s. Hydraulic linkage, belt pulley and a $1^{1}/_{8}$ inch diameter power take-off were optional extras. The hydraulic unit was bolted on to the side of the tractor and gearbox oil was pumped to external rams which operated a mid-mounted tool frame and three-point linkage. A simple depth-limiting device with two metal blocks fixed to the mid-mounted tool bar and supported by the front axle controlled the working depth of hoe blades or cultivator tines. Screw handles were provided to vary working depth and the pivoting action of the front axle maintained an even depth when working on uneven ground.

A vineyard version appeared in 1954 but sales of the B.M.B President and similar small tractors were in decline and production ceased in 1956. A later version of the B.M.B President tractor made by H.J. Stockton Ltd of London was exhibited at the 1957 Smithfield Show.

26. The B.M.B President with a top speed of 8mph was launched at the 1950 Royal Show.

BRAY

Formed in the early 1900s the Bray Construction Co made loader shovels and dozer blades, mainly for industrial use. Four-wheel drive loaders were added to the product range in the 1950s and the Bray Centaur tractor designed by Essex farm contractor John Suckling was based on a Bray loader shovel skid unit. The four-wheel drive Centaur with a live hydraulic linkage at the front and rear was really a high output self-propelled plough with a hydraulic pump driven from the tractor's 69hp 6 cylinder Ford diesel engine crankshaft. The Centaur, with a 6 speed gearbox and a mechanical forward/reverse shuttle mechanism, went into production in 1959. It had a 5 furrow plough at each end and could plough up and down from one side of a field to the opposite hedge just like the steam-powered balance plough of earlier days. Front-wheel drive was growing in popularity by the early 1960s and the Bray Construction Co, now at Feltham in Middlesex, re-entered the tractor market in 1966 with the equal-size wheel four-wheel drive Bray Four 10/60. It was based on the Nuffield 10/60 with the front wheels driven from a transfer box via a centre prop-shaft to the differential housing and epicyclic reduction units on the front axle.

The Bray Four 4/65 with power-assisted steering, front diff-lock and self-energising disc brakes was launched in 1967. The front-wheel drive arrangement was similar to that used for the Bray Four 10/60. Several major manufacturers were making their own four-wheel drive tractors in the late 1960s but the Leyland 384 was also given the Bray front-wheel drive treatment and it superseded the Nuffield 10/65 in 1969. The Bray Four 384 was the last four-wheel drive conversion made by the Bray Construction Co who moved to Tetbury near Gloucester in 1971. The company was taken over by Matbro in 1973 and the new owners concentrated on the production of mechanical handling equipment.

27. The Bray Four 4/65 introduced in 1967 was based on the 65hp Nuffield 4/65.

BRISTOL

The first Bristol crawler tractor was made at the Douglas motorcycle factory at Bristol in 1933. The tractor, made by the Bristol Tractor Co who had links with Roadless Traction Ltd was less than 3ft wide, weighed about one ton, used a gallon of petrol per hour and, like the more popular Ransomes MG crawler, it was mainly used by smallholders and market gardeners. Power was provided by a twin-cylinder horizontally opposed Douglas engine with a twist grip throttle on the tiller-style steering lever. The Bristol had a 3 forward and a reverse gearbox and power was transmitted through independent differential brakes to 7 inch wide Roadless rubber-jointed tracks. Later models had a 7hp Jowett water-cooled petrol engine or a 10hp Coventry Victor diesel. Production ceased in 1942 and when the Bristol crawler re-appeared in 1945 the company was owned by an Austin car dealer called H.A. Saunders. The tractors were made at Earby in Lancashire and an Austin 10 car engine provided the power.

The new Bristol 20, with a modified low compression 22hp Austin 16 car engine which could run on petrol or paraffin was introduced in 1948. Power was transmitted through a single-plate clutch, 3 forward and reverse gearbox, spur gear final drive and independent foot brakes. The standard model had $29\frac{1}{2}$ inch track centres and a special high-stability model with 44 inch track centres was made for hillside work. The Bristol 20 with a power take-off cost £480 while electric starting was an extra £22.10s.

28. Roadless Traction Ltd designed the rubber-jointed tracks on the Bristol 20.

The Bristol 20 was one of very few tracklayers made in Europe or America in the late 1940s with an optional bolt-on three-point linkage, the cost of which was £47.10s. A 4 cylinder pump constantly driven by the gearbox layshaft supplied the hydraulic system with oil from the transmission housing. The power take-off shaft, which could be used with a belt pulley, was extended through the hydraulic unit on tractors with three-point linkage.

Bristol Tractors' sales literature for 'unit-attached' (mounted) implements explained that when using a plough, cultivator or ridger 'the Bristol 20 could turn on its own axis and the front of the tractor could be driven right up to the hedge before making a headland turn'. The leaflet also pointed out that 'the Bristol has always been the ideal tractor for cultivations – now perfect ploughing has been added to its other virtues'.

A modified 23hp Austin A70 car engine was used for later versions of the Bristol 20 and the same petrol or paraffin engine provided the power for the Bristol 22 introduced in 1952. An optional 23hp Perkins P3 diesel engine was available from 1953. There was a choice of 7 inch or 10 inch wide track plates and adjustment was provided to give track centre settings between 30 and 47 inches. The optional Bristol 20 bolt-on hydraulic linkage could also be used on the Bristol 22 with an extended range of equipment which included single- and two-furrow ploughs, a tool bar, circular saw, post hole digger and a winch.

The Bristol 20 and the 22 became the Bristol 25 in 1956. It had standard pin and bush tracks and there was a special model for forestry work. The Bristol 25 was available with 30 inch, 44 inch and 52 inch track centres, the PC (petrol) and VC (vaporising oil) series had a 23hp Austin A70 and the D series had a Perkins P3 diesel power unit. The basic price with an electric starter ranged from £783 for the PC 30 to £952 for the D 52. Hydraulic linkage was an additional £93.10s.

The more powerful PD series with a 32hp Perkins P3 TA indirect injection engine and Kigass cold starting were the last Bristol crawlers. The PD (Power Diesel) tractors had a hand lever operated single-plate clutch, a 3 forward speed and reverse gearbox, clutch and brake steering and a Dunlopillo upholstered seat with a backrest. There was a choice of 7, 10 or 12 inch wide track plates for the PD 30, 33, 44 and 48, the model number denoting track centre widths in inches.

The Bristol Taurus made from the early 1960s and marketed by Bristol-Saunders at Worcester had a 46hp Perkins direct injection engine, 6 forward and 4 reverse gears, clutch and brake steering and hydraulic track tension adjustment. A 540/1050rpm power take-off, hydraulic linkage and a weather cab were included in the list of extras. Bristol Tractors were bought by Marshall Sons & Co of Gainsborough in 1970 when the Taurus crawler was discontinued but the loader version was made for a while as the Track Marshall 1100.

29. This Bristol PD series (Power Diesel) crawler had track guards for working in orchards and vineyards.

BYRON

The three-wheeled Byron Mk I with an industrial version of the Ford 10 petrol engine, electric starting and a 3 forward speed and reverse gearbox was introduced in 1947. The Ford 10hp petrol engine was a popular power unit for small tractors because it was inexpensive and spare parts were readily available. The tractor had independent brakes and a mid-mounted tool bar which was raised and lowered from the tractor seat by a hand-operated lift lever.

It was made by Byron Farm Machinery at Walthamstow in London who eventually changed their name to Byron Horticultural Engineering and moved to Hucknall in Nottinghamshire. The manufacturers claimed that the Mk I Byron was an ideal tractor for rowcrop work and that it could pull a two-furrow plough in average soil conditions.

The Byron Mk II which appeared in 1949 was the same basic machine and the mainly cosmetic changes included slimmed down mudguards to improve visibility in rowcrops. The Mk II tractor cost £247.10s and the rowcrop model was an extra £44.10s. Even at this price the Byron was considered an expensive machine when compared with a petrol-engined Ferguson TEA 20 priced at £325 and the rowcrop version of the E27N Fordson Major which cost £226. There was little demand for the Byron and it went out of production in 1953.

CABS

Lambourn, Scottish Aviation, SunTrac, the Victoria Sheet Metal Co and Weathershields were some of the companies making steel-framed tractor cabs covered with canvas or sheet metal. Weather cabs were made for most popular tractors in the early 1950s and although they were rather draughty they provided welcome protection from wind and rain.

The Weathershields sheet metal cab made in Birmingham had a safety glass windscreen, removable doors, foot plates and fabric gaiters over the steering linkage. A sales leaflet explaining the benefits of the cab noted that 'as it was essential to carry out farm work in all weathers the protection of a cab would reduce to a minimum the time lost through bad weather'.

The Victor Stormguard cab made by the Victoria Sheet Metal Co had a safety glass windscreen and sliding glass side panels. Prices started at £42, an electric windscreen wiper was an extra £4.9s and a roll-up rear curtain with a flexible plastic window cost £2. The Minster steel cab approved by International Harvester for Farmall tractors was bolted to the mudguards and canvas wind guards helped keep the driver's feet warm.

Cabs were becoming an essential item by the mid-1960s and some tractor manufacturers offered their own weather cabs. Innes Walker Engineering Co at

30. Farmers could fit the Weathershields cab to the TE 20 without using a drill or a welder. The waterproof bonnet muff was said to 'keep the engine warm in the coldest of weather, no matter whether the tractor was garaged or left standing in the open and would promote easy starting'.

Paisley in Scotland advertised the Clydebuilt 'Speedifit' cab which cost £28.10s with carriage paid for most popular makes of tractor. Delivered in a flat pack the steel cab had sliding side windows and a roll up rear curtain with a plastic window but no doors. The cab was hinged on the back axle and access to the seat was either from the rear or by tipping the cab back and mounting the tractor from the side. Sta-Dri cabs made by Bristol Metal Components Ltd had two doors, sliding safety glass side windows and a fibreglass roof. According to an advertisement the cost of a cab would mean 'no lost output and no wasted hours for machinery or men'. Sta-Dri also manufactured a cheaper

31. The Victor Stormguard cab had an easily detached fibreglass roof panel which reputedly solved the drumming problem experienced in metal weather cabs.

32. The Scottish Aviation cab for the Fordson Major cost £29.15s, including carriage to the nearest railway station. Made for most popular tractors, this light alloy cab, which weighed about 100lbs, could be lifted off after releasing three spring clips.

33. The Minster cab made at Wimborne in Dorset was approved for Farmall BM and BMD tractors. A hand-operated windscreen wiper was included in the £41 price tag.

Tip-Top canvas cab with a wrap-around windscreen which gave 'ample elbow room' and could be folded back to 'give exceptional ease of entry'.

Massey Ferguson introduced an optional steel framed fibreglass cab with removable roof and doors for the new 1965 Red Giant range. According to publicity material the stylish looking cab was free from drumming and rattles, completely rain proof and shaped to give the driver maximum vision, comfort, operating room and convenience.

Cabs were an important sales feature by 1970 so manufacturers took steps to reduce noise levels. Massey Ferguson fitted a low-sound cab on the new MF 595, John Deere provided tractor drivers with a quieter 'operator protection unit' (cab) and Lucas marked improved cab design with the launch of a new in-cab stereo cassette player at the 1974 Smithfield Show.

It was a legal requirement for all new tractors sold after September 1970 to have a safety cab or roll bar tested and approved by the National Institute of Agricultural Engineering at Silsoe. A sample cab was subjected to crushing and impact tests with a 2 ton weight and only a minimum of deformation of the structure was allowed. Impact tests were made on the front, side

34. The Comfort tractor heater was sold in the early 1960s for the Fordson Power Major.

and rear of the cab by swinging the weight, suspended on a chain into the cab. The regulations also required the provision of a step for climbing on to the driving platform. Safety cabs gave protection from injury but some drivers took to wearing ear muffs to help deaden the noise from the engine and transmission.

Legislation finally solved the noise problem in June 1976 when the law demanded that all new tractors be supplied with a quiet cab. A radio was usually an optional extra and many farmers made their views on the subject heard by commenting that although good money had been paid for a quiet cab there seemed little point in doing so as the driver had the radio at full volume! The final part of the safety cab regulations came into force in September 1977 when all tractors made before that date and driven by an employee were required to have a safety cab or frame. Safety cabs were blamed by some experts for the steep increase in tractor prices in the mid-1970s. A 70hp model which cost about £2,000 in 1973 was listed at £5,200 three years later. The price of a 40hp tractor with the addition of a safety frame increased the price from £1,500 to £3,700 over the same period.

35. The hinged doors could be removed from the Massey Ferguson fibreglass cab in a matter of seconds.

36. Safety frames were required by law on all new tractors sold after September 1970. Special frames were made for vineyard tractors and other designs could be folded down when working in low buildings. Some safety frames had a canopy to protect the driver from the worst of the weather.

CARTERSON

Very few Carterson tractors were made, the first ones had a tricycle front wheel but this was soon changed to a more conventional four-wheel layout. The tractor had a kick-start Norton side- valve engine which developed 8hp at 2,600rpm and a 3 forward speed and reverse gearbox with a top speed of 10mph. The tractor was steered with a system of pulleys and wire rope and an unusual clutch control mechanism returned the engine to tick-over speed when the pedal was depressed.

37. The Carterson was designed and built by Horace Carter and his son. A small number of these tractors were made in Cheshire between 1948 and 1950.

CASE

The J.I. Case Threshing Machine Co founded at Racine, Wisconsin, in 1842 by Jerome Increase Case made threshing machines and steam engines. The company built a petrol-engined tractor in 1895 but little more was heard of Case tractors until the 1920s when three models with 27–40hp transverse engines (see plate 4 on page 6) were made.

Associated Manufacturers Co (Amanco), with premises at Kings Cross in London and later at the Palace of Industry in Wembley, were the UK distributors of Case farm equipment between the late 1920s and the mid-1950s. Case tractors imported in the 1930s included the Model L, Model C and Model CC rowcrop with an enclosed roller chain drive to the rear wheels. A power-lift system for the rear-mounted tool bar which was shaft-driven from the engine and activated by a pedal on the footplate was available from 1935 as a factory-fitted option for some Case tractors, including the CC rowcrop model. At the time Case tractors were painted grey and carried the American civil war bald eagle badge originally used by J.I. Case in the mid-1860s.

The Model C and the 4–5 plow Model L were re-styled in 1939 as the Model D and Model LA. A new Flambeau red colour scheme was used for the Models D and LA and for the Case DEX when it was introduced in 1941. The DEX was the export version of the Model D modified to suit the needs of British farmers who bought this tractor in considerable numbers.

Flambeau red gave way to a desert sand colour scheme for the 6 cylinder 65hp diesel engined Case 500 which replaced the Model LA in 1953. Other models launched in

38. Associated Manufacturers Co (Amanco) of London were selling a range of Case tractors, including the LA with an optional power lift system. Case tractors with their famous Bald Eagle badge disappeared from the UK tractor in the mid-1950s.

39. The Case Comfort King was described as the 'King of 6 plow tractors' when it was introduced to American farmers in 1962.

40. A special edition of the Case 1570 was made in 1976. Called the Spirit of '76, the stars and stripes design on the bonnet commemorated the company's 200 years of agricultural achievement.

America in the mid-1950s included petrol, tvo and LP-gas versions of the Case 400 and 600 with live power take-off and a dual range 8 forward and 2 reverse speed gearbox. The 4 cylinder 35hp petrol or diesel-engined Case 300 with a 12 forward and 3 reverse gearbox for smaller farms was added in 1956.

The Case 1200 Traction-King launched in America in 1964 and the improved Comfort King which replaced it in 1966 were not sold in the UK. Tenneco had already acquired 90 per cent stake in Case when the first of the 70 series Case Agri-King tractors appeared in America in 1969 and within a year Tenneco was the outright owner of J.I. Case & Co. The company acquired David Brown Tractors in 1972 and within a few years the Case name appeared on David Brown tractors sold in the UK.

Six models of the two-wheel drive Case Agri-King were being made in America in the mid-1970s when, in common with other North American tractor makers, Case quoted power take-off horse power in preference to engine power for the Agri-King 70 series. The smallest Case 970 was rated at 93hp while the top-of-the-range 1570 launched in 1976 developed 180hp at the power shaft. The 1570 had a four-range gearbox with three power shifts in each range and its air-conditioned cab was isolated from tractor vibration by rubber mounting blocks. A seat belt was standard equipment for the farmer who spent 'a lot of time in the cab on the Easy Rider 7-way adjustable swivel seat'.

The four-wheel drive 2470 and 2670 Traction Kings launched in 1974 completed the mid-1970s Case tractor range. Rated at 176 and 221 pto hp respectively, both tractors had a 12 forward and 4 reverse powershift transmission with an all-wheel steering system that gave the driver the choice of front, rear, four-wheel or crab steering. The turbo-charged, 6 cylinder Case 2670 was introduced to British farmers on the David Brown stand at the 1976 Smithfield Show. Advertisements for the 243hp Case 2670 with £30,000 price tag explained that the tractor 'had acre eating power plus weather beating traction' and the cab was 'the nearest thing yet seen to an airliner cockpit'. American farmers were able to buy even more horse power in 1974 when Case launched the 300 SAE hp 2870 Traction King.

41. The 243hp Case Traction King made its UK debut at the 1976 Smithfield Show.

The Case 970 Agri-King with a 12 forward and 3 reverse gearbox, hydrostatic steering, self-adjusting disc brakes, independent power take-off with a hand clutch and lower link sensing hydraulics was marketed by David Brown in the UK in the mid-1970s. Power take-off horse power was still given in sales literature when the Case 90 Series Agri-King replaced the 70 series tractors in 1978. The twelve 90 Series models ranged from the 1190 rated at 43 pto hp to the four-wheel drive Case 4890 with 253hp available at the power shaft.

The David Brown Case 2090, 2290 and 2390 with 120hp, 139hp and 171hp engines and power shift transmissions were launched in 1979 to meet British farmers' demands for more horse power. According to publicity material the new tractors had 'style, technical superiority and a hefty surge of raw power to make even the biggest operator feel at home in the cab'.

The David Brown name disappeared from the tractor scene in 1983 and Case Tractors Ltd at Meltham in Yorkshire were marketing 34 different models in the UK in 1984, including the 94 series launched in that year. The ten model 94 series included the two-wheel drive 48hp 1194 and the 61hp, 72hp, 83hp and 95hp medium-power range tractors with two- and four-wheel drive. The flagship four-wheel drive 277hp Case 4894 had equal-sized wheels and the cab was filled with the latest electronic technology. A 12 forward speed gearbox was standard on the 94 series with the Hydrashift semi-automatic change-on-the-move gearbox optional equipment for the medium-powered tractors. Case acquired International Harvester in 1985 and the complete tractor ranges made by both companies were retained until the new Case IH Magnum series appeared in America in 1987. Case IH also introduced an improved International Harvester 1056 for the European market in the same year. It had a 16 forward and 8 reverse synchromesh gearbox, independent power take-off and a new safety feature which automatically engaged four-wheel drive when the driver applied the brakes.

The Magnum 7100 series already on sale in America was introduced to British farmers in 1989. The four-wheel drive 7110, 7210 7310 and 7410 Magnums rated at 155hp, 180hp, 205hp and 230hp had 18 speed powershift full transmission, a central drive shaft to the front axle and electronic linkage control (elc) hydraulics. The four-wheel drive 90hp Case IH 985 Turbo with a two-speed powershift gearbox, trailer brakes and XL cab was announced at the 1989 Smithfield Show as a grassland farmer's special edition of the ageing International Harvester 85 series.

42. The driving controls of the David Brown Case 2290 were located on the right-hand side of an eight-way adjustable seat in the 'silent guardian' cab.

43. An electronic implement hitching system and computer to monitor performance were features of the turbocharged Case IH Magnum range launched in 1987.

Three 90–110hp 5100 series Maxxums with a 16 forward and 12 reverse semi-powershift gearbox with shuttle reversing and electro-hydraulically engaged front-wheel drive appeared in 1990. The lower link sensing Maxx-o-Draulic hydraulic system which automatically matched hydraulic power output to the load requirement of the tractor was a new feature on the Maxxum range.

Production of the 45hp four-wheel drive Case IH 844 XL with a 16 forward and 8 reverse synchromesh transmission, self-adjusting inboard disc brakes and the International Sens-o-Draulic hydraulic system was moved to Doncaster in 1990. Case IH were marketing 23 models in the 17–246hp bracket (including the long lived 844XL), when the 95 series appeared in 1990. There were seven 95 series tractors with 45–90hp engines in 22 build combinations selected from three types of cab, two- and four-wheel drive and synchromesh or powershift transmission. A limited number of a no-frills Stockman's Special version of the 69hp 695 and 82hp 895 with a basic cab and no heater were made in 1992. Case IH decreed that no discounts could be allowed on the £9,999 and £13,250 price tags.

A ready-made supply of powerful four-wheel drive articulated tractors was the prize when Case IH acquired Steiger Tractor Inc of North Dakota in 1986. The 380hp 16 ton articulated four-wheel drive giant 9280 made at the Steiger plant was the most powerful Case IH tractor yet seen when it appeared in 1992. It had a 12 speed powershift transmission with a skip-shift mechanism which could be moved up two gears at a time to get the 9280 from 0 to 8mph in about three seconds.

The 6 cylinder 5150 with 24 forward and 20 reverse speeds launched in 1993 extended the improved Maxxum Plus power range to 125hp. The smaller 90hp, 100hp and 110hp models had a 16 forward and 12 reverse synchromesh gearbox with an optional creep speed box adding another 8 speeds in both directions.

44. The 360 hp Case IH Quadtrac from the Steiger factory had a power shift transmission and four independently suspended rubber tracks.

45. Increased engine power, improved manoeuvrability and numerous electronic management systems were features of the American-built 170–261hp Case Magnum Pro 7200 series launched in 1997.

Improved Maxxum Pro models and the new CS range, which were the first Case IH tractors to appear with the Steyr pedigree following the company's link with the Austrian tractor maker, made their debut at the 1996 Smithfield Show. Increased engine power, improved cab visibility and single lever control of the range and powershift gearboxes were the main improvements on the Maxxum Pro range which replaced the Maxxum Plus tractors. Features of the 150hp Case IH CS 150 included a 40 forward and reverse powershift transmission and a computerised headland turn management system. The 94hp CS 94 had a 16 forward and reverse powershift transmission and a four-speed power take-off.

The Steiger name re-appeared on farm tractors when the first of six new articulated four-wheel drive 205–425hp Case IH Steiger 9300 series with turbocharged, after-cooled engines and a 12 or 24 speed synchromesh transmission was introduced in 1996. The addition of the 360hp Quadtrac 9380 with four independently suspended rubber track units and three rowcrop versions in 1997 increased the Steiger range to ten big tractors with 'luxury operative protective structures' (cabs). Although more suited to wide open spaces in America some Steiger wheeled 'rowcrop' models and Quadtracs were sold to UK farmers in 1997.

The more powerful American-built Magnum Pro 7210 series replaced the Magnum 7200 tractors in 1997. The 170hp 7210 was the only one of a five model range without a wastegate turbocharger which increased engine power to 190hp, 214hp, 239hp and 261hp. The Maxxum or MX series was extended in 1998 to give nine models from the 80hp MX 80C (compact) to the MX 170 with 170hp under the bonnet. The letter X denotes a Doncaster-built tractor, M is used for models with more gears and a higher specification than those joins the C range. Steyr-sourced tractors have the letter S included in the model number.

CATERPILLAR

The Caterpillar Tractor Company of Illinois was formed when the Holt Tractor Co, who had already registered the Caterpillar name, and the Best Tractor Co merged in 1925. The Best Tractor Co made tracklayers and Benjamin Holt introduced the first practical steam-powered tracklayer in 1904 and a petrol-engined model in 1906.

The Caterpillar Twenty was one of the more successful early crawlers. It had a 25 belt hp 4 cylinder petrol/paraffin engine, a 3 forward and reverse gearbox and was steered with multi-disc clutches and band brakes. Caterpillar Twenty tractors were sold in the UK but the Caterpillar 22 made between 1934 and 1939 with a 26hp petrol/paraffin engine was more popular than the Twenty. The future lay in diesel power and Caterpillar introduced the 4 cylinder four-stroke engined Caterpillar 65 in 1931 and, like many later models, it was started with a 10hp horizontally opposed 2 cylinder donkey engine. Other diesel crawlers made in the 1930s included the 41hp Caterpillar 35 and the 82hp Caterpillar 75 used mainly for construction work.

Caterpillar tractors first appeared in Britain in 1915 and by the mid-1930s they were being imported by Jack Olding & Co at Hatfield, Hertfordshire, and H. Leverton & Co at Spalding, Lincolnshire. Coupar Angus were Caterpillar concessionaires in Scotland. H. Leverton & Co, who imported their first Caterpillar tractors in 1936, were marketing agricultural versions of the D2, D4, D6 and D8 in the mid-1940s. The American Caterpillar company set up its own spares depot near Leicester in 1950 and the first British-built Caterpillar tractors were made at Glasgow in 1958.

Nebraska tractor tests completed between 1939 and 1941 for the D2, D4, D6, D7 and D8 recorded maximum power outputs of 30, 40, 78, 89 and 127 belt hp respectively. The D6 and D8 had 6 cylinder engines while the others had 4 cylinders. They were all started with 2 cylinder donkey engines ranging from 10hp for the D2 to 24hp on the D8. The Caterpillar R2 and R4,

46. The D2 was the smallest of the famous Caterpillar D series tractors introduced in 1935; this model shown at the Suffolk Show was originally sold to plough the land when the showground was farmed.

which were only made for a few years, were petrol-engined models of the D2 and D4. The D2 was discontinued by the mid-1950s but other D series tractors were made well into the 1970s. Improved versions of the D4, D6, D7 and D8 were made in the mid-1960s. The D6B, for example, had 5 forward and 4 reverse gears and a 93hp engine which was still started with a donkey engine. A special farm version of the 68hp D4D designed for drawbar work appeared in 1967 with all five of its forward gears within the 2.5–5mph range used at the time for cultivation work.

47. Caterpillar VHP crawlers developed more horse power as the driver changed up through the gears. Brake horse power ranged from 165–216hp on the D6D (SA) tractor.

Many Caterpillar tractors were used by the construction and civil engineering industries in the mid-1970s when Levertons were also selling agricultural versions of the Caterpillar D3, D4D, D5 (SA) and D6C with 62hp, 68hp, 90hp and 125hp engines and a Leverton hydraulic linkage.

The Caterpillar range of variable horse power crawlers launched in America in 1980 made their UK debut at the 1982 Smithfield Show. VHP models had an electric switching system linked to the transmission which could be used to increase engine horse power when field conditions required more power at the drawbar. This was achieved by a solenoid in the injection pump which increased the quantity of fuel supplied to the injectors when the driver changed up through the higher gears on the six speed transmission. The horse

48. The steering wheel on the Caterpillar Challenger controls the hydrostatic motors which drive the tracks. Turning the steering wheel increases the speed of one track while the other one is slowed down.

49. The Challenger 35 with Caterpillar Mobil-Trac rubber tracks was introduced to British farmers at the 1994 Smithfield Show.

power ratings of the D4E, D5B and D6D (SA) could be varied from 97 to 125, 120 to 160 and 165 to 216 SAE hp respectively.

The Caterpillar D4E VHP specification included a 24 volt electric starter with an optional cold start system, an oil-cooled transmission clutch, hydraulic clutch and brake steering, a forward/reverse shuttle 5 speed gearbox and 1,000rpm power take-off. The D4E SA-T introduced in 1982 shared the D4E VHP specification with a standard 97hp turbocharged 4 cylinder direct injection engine providing the power.

Slow working speeds and problems with road transport were always a handicap for steel-tracked crawler tractors. The high speed Mobil-trac rubber-tracked Caterpillar Challenger 65 with a top speed of 18mph introduced to British farmers in 1989 overcame the problem. The Challenger 65's 6 cylinder turbocharged 270hp Caterpillar engine transmitted power to a 10 forward and 2 reverse powershift gearbox and mechanical drive to a differential steering system.

Caterpillar replaced the original model with an improved 285hp Challenger 65C and launched the new 325hp turbocharged and intercooled Challenger 75C in 1993. The main difference on the C series Challengers was the use of steel front idlers in place of the earlier inflatable rubber units which were liable to puncture on some stony soils. An ADAS report suggested the cost of the Challenger was difficult to justify on farms under 1,200 acres and on even bigger areas shift work was needed to make maximum use of the tractor.

The smaller Challenger 35 and 45 Mobil-trac tractors were introduced to UK farmers at the 1994 Smithfield Show. Rated at 205 and 235 gross engine hp with five belt widths and five track centre settings, the new models had a 16 forward and 9 reverse powershift transmission and Caterpillar differential steering.

When the 330hp 75D replaced the 75C and the 272hp Challenger 55 was launched in 1996 there were six Caterpillar crawlers, ranging from the 212hp Challenger 35 to the 330hp Challenger 75D, on the British market. An agreement between Caterpillar and Claas resulted in the German company marketing Challenger tractors in the Claas colour scheme to European farmers from 1997 while a reciprocal arrangement saw Claas combines on sale in America with Caterpillar yellow paintwork.

CLAAS

The German combine manufacturer Claas made the Huckepack self-propelled tool carrier between 1955 and 1962. It was similar to the Lanz Alldog with a 15hp Hatz or MWM diesel engine. The Huckepacke provided the power and transmission system for a wrap-around combine harvester with separate cutting and threshing units. The combine could be removed without difficulty, leaving the tool carrier free for other work throughout the year. The driving platform placed above the left-hand rear wheel gave the driver a clear view when mowing grass or cultivating rowcrops. The Huckepacke could also be used with a load carrying platform for transport work.

Claas took no further public interest in tractors until the early 1990s when they co-operated with Schluter in the

50. This model of the prototype Claas Xerion 2000 was first shown to the farming public in 1993.

51. The first production models of the Xerion 2000 appeared in 1997.

52. Caterpillar Challengers with the Claas green livery first appeared in Europe in 1997.

design of a bi-directional Euro-Trac systems tractor (see plate 267 on page 195). This was followed by public demonstrations of a prototype multi-function tractor in 1993. The Claas Xerion, with some resemblance to the Euro-trac, was designed for use with conventional front- and rear- mounted equipment and as a power unit for a root harvester or cultivator/drill combination. With development work complete the first 200hp Xerion 2000 tractors which cost just under £100,000 were made in 1997. The range was soon extended with the addition of the Xerion 2500 and 3000 with 6 cylinder 250hp and 300hp turbocharged and intercooled engines equipped with electronic controls and performance monitoring system. The Xerion has a hydrostatic/mechanical transmission with eight mechanical ratios and stepless speed variation in each gear, three mode four-wheel steering and power take-off shafts at the front, centre and rear of the machine. The Xerion's cab rotates hydraulically through 180 degrees to give the driver full vision and control.

An agreement with Caterpillar in 1997 resulted in the German harvest machinery manufacturer marketing the 212hp, 242p and 272hp Challenger 35, 45 and 55 crawlers in Claas green livery throughout Europe. Within a few months the improved and re-styled E series Claas Challengers were launched and sales literature claimed their introduction to 'herald the arrival of user friendly crawler tractors'. The electronically controlled Caterpillar engines on the rubber-tracked Challenger 65E and 75E were rated at 310hp and 340hp. The 85E and 95E also develop 340hp in first and second gear but this could automatically be increased to 375hp and 410hp when used in gears 3 to 10. The Challenger specification included a 10 forward and 2 reverse powershift transmission, hydraulic differential steering and load sensing category 3 and 4 hydraulic linkage. An 8-way adjustable driver's seat and a buddy seat were provided in the air-conditioned cab.

CLAYTON

Lucassen Young of Stockton-on-Tees in Cleveland launched the Clayton 4105 Buggi lightweight tractor and low-ground pressure spray vehicle at the 1992 Royal Agricultural Show. The two- and four-wheel drive tractor had a 110hp John Deere turbocharged diesel engine and a 10 forward speed and 2 reverse transmission with all-round suspension. Other features included hydrostatic two- and four-wheel steering, a fully automatic trailer braking system, a rear load platform and optional hydraulic linkage. There were three models of Clayton Buggi when the 85hp or 110hp 4090 and the 120hp 4120 were added to the range in 1994. The new models had a similar specification to the original Buggi which included a John Deere engine, full suspension system and a moveable 6-spline power take-off shaft driven by a hydraulic motor. Options included three wheelbase lengths and a rubber block, coil spring or hydraulic rear axle suspension system.

The multi-function Pentronic steering unit introduced in 1997 was an additional option for the Clayton 4105 and 4120 Clayton Buggi tractors. The new design added a delay period to the four-wheel drive system

53. The 1997 Clayton Buggi systems tractor has a load sensing power take-off and an air compressor for its trailer braking system.

which allowed the front wheels to turn through 10 or 15 degrees before the rear wheels moved to match the front wheel angle when in four-wheel or crab steer mode.

The four-wheel drive C-Trac 6700 and 6800 with 6 cylinder John Deere engines were added to the Clayton range in 1998. Features of the new models included a 10 speed synchromesh gearbox, four-wheel steering and a choice of 3 wheel base lengths.

CLETRAC

The Cleveland crawler tractor made by the Cleveland Motor Plough Co in Ohio became the Cletrac when the company became the Cleveland Tractor Co in 1918. The 12–20hp Cleveland Model R had the distinction of being the first tractor with controlled differential and independent brake steering instead of the more usual clutch and brake system. It was steered by applying one brake lever which slowed the track on one side and the differential automatically increased the speed of the opposite track to change the direction of travel.

Early Cletracs included the lightweight Model F made between 1920 and 1922, while the 22–30hp Cletrac 15 with a 4 cylinder Hercules engine and the 27–33hp Cletrac 25 with 6 cylinder Hercules engine were made in the early 1930s. The Model E introduced in 1935 with a choice of five track centre widths from 31 to 76 inches was sold in considerable numbers by H.G. Burford Ltd of London who imported their first Cletracs in the early 1920s.

The Cletrac HG crawler with a 4 cylinder 26hp Hercules petrol engine and a 3 forward and reverse gearbox with a top speed of 5¼mph was the smallest of the three petrol- or diesel-engined crawlers

advertised by Cletrac in the early 1940s. The Cleveland Tractor Co recommended the petrol-engined 30–38hp Model A series for medium-sized farms and the 38–50hp Model B series with a petrol or diesel engine for 'large farms and for farmers who did custom (contract) work'. American farmers were reminded that wartime regulations meant that it would only be possible to buy a Cletrac crawler if they could prove the need for a new tractor. The Oliver Corporation retained the Cletrac crawler range when they bought the Cleveland Tractor Co in 1944 but the tractors were sold with an

54. The 18–22 hp Cletrac HG crawler was introduced in 1939 by the Cleveland Tractor Co of Ohio.

Oliver name badge. Following the acquisition of the Oliver Corporation by the White Motor Corporation in 1960 the Oliver (Cletrac) crawler range was made for another five years.

The lightweight Cletrac General GG launched in 1939 with a 14–19hp Hercules engine and 3 forward gears and reverse was the first and only wheeled Cletrac model to be made. The Oliver Corporation dropped the tricycle-wheeled General GG when they acquired the Cleveland Tractor Co. However, the General, now with an improved Hercules engine, was made by B.F. Avery & Sons at Louisville, Kentucky as the Avery Model A and a few of these tractors were sold by Blaw-Knox Ltd to British farmers in the mid-1940s. The Avery Model A and Model V wheeled tractors with a strong family resemblance to their Cletrac General ancestor were still being made when Minneapolis-Moline bought B.F. Avery & Sons in 1951.

COLD STARTING AIDS

When atomised diesel fuel is sprayed into air heated to a temperature of approximately 550 degrees centigrade it will burn rapidly and the expanding gases in the cylinder drive the piston downwards on the power stroke. Early diesel engines, known as hot bulb or semi-diesels, were started by using a blowlamp to heat an iron bulb on the cylinder head and raise the temperature high enough to ignite the fuel. Most diesel tractors made in the late 1940s and 1950s had an indirect injection diesel engine which was fuel efficient but could be difficult to start in cold weather without the use of some form of starting aid.

A smouldering paper wick placed in a holder and screwed into the cylinder head was used to ignite the fuel when starting a Field Marshall tractor. In cold conditions a special cartridge could be placed in a chamber above the piston; when the cartridge was fired with a sharp blow from a blunt instrument the engine rarely failed to start.

An electric heater coil in the inlet manifold and a small hand operated pump was a common type of cold start aid on multi-cylinder indirect injection engines. Fuel from the main tank was pumped on to the red hot coil and the resulting flame was drawn into the cylinders by the starter motor. The Fordson Dexta instruction book advised that this procedure could be repeated three times but should the engine still refuse to start the driver should refer to the fault-finding chart! The Ki-gass cold start system used on the Ferguson TEF 20 and other tractors was used in the same way but a separate tank stored the fuel which was pumped on to the heater coil. The TEF 20 also had a de-compression lever which held some of the valves open to reduce the load on the starter motor. International Harvester tractors usually had a 'glow plug' pre-heater coil in each cylinder with a pilot unit on the instrument panel. The engine invariably refused to start when cold without pre-heating the cylinders and this procedure was often necessary even when the engine was warm.

If all else failed the driver could always spray ether from an aerosol into the tractor's air cleaner. Most aerosols also contained an upper cylinder lubricant and one manufacturer claimed that it was amazing how many starts could be made with a single canister. The engine usually responded to this treatment but a cloud of black smoke and loud knocking sounds coming from the cylinder block could be a cause for concern. Some drivers were convinced their tractor had become addicted to it and refused to start without its daily dose from an aerosol can. The truth was that worn cylinders and leaking valves made most of these engines so short of compression that they could no longer be started in any other way.

The transition to direct injection engines solved most cold starting problems and those with an in-line fuel injection pump normally had an excess fuel button for cold starting. A combined heater coil and automatic thermostatically operated excess fuel device in the inlet manifold was usually provided on engines with a distributor-type injection pump.

55. An aerosol can of ether was the solution to starting worn engines on cold mornings.

COUNTY

Edward and Percy Tapp established County Commercial Cars at Fleet in Hampshire in 1929. Initially concerned with converting lorries to increase their load-carrying capacity they used their wartime experience gained in development work with battle tanks to design the County CFT (County Full Track) agricultural crawler.

An E27N Fordson Major was used for the CFT crawler launched in 1948. It had a 36hp petrol or 30hp paraffin Fordson engine and an optional Perkins P6 diesel-engined version was added in 1950. The CFT had the Fordson Major's gearbox and a fixed spiral bevel on a countershaft transmitted power to the spur gear final drive which gave a top speed of 3.4mph. The tractor was steered with lever-operated steering clutches assisted by pedal operated band brakes for tight turns. Hydraulic linkage, power take-off, electric starting and lights were optional extras.

56. A County CFT with a Perkins P6 diesel engine.

The industrial County CFT B was added in 1951 and, following the launch of the New Fordson Major at that year's Smithfield County Show, introduced the Model Z agricultural crawler with the new Fordson tractor's diesel engine and 6 forward speed gearbox.

The County Four-Drive – also based on the New Fordson Major Diesel – was launched in 1954. The front wheels were driven by heavy roller chains from the rear wheels and the tractor was skid steered with a crawler tractor clutch and brake mechanism. A Fordson Power Major skid unit was used for the Mk II Four-Drive which appeared in 1958 and a few Mk II tractors based on the Fordson Super Major were built before the County Super-4 replaced the Four-Drive in 1961.

57. County entered the four-wheel drive market with the Four-Drive which was really a crawler tractor on pneumatic tyres.

58. The County Super-4 had two drive shafts to the front axle.

The County Model Z crawler had been improved several times before it was replaced by the County Ploughman in 1957. The new model was also based on the New Fordson Major Diesel and the introduction of the Fordson Power Major brought the launch of the 51.8hp Ploughman P50 in 1958. The Ploughman 55 with the Super Major transmission and a 55hp Ford industrial engine appeared in 1961 and the Clydesdale crawler (a no frills version of the P55) was added later that year. As County was well established in the four-wheel drive market in the early 1960s the company decided to concentrate on wheeled tractors. The Clydesdale was discontinued in 1964 and the last P55 Ploughman was made in 1965.

59. County forward control tractors were better suited to industrial use but this FC1004 was working in Suffolk with a set of mounted disc harrows.

The County Super-4 was a conventional front-wheel steered tractor with a Fordson Super Major engine and transmission, four equal-size wheels and power-assisted steering. The front wheels were driven by two forward-running telescopic prop-shafts from the final reduction gears in the back axle. An optional rear-axle diff-lock gave a positive drive on all four wheels, the independent steering brake pedals operated both wheels on each side of the tractor and with the pedals locked the Super-4 had four-wheel braking for roadwork.

Announced in 1962, the County Super-6 with a 95hp 6 cylinder Ford industrial engine was very similar to the Super-4 but, according to press publicity, the Super-6 could do 'two hours work in 60 minutes' on its 'four big equal-size wheels that hardly know what wheelspin means'.

The Super-4 and Super-6 were replaced by the 654 and 954 when Ford launched the 1000 series in 1964 and County Commercial Cars used the new Basildon tractor range for the next ten years. The new model numbers denoted brake horse power and the figure 4 indicated four-wheel drive. The 654 had a Ford 5000 engine while a 95hp Ford industrial power unit was used for the 954. Both tractors had twin prop-shaft drive to the front wheels. Other equal-size wheel County tractors based on the Ford 5000 series included the 854T, 1104 and 1124. A Ford 5000 engine was used on 854T but the other two had Ford industrial engines. Launched in 1967, the 854T was the first turbocharged County, the turbocharger being made by CAV. Model numbers still indicated engine power, the twin prop-shaft front-wheel drive arrangement was retained and there was a choice of the Ford 8 speed manual gearbox or 10 speed Select-O-Speed transmission.

The forward control County FC 654 introduced in 1965 had a front-mounted cab with full-width rear-view driving mirrors and rear-load carrying platform. The first of several County forward control tractors made in the 1960s and 1970s, it was bought by contractors for spraying and fertiliser spreading but was mainly used for industrial work and forestry. The FC 754 replaced the FC 654 when the Ford Force range appeared in 1968 and this tractor was made for several years. Four versions of the FC 1004 with Ford industrial engines were made between 1967 and 1977; 5000 series skid-units were used for three of them and the last model was based on a Ford 6600.

60. The County 4000-Four four-wheel drive conversion kit could be fitted to new or used tractors.

The 4000-Four made between 1968 and 1975 was the first County four-wheel drive tractor with smaller wheels at the front. Select-O-Speed was optional and apart from the transfer box and single prop-shaft drive to the front axle the County version was virtually the same as the Ford 4000.

The re-styled County 1164, with an integral cab, sloping bonnet and fibre glass fuel tank, replaced the 1124 in 1971. This tractor had the 6 cylinder engine used on the American-built Ford 8000 and a strengthened 5000 transmission system. Later versions of the 1164 had a Ford 7600 transmission and Ford 8600 or TW engines. The County 944, made between 1971 and 1975, had a Ford 7000 engine and an 8 forward and 2 reverse gearbox, Load Monitor and a Duncan cab. County were still using the twin prop-shaft front-axle drive system for the 1254 and 1454 launched in 1972. The 1254 with a Ford 8000 engine was made for three years and the 1454 with a Ford 9000 power unit was discontinued in 1978. Both tractors had a 16 speed Dual Power transmission and a Swedish-built cab.

County Commercial Cars established a separate company called County Power Drives Ltd to manufacture specialist models including the County

61. County high-clearance kits were made for a succession of Ford tractors in the 1960s and 1970s. The County 762H conversion for a Ford 6600 was introduced in 1975.

11F. This two-wheel drive tractor, based on a Ford 7000, had a torque converter and an inching pedal for manoeuvring in confined spaces replaced the conventional clutch. The Ford 600 and 700 series provided the skid-units for five different County four-wheel drive tractors with small front wheels. Made between 1975 and 1981 they were all virtually identical to the Ford two-wheel drive tractors with a single prop-shaft drive to the front axle. Ford 600 and 700 series tractors were also used for the equal-size four-wheel drive County 774, 974, 1174 and 1474 with flat floor cabs. County were building twelve different four-wheel drive tractors in 1979 including the 1184 which had replaced the 1174 and an improved flagship 1474 with a 153hp Ford TW 20 engine.

Fordson and Ford skid-units were used for most County tractors but four-wheel drive conversions were made for other models, including the International Harvester 614 and 634 and some Leyland tractors. County

62. County Power Drives Ltd was established in the early 1970s to build specialist tractors, including this County 11F with a Brockhouse torque converter.

sales were in decline when the improved 1184, now based on the 177hp Ford TW 30, was launched in 1980. A TW 35 skid unit was used in later years and both models were similar to the 1474 with a 16 forward and 4 reverse Dual Power transmission. County Commercial Cars went into receivership in 1983 and the business was purchased by a County tractor dealer at Ludlow. Renamed County Tractors Ltd, production of four-wheel drive tractors with equal-sized wheel continued at Fleet in Hampshire. The Benson Group bought County Tractors Ltd in 1987 and moved to a factory at Knighton in Wales. Production of the 774, 974 and 1184 was scaled down. The last County tractor was made at Knighton in 1990.

After receiving permission to use the County name, SEM Engineering at Basildon introduced the County HSH 140, based on a Ford New

63. County launched the new 120hp 1184 TW with a Ford TW engine and Ford 7600 transmission in 1979 to celebrate their 50th anniversary.

Holland 40 series tractor, in 1994. It was a high speed haulage tractor with an industrial front axle, coil spring suspension, shock absorbers and a top speed of 25mph. Designed for worldwide use, the HSH 140 had a 6 cylinder 143hp Powerstar engine with a large capacity radiator and an additional engine cooler for tropical conditions. There was a choice of an 8 forward and 2 reverse gearbox or optional 6 speed power shift transmission with a torque converter. Other features included a diff-lock, hydrostatic steering, three-point linkage and an air over hydraulic brake system with a built-in compressor. SEM Engineering was also involved in the production of some new prototype County tractors, mainly for overseas use, based on the Ford 40 series but within a year the company had ceased trading and the project came to an end.

64. The County HSH 140 was made by SEM Engineering.

CUTHBERTSON

The Water Buffalo was introduced in 1951 as a specialist tracklaying machine with a watertight welded steel hull designed for land reclamation work on hills, bogs and swamps. Made by James A. Cuthbertson at Biggar in Scotland it had an 80hp Albion engine and mechanical transmission with a 5 forward speed and reverse gearbox, multi-plate steering clutches and rubber-jointed steel tracks. An industrial version of the Water Buffalo with a 150hp Leyland engine was introduced in the late 1950s and a hydrostatic model appeared in 1964. Two variable speed, reversible hydraulic motors were used to drive the tracks and the machine was steered by varying the speed of one of the hydraulic motors to slow the inner track when turning a corner.

DAVID BROWN

A small factory established in Huddersfield by David Brown in 1860 had become an important gear wheel manufacturing business by the early 1900s. In 1936 the founder's grandson, also named David Brown, joined forces with Harry Ferguson to manufacture the Ferguson-Brown A type tractor with the revolutionary Ferguson draught control hydraulic system. The first Ferguson-Browns were made that year with a 20hp petrol/paraffin Coventry-Climax engine; later models had a similar engine made by David Brown. The A type had a 3 forward and reverse gearbox with a top speed of just under 5mph, spade lug steel wheels and independent drum brakes with optional power take-off and side-mounted belt pulley. The left-hand brake pedal operated the clutch before it applied the brake and for left-hand power turns it was necessary to pull the pedal up by hand. The steel wheeled Ferguson-Brown with a petrol engine cost £198 in 1938 and the vaporising oil model was an extra £10. Pneumatic tyres added £40 to the bill and many farmers considered the tractor to be too expensive when compared with the £100 price tag for a Fordson Standard.

65. Hunting pink was the standard colour used for early David Brown tractors such as this VAK 1C made in 1946.

Approximately 1300 Ferguson-Browns had been made at Meltham by 1939 when the relationship between the two tractor men came to an end and Ferguson tractor production was transferred to America.

Plans to build the David Brown VAK 1 tractor were well advanced when Harry Ferguson and David Brown parted company and the new model was launched at the 100th Royal Show held at Windsor in 1939. The 35hp VAK 1 had an overhead-valve 4 cylinder, water-cooled petrol/paraffin engine, a 4 forward speed and reverse gearbox and independent brakes. A power take-off shaft and hydraulic linkage which required wheels to control implement depth were optional extras. The VIG 1 was an industrial version of the VAK 1 made during the war period and many of them were used by the Royal Air Force to tow aircraft and bomb trolleys.

The VAK 1A with a modified engine manifold to give a faster warm up and a patented adjustable top link was made from 1945 until 1947 when it was replaced by the VAK 1C. It was the first David Cropmaster Brown tractor and was also the first British tractor with an optional 6 speed gearbox and two speed power take-off. A pedal and a hand lever were provided to control the clutch while other features included hydraulic linkage, swinging drawbar and electric lighting. David Brown made their own range of mounted ploughs and cultivating implements while other machines, including Allman sprayers, Robot planters and Byron disc harrows, were officially approved for use with Cropmaster tractors.

An optional 49hp diesel engine was introduced in 1949 and the VAK 1C Cropmaster remained in production until 1953. The Super Cropmaster with a bigger engine, side panels on the engine bonnet and wider tyres was added in 1950. There was also a vineyard model of the Cropmaster and the Taskmaster version was made for airports and industrial use.

David Brown entered the agricultural crawler market in 1942 when they launched the DB4 with a 38hp Dorman diesel engine and a 5 speed gearbox. The Trackmaster 30, a crawler version of the Cropmaster with differential steering and a 6 speed gearbox which replaced the DB 4 in 1950 was made for three years. The petrol paraffin/engined model was initially known as the TAK 3 (Tracklayer Agricultural Kerosene) while the

TAD 3 (Tractor Agricultural Diesel) had a diesel engine. Another new crawler, the Trackmaster Diesel 50 with a 6 cylinder engine and 6 speed gearbox, made its debut in 1952. David Brown introduced the 25, 30C and 30D in 1953 and the crawler model numbers were changed to match the new wheeled tractors. The Trackmaster 30 and 30 Diesel became the 30T and 30TD and the Trackmaster 50 Diesel became the 50TD.

The David Brown 25 and 30 tractors made between 1953 and 1958 retained some features of the earlier Cropmaster range. The David Brown 25 had a 32hp vaporising oil engine or 37½hp petrol engine and the 25D launched in late 1953 had a 31½hp diesel power unit. The 30C and 30D with petrol, vaporising oil and diesel engines rated at 41, 37½ and 34hp respectively were similar to the David Brown 25. Standard equipment included a 6 speed two-lever gearbox with a top speed of 15mph, a two speed power take-off and belt pulley, hydraulic lift,

66. The David Brown Trackmaster 30 diesel, the crawler version of the 30D, became the 30TD in 1953.

67. The bench seat and wide mudguards had disappeared when the David Brown 25 was launched in 1953.

68. The 50D was the only David Brown tractor with a side-mounted belt pulley. Some of these tractors were used by agricultural contractors to drive threshing tackle.

independent expanding shoe brakes and a parking brake. The clutch was operated with the usual foot pedal or a hand lever at the back which provided the driver with 'full control of the tractor while standing at the rear'. An optional hydraulic overload mechanism in the top link, connected by a cable to the clutch hand lever, automatically disengaged the clutch if the implement hit an obstruction. Ferguson's draft control hydraulic linkage was still protected by patents and, in common with other manufacturers, David Brown developed their own weight transfer system. The Traction Control Unit (TCU) introduced in 1953 still required depth wheels on the implement but varying amounts of the implement's weight could be transferred on to the tractor until wheel-slip was eliminated. TCU could also be used with a special linkage to transfer some of the weight of trailed equipment on to the tractor.

The David Brown 50D and 50TD tracklayer launched in 1953 had the same 50hp 6 cylinder diesel engine but the 50D could only manage a sustained pull of 6,550lb at the drawbar compared with a 9,800lb pull by the crawler. Designed mainly as a towing tractor, the 50D had a four speed power take-off shaft and optional belt pulley but there was no hydraulic linkage.

Harrison, McGregor and Guest, manufacturers of Albion binders, mowers and other machinery since the 1870s, was acquired by David Brown Tractors in 1955. This enabled the Meltham company to add the David Brown Albion trailed combine harvester, the Hurricane forage harvester and a pick-up baler to their product range.

The 14hp David Brown 2D had a four-stroke, air-cooled, 2 cylinder diesel engine, single-plate clutch and a 4 forward and reverse gearbox mounted above the rear axle. Independent drum brakes, adjustable wheel track and a compressed air Air-Light implement lift system were standard equipment. A compressor driven by the tractor engine provided compressed air for two lift cylinders which raised and lowered the underslung and rear mounted tool bars. The two control levers could be locked together or used separately for independent control of either lift cylinders. The tubular steel chassis served as an air reservoir and a connection for a tyre inflator was an added bonus. Although claimed to be a maid of all work the David Brown 2D was more at home working in rowcrops with an 8ft or 10ft wide mid-mounted tool bar.

The distinctive hunting pink David Brown 900 with blue wheels and radiator grille was launched at the 1956 Smithfield Show. The tractor had 6 forward and 2 reverse gears and there was a choice of 40hp diesel, 37hp paraffin or 40hp or 45hp petrol engine. The tractor was one of the first diesel models with a distributor type injection pump and mechanical governor. An improved model with a live two-speed power take-off and dual category TCU hydraulics appeared in 1957.

Not the most successful tractor made by David Brown the 900 was replaced in 1958 by the 950. The new model had yellow wheels and radiator grille to distinguish it from the 900 but otherwise it was much the same at its predecessor. The main changes were an improved diesel fuel injection system which added an extra 2½hp, a modified

69. The rear-engined David Brown 2D designed for smallholders and market gardeners was made between 1956 and 1961.

drawbar and a re-designed steering system.

It was claimed that the David Brown 950 Implematic tractor, introduced in 1959, was able to overcome the need to choose a new tractor which could be used with existing implements on the farm rather than buying the best available model. According to sales literature the 950 Implematic would give the best possible results regardless of whether the farmer was using the TCU system for mounted implements with depth wheels or the new Implematic Traction Depth Control system for Ferguson-type implements without depth wheels. The Traction Depth Control system transferred variations in the forces acting through the top link by means of a

70. The David Brown 900 was launched at the 1956 Smithfield Show.

Bowden cable which ran from the tractor end of the top link to the hydraulic control valve. Any change in these forces automatically raised or lowered the implement to maintain the pre-selected draft setting and, in ideal conditions, a constant depth.

David Brown launched the 850 tractor in 1960, followed by the 880 and 990 in 1961. The standard and narrow width 35hp 850 and 42½hp 880 Implematic tractors had a 6 forward and 2 reverse gearbox and diff-lock with optional Live-drive power take-off and hydraulics. The 880 had category I and II hydraulic linkage but the 850 was restricted to category I implements. Tractor electrical systems had a positive earth at the time and the 880 had the distinction of being the first tractor with a negative earth electrical system to comply with new European standards. A 35hp petrol engine was available for the 850 but few were sold and it was only made for a short while. A number of David Brown 850 and 950 tractors, painted green and white, were sold in America in the early 1960s by the Oliver Corporation as the Oliver 500 and Oliver 600. The 52½hp 990 with a Live-drive or standard transmission had a cross-flow cylinder head and a dual range 6

71. Live power take-off and hydraulics were optional equipment for the David Brown 950 Implematic made from 1959 to 1962.

forward and 2 reverse gearbox. An optional automatic gearbox for the 990, which changed gear according to the load on the tractor, was announced at the 1961 Smithfield Show. However, farmers were not willing to pay an extra £250 for an automatic gearbox and the idea was dropped. An improved 990, announced in 1963, had the battery re-positioned in front of the radiator, a strengthened front axle and an optional 12 speed gearbox. The 3 cylinder 33hp 770 with 12 forward and 4 reverse gears launched at the 1964 Smithfield Show was the first David Brown tractor with the new Selectamatic hydraulic system. The driver could select depth

72. The David Brown 880.

73. A new chocolate brown and orchid white colour scheme replaced the David Brown red and yellow paintwork in 1965. This 990 has a Vicon Rotaspa spading machine on the three-point linkage.

control, TCU, height control, or external services on the Selectamatic dial and then control the chosen system with the hydraulic lever.

A chocolate brown and orchid white colour scheme replaced the David Brown red and yellow paintwork in October 1965 and the Selectamatic hydraulic system with an engine-mounted pump replaced the Implematic hydraulics on the 880 and the 990 in the same year. Engine outputs on the 770 and 990 were increased to 36hp and 55hp respectively. The 3 cylinder 48hp David Brown 885 replaced the 880 in 1971; the new model with a synchromesh gearbox and dual category linkage was made for the next five years.

David Brown were making about 30,000 tractors each year when the 67hp 1200 Selectamatic was launched in 1967 to meet farmers' demands for more horse power. The 1200 had a 4 cylinder direct injection engine, 6 forward and 2 reverse gears with a top speed of 14.7mph and an optional 12 forward speed gearbox. Other features included an independent power take-off with a hand-lever operated clutch, diff-lock, Selectamatic hydraulics, drum brakes and a pedal-operated exhaust brake. This device was a form of pneumatic engine brake which, when the pedal was depressed, restricted the flow of exhaust gases from the engine and in so doing slowed the transmission and rear wheels. Engine power was increased within a couple of years and the 72hp David Brown 1200 Selectamatic remained in production until 1971.

The 64hp 995 with a live multi-speed power take-off and the 996 with an independent power shaft were added to the David Brown range in the mid 1970s when the 900 had been improved with a 58hp engine, a 12 forward and 4 reverse synchromesh gearbox, Selectamatic dual-category hydraulics and a quiet cab.

The attempt to market an automatic David Brown gearbox in 1961 was a failure but the semi-automatic Hydrashift transmission introduced ten years later proved to be an award winner. The 72hp 1212 Hydrashift tractor which replaced the 1200 in 1971 had 12 forward and 4 reverse speeds provided by four clutchless change-on-the-move gears in each of 3 forward ratios and reverse.

Tenneco, who already owned Case, completed the acquisition of David Brown Tractors in 1972 and the 72hp 1210 Selectamatic with a synchromesh gearbox was launched that year. The four-wheel drive 1210 introduced in 1973 was the first David Brown tractor with two driven axles and power to the front axle could be engaged or disengaged on the move. The Case influence became more apparent in the UK in 1973 with the introduction of the orange and white Case 970 Agri-King.

The synchromesh 1410 and Hydrashift 1412 with turbocharged 91hp engines, 12 forward and 4 reverse gears, live hydraulics, independent power take-off and disc brakes were launched in 1975 and four-wheel drive models were added in 1976. There were fifteen different David Brown-Case tractors in the late 1970s ranging from the 48hp David Brown 885 to the 243hp Case 2670 Traction King. Some of the small and medium sized tractors were also made in high clearance rowcrop, narrow orchard and vineyard format. The 1210, 1212, 1410 and 1412 were made until 1980 when they were replaced by the David Brown-Case 90 series (plate 42), launched two years earlier in America. The David Brown name disappeared in 1983 when Case Tractors Ltd at Meltham launched the new 94 series tractors.

74. David Brown entered the 90hp class with the launch of the 1410 and 1412. The 1410 had a synchromesh gearbox while the 1412 had the David Brown Hydrashift semi-automatic transmission.

DEUTZ

Nikolaus August Otto, who perfected the four-stroke or Otto cycle engine in 1876, and Eigen Langen founded an engineering company at Deutz near Cologne in the 1860s. The first Deutz farm tractor with four large steel wheels and two equally large flywheels was made by a subsidiary Deutz company in America in 1894 and a 25hp Deutz tractor with a plough at each end was made in Germany in 1907. The tractor had two seats and a central steering wheel so that the driver could change position after each run to get a clear view of the plough as it worked its way back and forth across the field. Another 1919 vintage Deutz tractor for farming and forestry work looked more like a short wheel-base lorry than a 40hp farm tractor.

Dr Rudolph Diesel, who worked with the Deutz company in the 1890s, made the world's first high compression self-igniting (diesel) engine in 1897. An improved version of this semi-diesel engine was used for the 14hp Deutz MTH 222 tractor introduced in 1924. A 25–28hp Deutz water-cooled diesel engined tractor with two vertical cylinders, a 5 speed gearbox, power take-off and belt pulley appeared in 1933. The 11hp Deutz Bauernschlepper or smallholder's tractor introduced in 1936 played a major role in the mechanisation of small farms in Germany.

There were many mergers in the German engineering industry in the 1930s, such as the formation of Klöckner-Humboldt-Deutz AG (K-H-D) in 1938. Within four years the new company was mass producing water-cooled Deutz diesel engines. The F1L514 tractor with a 15hp single-cylinder engine and 4 forward gears introduced in 1949 was the first of many Deutz tractors with air-cooled diesel engines made in the 1950s. Other models included the 11hp F1L 612 rowcrop tractor, wheeled and crawler versions of the 28hp F2L 514 with 5 forward gears, the 50hp F3L 514, the F4L 514 with a 60hp engine and 7 forward speeds and the 100hp 6 cylinder DK 100 crawler. The figure after the letter F in the engine model number (eg, F4L) indicated the number of cylinders. The new Deutz FL 712 series tractors including the F1L 712/D-15 and F2L 712/D-25 launched in 1959 were at the lower end of K-H-D's early 1960s range of twenty-five wheeled tractors up to

65hp and two tracklayers with 75 and 100hp air-cooled engines. Independent front axle suspension was a feature of the 15hp D-15, which had 6 forward and 2 reverse gears and a diff-lock. The 22hp twin-cylinder D-25 had 8 forward and 2 reverse gears and the new Deutz Transfermatic three point linkage hydraulic system was optional on both models. The Deutz range had been extended to seven wheeled tractors in the 15–65hp bracket and two crawlers with 75hp and 100hp engines when British Deutz Ltd opened an office on the Strand in London in 1961.

The 28hp D 30 and D 30S with 8 forward speeds had replaced the D25 when British Deutz introduced the D 15 and D 30 to British farmers at the 1961 Smithfield Show. Press advertisements explained the benefits of air cooling and pointed out that there was no laborious nightly draining of the radiator on tractors left outside in

75. The Deutz D 30 and D 30S had a twin cylinder air-cooled engine, sprung front axle and a side pulley to drive a mid-mounted mower. Live power take-off was standard on the D 30S.

frosty weather. Air-cooled engines were popular with continental farmers and the Deutz design with many interchangeable parts made it possible to build 1, 2, 3, 4 or 6 cylinder in-line engines and vee engines with up to 12 cylinders on the same production line. The 2 cylinder 28hp rear-engined Multitrac introduced in 1962 was the first of many Deutz tool carriers. The 39hp Allrad (four-wheel drive) with four equal-size wheels and a front-mounted engine was another early Deutz tool carrier. The more powerful D 40, D 50 and D 80 standard-wheeled tractors with 3, 4 and 6 cylinder engines were added to the Deutz range in 1962.

K-H-D became part owners of Fahr Machinenfabrik in 1968. The acquisition of this well-established German tractor and farm machinery company, who also made a range of implements for Deutz tractors, was completed in 1970. Watveare Overseas Ltd, derived from Watkins & Roseveare, became UK distributors for the Deutz two- and four-wheel drive 06 series in 1974. Three models were available in Britain at the time, the D 7206/A and D 8006/A had 72hp and 80hp 4 cylinder air-cooled direct injection engines and the D 100 06A was a 6 cylinder 100hp four-wheel drive tractor. The model number indicated horse power and the letter A denoted four-wheel drive. The D 100 06A had 16 forward and 7 reverse speeds while the other models had a 12 forward and 4 reverse gearbox. All three were equipped with Deutz Transfermatic hydraulic system and hydrostatic steering. Sales literature described Transfermatic hydraulics as a system with 'joltless control and even working depth' and 'single lever operation after selecting either draft or position control'. The raised implement was 'carried on a cushion of oil in the service cylinder to give a shock absorber effect' so that the tractor and implement were subject to less fatigue. The 06 series, with various improvements and additions including D 4506 with a 3 cylinder Deutz engine and an 8 forward and 4 reverse gearbox, were made until the

76. The 100hp 6 cylinder Deutz D100 06A with a 16 forward and 7 reverse speed gearbox cost £8,290.

early 1980s. Later models were sold with a safety cab.

A new generation of Deutz self-propelled tool carriers appeared in 1972. The four-wheel drive Intrac 2003A with a glass-walled cab and the driving seat in front of a 62hp air-cooled diesel engine had an 8 forward and 4 reverse synchro-mesh gearbox with an optional creeper box adding four extra speeds from 0.2mph to 1mph. Front and rear independent power take-off shafts and live hydraulic linkages with top link sensing and power-assisted steering were standard equipment.

The 80hp DX 85 and 102hp DX 110/A which took part in the 1979 Long Sutton tractor tests were early models in the new Deutz DX range. K-H-D adopted the Deutz-Fahr name for its agricultural equipment in 1981 and the four-wheel drive DX 120A and DX 145A were launched in the same year. The new tractors had 110hp and 132hp engines with a thermostatically controlled cooling fan claimed to reduce fuel consumption by 10 per cent and a 24 forward and 8 reverse Powermatic change-on-the move transmission.

The Deutz-Fahr 07C medium-power tractors, ranging from the 52hp 5207C to the 75hp 7807C, were announced during 1981 and 1982. The smaller models had a 9 forward and 4 reverse synchromesh transmission and telescopic front axles while the other tractors were equipped with a 12 forward and 4 reverse gearbox. The Deutz-Fahr range on the UK market had increased to 17 models in two- and four-wheel drive format in 1983 with 07C tractors from 54hp to 82hp and DX range from 78hp to 220hp.

The new 78–117hp 4 and 6 cylinder DX 4 and DX 6 tractors introduced at the 1983 Smithfield Show had a central drive shaft to the front axle, independent front hydraulic linkage and improved ground clearance. The DX 3 models with 3 cylinder 50–82hp engines superseded the 07C series in 1984 and the DX range was completed with the launch of the flagship 220hp 8 cylinder DX 8.30 with Powermatic transmission and electronic linkage control hydraulics in the same year.

K-H-D bought the engine manufacturer Motoren-Werke Mannheim (MWM)and launched six new 50–98hp Deutz DX 3 and DX4HPE (High Performance and Economy) tractors in 1985. Features of the HPE models included a synchromesh gearbox and a new cab which according to publicity material brought new standards of luxury to the 50–100hp tractor market.

Deutz-Fahr celebrated 60 years of tractor production in 1986 with the Diamond range which had a multi-speed transmission, remote hydraulic linkage control and improved sound proofing for the cab. The Deutz Agtronic performance monitoring system also introduced in 1986 as optional equipment for tractors

77. The 1984 Deutz Fahr DX range included the 50hp DX3.70 and the mighty DX8 30 with a 233hp engine, hydrostatic steering and a walk-through cab.

over 100hp could be used to record data on forward speed, area covered, power shaft speed, etc.

The 72–117hp DX Commander series introduced in 1989 had the latest Command Centre cab, an improved four-wheel drive and four-wheel braking system and OptiTrac self-locking differential on the front axle with automatic disengagement when the wheels were turned to the left or right. There was a growing interest in the use of bio-fuels in diesel engines in the late 1980s which prompted Deutz-Fahr to approve the use of rape seed oil for all Deutz tractors made after 1989. It was pointed out that although power output would not be affected the engine would require more frequent servicing.

Five new Deutz-Fahr Agrostar DX 4 and DX 6 4 and 6 cylinder 88–143hp tractors were launched in 1990. They had a 48 forward and 12 reverse synchromesh transmission and the new suspended flat floor cab, with its Agrotronic performance monitor, claimed to be the quietest on the market.

78. The Trac-technic division of Watveare introduced the Intrac multi-functional tractors with front and rear hydraulic linkage and power take-offs in 1990. The 115hp Intrac 6.30 and the turbocharged 150hp 6.60 had a 50-50 load distribution on the axles. The cab could be tilted hydraulically when servicing the tractor.

58

79. Deutz-Fahr had made tractors with air-cooled engines for 47 years when they introduced the Agrotron series. the first Deutz tractors to have water-cooled engines. Other features of the Agrotron range launched in 1997 included load sensing hydraulics, front axle suspension and a high visibility air-conditioned cab packed with electronic technology.

K-H-D introduced the first high visibility Deutz AgroXtra tractors in 1991. With other model changes the 1992 Deutz-Fahr range consisted of the AgroPrima, AgroStar and AgroExtra tractors. The high visibility AgroExtra 4.17A, 4.47A 4.57A, 6.07A and 6.17A tractors with streamlined sloping bonnets had air-cooled Deutz engines in the 80–113hp bracket, a choice of transmissions with up to 24 forward and 8 reverse speeds and hydraulic self-adjusting disc brakes.

The computerised AgroTronic HD system designed to combat the see-sawing effect caused when driving across rutted ground was an optional extra on the Agro Extra Power Plus models launched in 1993. The ASM drive control management system for the front and rear diff-locks and front-wheel drive, designed to give the driver maximum comfort and avoid operating errors, was a feature of the new 107hp, 115hp and 125hp AgroStar 6.08A, 6.28A and 6.38A launched in 1994.

K-H-D sold the Deutz-Fahr tractor business to SAME Trattori in 1995 and this led to the formation of the SAME Deutz-Fahr group. Watveare, who had moved to Warwickshire in 1990, retained the Deutz-Fahr distributorship until 1997 when SAME Deutz-Fahr established their own marketing organisation in the UK.

The Agrotron series initially launched in 1996 had been extended to ten models in the 75–150hp bracket in 1997. The biggest change was the use of low emission, water-cooled engines but other features included load sensing hydraulics, a front-axle suspension system and high visibility air-conditioned cabs which bristled with the latest electronic technology. More powerful Agrotrons with 230hp and 260hp engines were added in 1998.

DOE

80. This version of the Doe Dual Power tractor or Triple D was based on two Fordson Super Majors.

Farmers in Essex and surrounding areas were buying Allis Chalmers, Case and Fordson tractors from Ernest Doe in the 1930s. The family business of Ernest Doe & Sons Ltd at Ulting had become a leading Fordson tractor dealer when they introduced the Doe Dual Power four-wheel drive tractor in 1958. Some heavy land farmers who used a crawler for heavy cultivations wanted a more powerful wheeled tractor to overcome the transport problems experienced with a tracklayer. One of these farmers came up with the idea of linking two Fordson Power Majors in tandem to make a 100hp four-wheel drive tractor. The front axle was removed from both tractors and the rear unit was close-coupled on a 2ft diameter steel turntable attached to a strengthened drawbar on the leading tractor. An engine-mounted hydraulic pump supplied oil to the steering rams used to turn the front

81. Ernest Doe & Sons made heavy duty ploughs, cultivators and subsoilers for the Triple D.

tractor through an angle close to 90 degrees. The driver, seated on the rear unit controlled both clutches with a hydraulic master cylinder and slave rams. A linkage enabled the driver to select high or low range on the front tractor while seated on the rear unit but it was necessary to dismount in order to select the required forward gear on the leading tractor. The tractor was set in motion by engaging the front range gearbox and drive to the rear wheels after returning to the driving seat. The Triple D was reversed on the headland with only the rear wheels turning. The Doe Dual Power or Dual Drive tractor which became the Triple D could be supplied on pneumatic tyres or spade lug wheels. With about twenty tractors sold an improved version also with an assister ram for the three-point linkage was introduced in 1959.

The 1960 model of the Triple-D, based on two 52hp Fordson Super Major tractors, had a more efficient method of changing gear; a hydraulic master cylinder and slave rams enabled the driver to change gear on both units without leaving the seat. The front diff-lock was also engaged hydraulically from the rear tractor. The Triple-D had 108hp under its two bonnets when the improved 54hp Super Major appeared in 1963.

Ford launched the 1000 range in 1965 and two Ford 5000 tractors with a combined 130hp were joined to form the Doe 130. The clutch, gear changing and steering were hydraulically operated and a cable connected the throttle levers. An improved

82. The Doe 130, which cost £3,300 in 1967, had a strengthened hydraulic system to cope with the increased power at the drawbar.

Ford 5000 with a 75hp engine appeared in 1968 and a few of these tractors were used to build the Doe 150. Production had ceased by 1970, partly due to competition from County, Roadless, Muir Hill and other four-wheel drive tractors and partly because of the high development costs involved in complying with the new safety cab regulations.

Ernest Doe & Sons briefly returned to tractor production in 1971 with the two-wheel drive Doe 5100. Basically a strengthened Ford 5000 with a 100hp 6 cylinder Ford industrial engine and heavy duty clutch, the Doe 5100 was seen at several public demonstrations but only a handful were made.

83. The Doe 5100 was a stretched Ford 5000 with a 6 cylinder engine.

DUTRA

The Dutra story began in 1961 in Hungary with the introduction of a four-wheel drive tractor with equal-size wheels which had a power to weight ratio designed to give a high drawbar pull with almost complete elimination of wheelslip. The tractors were made in Budapest and exported by Technoimpex to several countries, including Britain where they were sold by the Guest General Trading Co at Brandon in Suffolk from the mid-1960s.

The Dutra D4K-B, with a Csepel 100hp diesel engine, 10 forward and 2 reverse gears and a top speed of 20mph, was demonstrated to British farmers in 1967. The advanced design of the D4K-B included a 540/1,000rpm power take-off and air brakes on all four wheels.

Dutra Tractors (GB) Ltd, also of Brandon, were marketing four Dutra models in the early

84. Dutra tractors were imported by the Guest General Trading Co in the mid-1960s.

1970s. The 6354, 6372 and 6354 Turbo had 6 cylinder Perkins direct injection engines rated at 102hp, 115hp and 125hp respectively while the Dutra 8613 had an indirect injection 110hp Csepel power unit. Standard equipment included 10 forward and 2 reverse gears, diff-locks on both axles, an independent closed circuit hydraulic system with lower link sensing and hydrostatic steering. The 10 forward gears were split to give 4 creep speeds, 4 field speeds up to 7½mph and 2 gears for roadwork. The clutch and diff-locks were operated pneumatically by compressed air rams connected to a small engine-driven compressor. An optional assister ram was available for the hydraulic linkage and a simple locking mechanism on the left-hand lift rod could be released to make it easier to attach mounted implements. The last Dutra tractors were made in 1973.

85. Four Dutra tractors from Hungary in the 102–125hp range were available in the UK during the early 1970s.

EBRO

The Spanish state-owned Motor Iberica company made Ebro tractors at their Barcelona factory in the early 1960s and a handful of these tractors were sold in Britain. Motor Iberica, who bought the production rights of the New Fordson Major from the Ford Motor Co, built the tractor in Spain as the Ebro. It was superseded by the Super Ebro, which was a Fordson Super Major in disguise. When the Super Major was discontinued in 1965 Motor Iberica continued production of the Super Ebro under licence until 1966 when a manufacturing agreement was made with Massey Ferguson.

The Ebro 115, also made by Motor Iberica, was virtually the same tractor with Massey Ferguson style wings and bonnet. Massey Ferguson established their own assembly line in Barcelona with a computer link to the Banner Lane factory to build MF tractors for the Spanish market. Motor Iberica used the 1980 Royal Show to test the British market when they exhibited the 130hp four-wheel drive Ebro 6125DT and two smaller tractors but achieved little success. Massey Ferguson was also involved in the production of two other Ebro models with 71hp and 82hp Perkins engines and Fordson Super Major transmission which were made until the early 1980s. Nissan, who bought the Massey Ferguson holding in Motor Iberica in 1980, eventually acquired the Spanish company.

EICHER

The Eicher brothers used a twin-cylinder Deutz engine to make a farm tractor in 1936. In the Second World War they joined a consortium of German farm equipment manufacturers which included Güldner and Fahr. Eicher were building tractors with their own single-cylinder air-cooled diesel engines by the late 1940s and the range was extended to include tractors with 2, 3 and 4 cylinder engines which had a separate cooling fan for each cylinder. The Eicher Kombi tool carrier with a rear-mounted 15hp Deutz diesel engine and a 5 forward and reverse gearbox was launched in 1952. Later Kombi tractors had 11hp and 19hp Eicher air-cooled diesel engines.

The Eicher 19/20 with a single-cylinder water-cooled Deutz engine, 5 forward gears and reverse and a 580rpm power take-off was the smallest of five Eicher tractors made in the 1950s. Air-cooled Deutz power units were used for the 25hp and 30hp 2 cylinder, 45hp 3 cylinder and 60hp 4 cylinder engined tractors which had a 5 forward and reverse gearbox. Deutz used the same range of engines for their own range of tractors.

The 13hp Muli and the New Kombi tool carriers with 19hp or 22hp Eicher air-cooled engines appeared in 1957. The New Kombi had 5 forward and one reverse gear but the Muli with a 6 forward and 2 reverse gearbox had a 540rpm rear power take-off and an

86. The Eicher 19/20 made in the early 1950s had leaf spring suspension on the front axle and a 580rpm power take-off.

unusual 982rpm front power shaft with an optional reverse drive. A 2 cylinder 26hp four-wheel drive Eicher with equal-size wheels launched in 1959 was one of ten models of the era with air-cooled diesel engines within the 15–60hp bracket. Big cat names were used for some of these tractors, such as the single-cylinder 15hp Leopard and the twin-cylinder 22hp and 29hp Panther and Tiger. The larger 50hp Mammoth I had three cylinders and the 55hp Mammoth II had four. The smaller tractors had 6 forward speeds and the others had 8 while the Mammoth had 4 reverse gears and the Leopard had 2.

A few Eicher tractors were sold in the UK, mainly to fruit farmers in the south east. They included the mid-1960s Puma with a 28hp engine, 6 forward gears and category I hydraulic linkage. Narrow versions of the Puma with two- and four-wheel drive and 2 or 3 cylinder 30hp and 50hp engines were imported in the early 1970s along with improved versions of the Mammoth and the 52hp Allrad four-wheel drive tool carrier. The two- and four-wheel drive Mammoth tractors had air-cooled turbocharged engines with a separate fan to cool each cylinder, a dual clutch, 12 forward and 4 reverse gears and draft control hydraulics.

Massey Ferguson bought a share in the German company in the early 1970s and some Eicher tractors were eventually made with water-cooled Perkins engines. A turbocharged 6 cylinder Eicher air-cooled power unit was used for the four-wheel drive Wotan tractor launched in the mid-1970s. Features of the Wotan included a 16 forward and 7 reverse gearbox, dual category lower link sensing hydraulics and front wheel drive which could be engaged or disengaged on the move. However, the Massey Ferguson connection was short-lived and the Indian division of the original Eicher company re-purchased the MF shares in the early 1980s. The Indian company continued to thrive and had an annual production of 20,000 two-wheel drive German-designed tractors with engines of up to 40hp in the late 1990s. Eicher were also making the Trantor fast tractor in India in the mid-1980s and the new Trantor 904, launched in 1999 and mainly for sale in India and China, was also made in their Indian factory.

FAHR

Johan Georg Fahr started making farm machinery in 1870 and he was producing binders and combine harvesters by the 1930s. The first Fahr tractors with Deutz and Güldner air- and water-cooled engines were made in 1938 while Fahr tractors made in the war years had gas-powered Deutz engines with a built-in wood gas generator.

Fahr Maschinfabrik introduced the first models of the lightweight D series tractors in 1949. The D15, D17N and high clearance D17H had a 15–17hp twin-cylinder, water-cooled diesel engine made by Güldner in Germany. Other models in the series included the 22hp D22 which, with the later addition of three extra horse power became the D25. These tractors, together with the D28 and D30, were all equipped with a 5 forward speed and reverse gearbox.

A mix of air- and water-cooled engines was used in the mid-1950s for Fahr-wheeled tractors and tool carriers. The wheeled D270, D400 and D540 had 32hp, 45hp and 60hp

87. A direct drive from the engine for a mid-mounted mower was a feature of the Fahr D 17. It was sold in Britain in the mid-1950s.

88. Passenger seats were provided on both mudguards of the D series Fahr tractors. This one has a power take-off driven Fahr spade harrow on the three-point linkage.

Deutz engines respectively and the 2 cylinder 17hp or 24hp engine for the GT 130 self-propelled tool-carrier was made by Güldner. The GT 130 had the driving seat at the rear and the engine was mounted above the front axle with the drive taken through a 5 speed gearbox to the rear wheels. The late 1950s saw the launch of the D88, the D131, and the D133 with 15hp, 17hp and 25hp Güldner engines respectively. The D 177 with a 4 cylinder 34hp Mercedes-Benz diesel engine and an 8 forward and 4 reverse gearbox was also launched during this period. Fahr and Güldner joined forces in 1961 and formed a working relationship with Deutz. K-H-D, who already owned Deutz, became part owners of Fahr in 1968 and the takeover was completed in 1970.

FARM TRACTOR DRIVES

The four-wheel drive FTD Chieftain based on new and re-conditioned Ford tractor components was exhibited at the 1981 Smithfield Show by Farm Tractor Drives Ltd of Shardlow in Derbyshire. Arthur Batelle established the company in 1977 to import Schindler front-wheel drive kits and transmission units from Switzerland and within four years several hundred Ford tractors had been converted to four-wheel drive.

Limited production of the low cost, no frills Chieftain tractor with a 6 cylinder 105hp Ford 2725 industrial engine and a mix of re-built Ford 5000 and 7000 transmission components started in 1982. The Schindler front axle with a torque biasing

89. The FTD Chieftain was aimed at an almost untapped market that wanted an economical general purpose four-wheel drive tractor.

differential enabled the front wheel with the best traction to absorb up to three times as much torque as the other one. Power-assisted steering and a Duncan safety cab with a radio and heater were included in the £13,750 price tag – about £5,000 less than many two-wheel drive tractors of the time. A front weight frame, hydraulic assister ram and auxiliary 18 gallon fuel tank were optional extras.

The main tractor manufacturers were not very interested in four-wheel drive at the time and left production of conversion kits to County, Roadless and other manufacturers who generally made tractors for the larger arable farm. This left an opening for FTD to sell the keenly priced Chieftain to farmers with small to medium-sized areas of grassland or mixed crops. However, David Brown initiated a price war in the early 1980s and within a couple of years the Chieftain tractor lost its price advantage. It had disappeared by 1985, with only a handful made.

FARMWELL

Workwell Engineering in Kent were using Massey Ferguson skid-units to build the Farmwell tractor in the early 1990s. Designed for under-developed countries, the 80hp Farmwell 480 was a very basic tractor on steel wheels with all electrical equipment removed. The engine was started by hand with a wind-up inertia or spring starter which provided instant starting for engines with capacities of up to one litre per cylinder. Inertia starters, made by CAV and Simms Motor Units

with a crank handle to compress a heavy spring in the starter housing, were a simple bolt-on alternative to an electric starter motor. With the spring fully wound a locking mechanism was released and the expanding spring turned the starter pinion and flywheel ring gear in the normal way.

90. The Farmwell 480 at the 1991 Royal Show.

The Farmwell was not a pretty tractor but the 3mm thick sheet steel bonnet and body panels protected the fuel tank, radiator and vulnerable engine components. An hour meter was its only instrument and a single grade of oil was specified for use throughout the tractor. A more powerful Farmwell 6110 was made for sugar cane production and other heavy work.

91. The inertia starter used on the Farmwell 480 was wound up with a cranking handle on the hexagon stub (left) and the handle (right) released the spring pressure which turned the engine.

FENDT

Johann-Georg Fendt and his son Hermann made a four-wheel self-propelled grass mower in 1928 with a 4pk petrol engine to cut the hay crop on their farm. The machine lacked power so the father and son built a 6pk steel-wheeled Dieselross (or Diesel Horse) tractor in 1930 and used it with various implements including a side-mounted mower and a mounted plough. Pk or ps is the German abbreviation for pferdestarke/n and like the French chevaux- vapeur (cv) it is one metric horse power and the equivalent of 1.014 imperial hp.

The F 9 Dieselross with a 9hp horizontal single-cylinder crosswise-mounted diesel engine, a sprung front axle and solid tyres appeared in 1932. The brothers Hermann, Xaver and Paul Fendt went into partnership as Xaver Fendt & Co at Marktoberdorf in 1937 and launched the single-cylinder 16hp F 18 Fendt Dieselross with an independent power take-off which could be disengaged under load. The F 22 Dieselross with a vertical 2 cylinder water-cooled 22hp engine and four-speed gearbox which appeared in 1938 was the last diesel tractor made by Fendt before the onset of war. The shortage of fuel in Germany led to a ban on the use of diesel tractors and Fendt developed a wood gas generator for their Dieselross tractors.

About fifty German tractor and farm equipment manufacturers, including Xaver Fendt & Co, spent the immediate post-war years re-building their industry. The Fendt 18hp Dieselross F 18H with 6 forward speeds and reverse launched in 1949 was the last tractor made at Marktoberdorf with a single-cylinder horizontal engine. A new era of Fendt tractors started when the F 15 Dieselross with a vertical single-cylinder 15hp MWM engine appeared in 1950. The low-profile F 15 had a short wheel base which gave it an old-fashioned look but an optional 8 forward speed gearbox was well ahead of its time.

The next generation of Dieselross tractors in the 12–40hp bracket was introduced in 1952. The 28hp Fendt F 28 added a little later with a twin-cylinder water-cooled MWM diesel engine with a 12 volt electric starter was typical. A starting handle was provided for emergency use. The 1952 range had a 5 forward and reverse gearbox with optional high speed and creep speed ratios, independent servo-assisted rear drum brakes, transmission hand brake, diff-lock and power take-off. The Fendt transverse leaf spring suspension was retained on the front axle and the steering was said to be 'light enough to control with one hand'. There was a belt pulley on the side of the transmission housing behind the rear axle and a direct drive system from the engine was provided for a side-mounted mower which many farmers kept permanently attached to the tractor. Optional equipment included hydraulic lift and linkage, weather cab, flashing indicators, a power take-off driven tyre pump and an electric hand lamp.

92. The 12hp Fendt Dieselross tractor was introduced to German farmers in 1952.

The first of many Fendt tool carriers, on this occasion with a 12hp MWM diesel engine above the rear axle and four implement attachment points, was launched in 1953. The first models of the new Favorit and Farmer range went into large scale production in 1958 and Fendt celebrated the production of their 100,000th tractor at Marktoberdoft in 1961.

Improved versions of the Farmer range appeared throughout the 1960s and a new self-propelled tool bar with a 45hp 3 cylinder diesel engine with front-, mid- and rear-mounted implement attachment points was launched in 1965. The Farmer 3S Turbomatik range introduced in 1968 set a new trend for Fendt tractors. The Turbomatik turbo-clutch or fluid flywheel was used to transmit drive through a single-plate clutch to the gearbox with the engine set at a pre-selected speed.

93. The Favorit 612 S, costing £7,300 in 1974, was one of the first Fendt tractors sold by Bill Bennett Engineering. Tractors sold in the UK had a safety cab with an adjustable seat and a large front opening window.

Bill Bennett Engineering of Chipping Sodbury near Bristol introduced Fendt tractors to British farmers in 1974. Early imports included the two-wheel drive 105hp Favorit 610S and the two- or four-wheel drive 6 cylinder 120hp 611S and 612S with water-cooled direct injection engines. A 6 speed synchromesh gearbox and high/low range lever provided 12 forward and 6 reverse speeds. The Favorit 612S had 16 forward and 8 reverse gears. The engines had individual cylinders for easy servicing and other standard features included the Fendt turbo-clutch, power steering, and a sprung front axle. The tractors

94. Improved models of the Fendt Favorit 600SL series introduced in 1976 with automatic diff-locks and disc brakes on both axles set new standards in tractor design.

had external assister rams for the hydraulic linkage which could be used in position or draft control and in a mix of both systems.

The two- and four-wheel drive, 3 cylinder 55hp Farmer 104S and the 4 cylinder 65hp Farmer 106S with a synchromesh transmission and optional reverser unit for quick directional changes for loader work were also available in the UK in 1974. The 36hp or 50hp rear-engined 250 GT (Gerate Trager or tool carrier) with a safety cab completed the 1974 Fendt tractor range available in the UK.

British farmers had a wider choice of Fendt tractors, including 85–150hp Favorit models, the full Farmer range and 55hp or 78hp tool carriers, in 1976. Five new Fendt Favorit 600 S and 600 SL Turbomatik models introduced later that year had 100–165hp direct injection engines. Other features included independent power take-off, lower link sensing hydraulics with automatic couplers and a heated quiet cab which tilted backwards to service the transmission and hydraulic system. A Bill Bennett Engineering advertisement claimed that 'more and more farmers were finding that high quality Fendt tractors gave them a new standard of reliability and operator satisfaction'.

The 100hp 610 S had 12 forward and 5 reverse speeds while the other models were equipped with a 16 forward and 7 reverse speed gearbox. An optional creeper box provided an extra 8 forward and 4 reverse

speeds. The more powerful 211hp 622 SL and the 252hp 626 SL four-wheel drive tractors were added to the Favorit range in 1979. The flag-ship 18 forward and 6 reverse speed 626 SL had 6 forward and 2 reverse synchromesh gears with a clutchless one-up and one-down change in each gear. A sideways tilt adjustment for the cab enabled the driver to sit level when ploughing with one wheel running in a furrow. Other features included electro-hydraulic control of the diff-locks and hydraulic linkage.

95. The F 275 GT was the biggest of three Fendt tool carriers launched in the late 1970s.

The re-styled two- and four-wheel drive Farmer 300 Turbomatik range with 4 cylinder 50–86hp engines launched in 1980 had an improved 14 forward and 4 reverse synchro-mesh gearbox, four-wheel braking and an optional 40kph (25mph) transmission. A safety cab on rubber mounting blocks, a two-speed power take-off and an automatically engaged diff-lock were included in the price of the 78hp 308 LS and 86hp 309 LS. The 92hp turbocharged 4 cylinder Farmer 310 with 21 forward and 6 reverse speeds was added to the range in 1984. The improved Fentronic hydraulics with electronic

96. Launched in 1993 the Favorit 800 series had electronic control systems for the four-wheel drive, diff-locks, power take-off and hydraulic system.

linkage control were operated with a joystick in the 'climate controlled workplace'. The 6 cylinder 115hp 312 LSA introduced in 1987 was similar to the other Farmer models. The two- and four-wheel drive 250S, 260S and 275S were the first models of the Fendt 200 series launched in 1988. The Farmer 312 LSA gearbox was used for the new 50hp, 60hp and 75hp tractors which were joined within a year or so by the 40hp 240S.

New models of the four-wheel drive Fendt GTA tool carrier with 65hp, 80hp, 100hp and 115hp air-cooled engines were introduced in 1991. The specification included Fendt's electronic hydraulic control unit with a shock load stabilizer system to reduce implement bounce on the rear linkage; two-wheel drive was available for the 65–100hp tractors.

There were 20 Farmer 200 and 300 series tractors, four 600 series

97. MAN four-cylinder engines with a turbocharger and intercooler provided the power for the Fendt Xylon 500 series launched in 1994.

Favorit models and eight tool carriers in 1992 when Bonhill Engineering Ltd at South Cave in Yorkshire were appointed Fendt distributors for the UK. Re-styled and more powerful Farmer 300 LS and LSA tractors with sloping bonnets and a new front grille were launched the same year. The smallest Farmer 304 LS/LSA had a 3 cylinder 70hp engine and the 6 cylinder 312 LSA rated at 120hp was the most powerful model in the range. An optional 21 forward and reverse speed shuttle gearbox with an electro-magnetic pre-selection system was available for tractors over 75hp.

The new 105–140hp 500 series and 165–230hp 800 series Favorit tractors announced in 1993 had the Fendt Turboshift single lever shuttle transmission system with 24 forward and reverse work speeds while an optional creeper box gave an extra 20 gears. Six-cylinder MAN engines, hydro-pneumatic front axle suspension with an optional levelling control, electronic front and rear hydraulic linkage controls and a spring mounted cab were features of the Flagship 800 series tractors.

The Farmer 300 series was revised in 1995 to give six models with 3, 4 and 6 cylinder engines in the 75–125hp bracket. Electronic control systems similar to those on the Favorit range were available at extra cost and the 75hp tractor was the only four-wheel drive model without an optional front axle suspension system.

The Fendt Xylon 520, 522 and 524 advanced tool carriers or 'systems tractors' with a choice of colour scheme were rated at 110hp, 125hp and 140hp when they made their debut at the 1994 Smithfield Show. The transmission system included the Turbomatik clutch and a four-stage powershift gearbox with pre-select reverse giving 24 field and 20 twenty creep speeds from 0.5 to 50kph. Other features included a swivel-joint front axle with lockable suspension, levelling control and a two-seater cab.

Introductions in 1997 included the Fendt 900 Vario tractors, the 150hp Favorit 515C, an improved transmission for the 900 series and the Farmer 307C, 308C and 309C rated at 75hp, 85hp and 95hp respectively, which replaced equivalent Farmer 300 LSA models. A mechanical gearbox combined with a new stepless hydrostatic transmission with a single joystick control was the special feature on the 170hp, 200hp, 230hp and 260hp 900 series Vario tractors with MAN 6 cylinder engines.

Xaver Fendt & Co were acquired by AGCO in 1997. The American company, which also owned Massey Ferguson, took over the distribution of Fendt tractors in the UK and within a year a number of MF dealers were selling the German-built tractors. Having lost the Fendt franchise, Bonhill Marketing Ltd were appointed UK distributors for Steyr tractors by Case Steyr Landmaschinntechnik AG in 1998.

FERGUSON

Harry Ferguson, christened Henry George, was born in County Down in 1884. His first experience with tractors was in Ireland in the 1920s where he sold the American Waterloo Boy Model N, marketed in Europe as the Overtime Model N. The Irishman built his first tractor in 1933, which was known as the Ferguson Black because of its colour. An agreement made with David Brown resulted in the production of Ferguson-Brown tractors at Meltham, Yorkshire between 1936 and 1939 with Ferguson's hydraulic weight transfer and draft control system. Anticipating the break-up with David Brown the Irishman concluded the famous 'gentleman's agreement' with Henry Ford which led to the production of Ferguson tractors at Detroit in the USA. Henry Ford made the Ford Ferguson 9N from 1939 until 1947 when it was replaced by the 8N which was sold as a Ford tractor. The 8N was virtually identical to the Ford Ferguson 9N and the resulting law suit dragged on for four years.

Ferguson was faced with the loss of his American market after the break-up with Ford so he bought a 72 acre factory site in Detroit and the first TO 20 (Tractor Overseas) was made at Ferguson Park on 11 October 1948. The TO 20, which was similar to the TE 20, was superseded by the 30hp TO 30 in 1951. The TO 35, which replaced the TO 30 in 1954, was made for the next six years.

The Ford Motor Co made 80 per cent of the tractors produced in the UK between 1936 and 1946 but the launch of the TE 20 (Tractor England) in 1946 heralded a revolution in farm mechanisation. The first Ferguson tractors made at the Standard Motor Company's Banner Lane factory in Coventry were similar to the 9N with an overhead valve 24hp petrol engine manufactured by the Continental Motor Co at Michigan in America. The TE (Con) 20 had a 4 forward and reverse gearbox with a safety-start mechanism built into the gear lever, re-shaped rear wheel centres, a front-hinged bonnet and a $1\frac{1}{8}$ inch diameter power take-off shaft. A master brake pedal which acted on both wheels was added to the independent steering brake pedals. The stock

98. American-built Ford Ferguson 9N tractors were sent to Britain during World War Two.

of Continental engines ran out in 1947 and new power unit based on the Standard Vanguard car engine was used and the tractor became the 24hp TEA 20.

Double shift work was started at Banner Lane in 1948 and production increased to about 5,500 tractors per month to meet the growing demand for Ferguson tractors. Launched in 1949 the TED 20 was identical to the TEA 20 apart from its vaporising oil engine. The TEH and TEJ lamp oil models were added in 1950 and modifications in 1951 increased the TEA engine power to 28hp and 26hp for the TED tractor.

Various gadgets were made during this period to make the grey Ferguson easier to use. Spanners were needed to alter the length of the standard Ferguson top link but the Speedy top link made by

FERGUSON TE TRACTOR MODELS, 1946–56

Model	Build	Fuel	Model	Build	Fuel
TE 20 (Con)	standard	petrol	TEA	standard	petrol
TEB 20 (Con)	narrow	petrol	TEC	narrow	petrol
TED	standard	tvo	TEE	narrow	tvo
TEF	standard	diesel	TEH	standard	lamp oil
TEJ	narrow	lamp oil	TEK	vineyard	petrol
TEL	vineyard	tvo	TEM	vineyard	lamp oil
TEP	industrial	petrol	TER	industrial	tvo
TES	industrial	lamp oil	TET	industrial	diesel

99. The Ferguson TEA 20 with a 24hp Standard petrol engine cost £325 in 1947.

Tamkin Bros of Maldon in Essex had a circular handle which made this adjustment a simple task. A large boot was useful when attempting to disengage the clutch and apply the left-hand steering brake at the same time but the Tamkin Slewstick made life a little easier for the driver. The Slewstick, which consisted of a tubular handle attached to the steering brake pedal, could be used to apply the left-hand brake while the left foot remained in full control of the clutch pedal. The Gray-Thompson safety clutch-release made by Grays of Fetterangus in Scotland was designed to stop the tractor if a mounted implement hit a buried object. The device, which cost £7.10s, consisted of a spring-loaded mechanism on the top link which was connected through a mechanical linkage to the clutch pedal. When a shock load from the implement was transmitted through the top link, the spring-loaded mechanism was released and the device disengaged the clutch.

A full range of Ferguson implements was available for the tractor but as Harry Ferguson lacked the necessary manufacturing facilities production was sub-contracted to other companies. Rubery Owen at Darlaston made the ploughs, the cultivators were produced by Midland Industries at Wolverhampton and James Sankey & Sons at Wellington made tipping trailers.

The original 6 volt electrical system on the TEA and TED tractors was changed to 12 volts when the 26hp 4 cylinder TEF 20 diesel tractor was launched in 1951. The TEF 20 had a heavy duty 12 volt starter with a safety switch on the side of the gearbox and two batteries located above the rear axle housings. A decompression lever and a Ki-gass system were provided to help start the in-direct injection engine in cold weather. A 3 cylinder Perkins diesel engine conversion was introduced in 1952 for the petrol- and paraffin-engined tractors. The Ferguson catalogue for that year included 14 models of the TE 20 tractor, 34 Ferguson implements and 20 different accessories including a tractor jack and tyre inflation kit.

Massey-Harris and Ferguson joined forces in 1953. Massey-Harris-Ferguson continued production of the TE series until 1956 by which time more than 517,000 grey Fergusons had been made at Banner Lane. The

grey Ferguson achieved average annual sales in excess of 20,000 in Britain and many more were exported with Scandinavia and Australia among the major customers.

The grey and gold Ferguson FE 35 with a 4 cylinder Standard engine, which, depending on build, could run on petrol, vaporising oil, diesel or lamp oil and was rated at 37hp, 30hp, 37hp and 29hp respectively was launched at the 1956 Smithfield Show. The FE 35 had a safety-start mechanism built into the range gear lever, a 6 forward and 2 reverse gearbox, live and ground speed power take-off and a new two-lever hydraulic system with position control, response control and

100. The grey and gold Ferguson FE 35 4 cylinder diesel engine with a 20:1 compression ratio and a pre-heater in the inlet manifold was not the easiest tractor to start on cold days.

two-way draft control. The American TO 20 style hinged bonnet with an access panel for daily engine maintenance was used on the new tractor. A tip-back cushioned seat with a back rest improved driver comfort and additional instruments recorded engine hours, registered power take-off speed and measured forward travel in each gear. The tip back seat made it possible for the operator to drive while standing on the foot plates, presumably allowing him to take a break from sitting on the not quite so comfortable seat cushion. The de-luxe FE 35 had a dual clutch with live hydraulics and power take-off.

Harry Ferguson relinquished his interest in M-H-F in 1957 and Harris was dropped from the company name. The grey and gold FE 35 became the Massey Ferguson 35 with the new MF red and grey colour scheme. Its triple triangle badge was also used for the MF 65 launched at the 1957 Smithfield Show.

FIAT

The Italian Fiat company founded by Giovanni Agnelli in Turin in 1899 to manufacture motor vehicles took its name from the initial letters of Fabrica Italiana di Automobili Torino. Fiat made their first tractors in 1919. The 702's water-cooled 4 cylinder Fiat truck engine developed 30hp when running on petrol but this fell to 25hp on paraffin. The tractor had 3 forward gears and reverse, a 3 speed belt pulley, a sprung front axle and an off-set driving position to improve the forward view when ploughing. The 700C, a crawler version of the 702 which followed at a later stage, was Europe's first mass-produced tracklayer. There was a shortage of good quality fuel in Italy when the 41½hp model 40 Boghetto crawler was introduced in 1938 but Fiat overcame this problem by using a multi-fuel engine which could run on petrol, fuel oil, diesel, natural gas, low octane gas or alcohol.

The Model 50 and 52 crawlers introduced when production resumed in 1945 were the first Fiat tractors with full diesel engines; they were started with a 10hp two-stroke auxiliary or donkey petrol engine. The 50hp 4 cylinder engine had two inlet and two exhaust valves for each cylinder and the water-cooling system shared with the donkey engine provided hot water to pre-heat the cylinders before starting the main engine. Both tractors had 5 forward gears and reverse and the multi-plate clutches were controlled with a steering wheel instead of the usual levers. The Model 52 crawler had slightly lower gear ratios and a 59 inch track centre compared with 46 inch track centre on the model 50.

Steel wheels were optional for the 22hp petrol or 18hp paraffin-engined Fiat 600 with a 4 forward speed and reverse gearbox launched in 1949. Variants of the Fiat 600 included the 602 tricycle-wheeled rowcrop model with adjustable wheel tracks and the 601 tracklayer with standard tracks for farm work or narrow tracks for orchards or vineyards. Standard equipment included a starting handle and a 6 volt lighting system with a friction-wheel driven dynamo which could be disengaged when the lights were not required.

The Fiat 55 crawler announced in 1950 had a 55hp diesel engine started with a 10hp twin-cylinder horizontally opposed petrol engine bolted to the flywheel housing. It was used in the same way as an

101. The Fiat Model 50 diesel-engined crawler was marketed in the UK in the early 1950s by Mackay Industrial Equipment Ltd of Feltham, Middlesex.

electric starter motor with a lever-operated clutch mechanism. This engaged the donkey engine starter pinion with the flywheel ring gear and turned the diesel engine while on full compression. The Fiat 55 crawler with a ground pressure of less than 5psi cost about £2,600. It had 5 forward gears and reverse with a top speed of 5mph and a steering wheel was used to operate the clutch and brake steering system.

102. 'Hydraulic or mechanical elevating gear for rear-mounted equipment' and a rear belt pulley were optional on the Fiat 600 which, according to publicity material, could 'pull a two-furrow plough at a depth of ten inches in average soil conditions'.

Fiat introduced 16 new two- and four-wheel drive tractors and five crawlers in 1959 and 1960. The 200, 300 and 400 series with 22–85hp diesel engines and the petrol engined Fiat 211 were not sold in the UK but McKay Industrial Equipment Ltd advertised the 30hp, 40hp and 70hp Fiat 311C, 411C and 70C diesel crawlers in the early 1960s. The more popular 70C had a 4 cylinder overhead-valve engine with an electric starter, 5 forward and 4 reverse gears and multi-plate steering clutches. A tool kit and grease bucket were standard but power-take-off, belt pulley and an alternative donkey petrol engine to start the tractor were optional extras.

Fiat, who had established a tractor and earth moving equipment division in the late 1960s, opened a head office in Berkeley Square, London, in

103. Hydraulic three-point linkage, front weights, power take-off and a belt pulley were optional on the Fiat 80C and 100C crawler tractors.

1972 to market their crawler tractors in Britain. The 80hp and 100hp 80C and 100C tractors launched in 1971 had 4 cylinder direct injection engines with a 24 volt electric starter. Other features included an oil-cooled dual-plate clutch, 5 forward gears and reverse, clutch and brake steering and hydraulic track adjustment. The smaller 65hp French-built 655C had 6 forward and 2 reverse gears and a 12 volt electrical system.

The Italian company established the Fiat Trattori agricultural division in 1974 and Fiat-Allis Construction Equipment Ltd was formed that year in a joint venture with Allis-Chalmers. Laverda joined Fiat Trattori in 1975 and Hesston became part of the group in 1977.

Fiat-Allis Construction Machinery (GB) Ltd were marketing Fiat 80C, 850C and 100C crawlers and Fiat 540, 640, 850, 1000 and 1300 two- and four-wheel (DT) drive tractors in the mid-1970s. Four-cylinder water-cooled direct injection engines rated at 54hp, 64hp, 85hp were used for the smaller models with 100hp and 130hp 6 cylinder engines providing the power on the Fiat 1000 and 1300. The 540 and 640 had 8 forward and 2 reverse gears while the others had a three range gearbox with 12 forward and 4 reverse speeds. The 1300 had hydrostatic steering while power-assisted steering was standard on the other tractors.

The 150hp Fiat 1300 Super and four-wheel drive 1300DT Super with a flat floor quiet cab replaced the 1300 and 1300 DT in 1977. The new models with the extra horse power provided by increased fuel injection pump capacity and a higher engine speed made them the most powerful tractors made in Italy at the time.

The 1300S and 1300DTS retained the lower link sensing hydraulics and telescopic lift arm ends used on the earlier models. They were also the first Fiat tractors with an

104. The Fiat 450 DT was the smallest of five models launched in 1979. Common features included disc brakes, steering column gear change and Controlomatic hydraulics with draft and position control.

external remote hydraulic control switch for the driver to use when attaching an implement. The optional four-speed creeper box, epicyclic final drive reduction units and the side-mounted drive shaft from a transfer box to the front wheels on the DTS model were carried over from the 1300 and 1300DT.

There were 62 models in 18 power bands between 28hp and 350hp in the Fiat range when the Turin factory celebrated 60 years of tractor production in 1979. They included the earlier 540, 640 and 850, already re-launched as the 58–88hp 80 series, together with four new two- and four-wheel drive tractors ranging from the 115hp Fiat 1180 to the 180hp 1880 launched in Turin's Diamond Jubilee year.

There was a growing demand for high horse power tractors in Europe in the late 1970s. About 9,800 tractors over 180hp were sold in North

105. The Fiat 44-35 with a 350hp Cummins engine was the largest of four articulated models made for Fiat by Versatile in Canada.

America in 1978 compared with only 1,700 in the rest of the world (excluding Eastern Europe). The apparent sales opportunities in Europe led to a trading agreement with the Versatile Tractor Co for the supply of articulated four-wheel drive tractors in Fiat colours. The Fiat 44-23, 44-28, 44-33 and 44-35 with a 12 forward and 4 reverse gearbox and category III & IV hydraulic linkage made by Versatile were launched in time for the 1979 Smithfield Show. The four articulated tractors had 230hp, 280hp, 330hp and 350hp Cummins 'Constant-Power' 6 cylinder turbocharged engines which maintained their rated power through a speed range of 1,600 to 2,100rpm.

Fiat extended the 80 series in 1981 with the 88hp 5 cylinder 880-5 and the 880-5DT originally introduced in 1975 as the Fiat 880 and 880DT. The Fiat 665C and 1355C crawler models with 68hp and 135hp engines were announced at the 1983 Royal Show. The 665C was based on the 4 cylinder, 8 forward and 4 reverse speed Fiat 680 wheeled tractor. It had clutch and brake steering, hydraulically tensioned tracks, independent power take-off and three-point linkage. An unusual gull-wing two-door cab was included in the basic price of

106. The Fiat 80-90dt with a Comfort cab independently mounted on rubber blocks cost £18,400 in 1986. An optional SuperComfort cab added an extra £2,100 to the price.

£13,000 for the 665C. This could be supplied with an optional 16 forward and 8 reverse creep speed transmission or an 8 forward and reverse shuttle box. The Fiat 1355C with a conventional air conditioned two-door cab had the same 6 cylinder engine as the 1580 wheeled tractor, 5 forward and 5 reverse gears and Turner hydraulic linkage. Provision was made for the optional one tonne front ballast weight to be lifted on to the 1355C with the hydraulic linkage on another tractor.

Fiat Trattori became Fiatagri in 1984 and the ageing 80 series was replaced by the 90 series tractors. There were eleven two- and four-wheel drive models from the Fiat 55-90 to the 180-90; the first two or three figures denoted engine horse power. The comfort cab was standard on the smaller models but there was a choice of a super comfort (S), comfort wide (CW) or super comfort wide (SW) cabs for the 115–180hp tractors. A 12 forward and 4 reverse synchromesh transmission was standard and a 16 speed shuttle box with optional powershift was available for the 130-90 and larger models. The Fiat 100-90 was the odd one out with a 15 forward and 3 reverse gearbox or a 20 forward and 4 reverse with an optional creep speed box. The flagship Fiat 180-90 distinguished itself in 1984 when it was used to set a world record by ploughing an acre in 11 minutes and 21.8 seconds.

Fiatagri also launched the medium horse power 65 and 66 series tractors in 1984 and 1985 but the 3 cylinder 45hp 45-66 and 45-66 DT were the only models shown in the price list when Fiatagri UK opened a retail depot in 1986 at Bury St Edmunds, Suffolk. The 12 forward and 3 reverse speed 45-66 had multi-disc wet brakes and Fiat Lift-o-Matic hydraulics with a four-position sensing control system. A creep speed box and a 12 speed shuttle gearbox were optional extras. The 1986 Fiat crawler range included the 4 cylinder 70hp 70-65, the 6 cylinder 1355C and the new Turbo-Hydro drive 180-55. This tractor had an automatic transmission with an over-ride pedal which could be used to vary forward speed to suit the load or gradient. The tracks were driven with hydraulic motors and a joystick was used to select gear ratios and steer the tractor.

There were at least 30 different makes and approximately 700 models of farm tractor on the British market including 70 or so with a Fiat or Ford badge on the bonnet when Fiatgeotech, the agricultural division of Fiat, merged with Ford New Holland in 1990. Separate Ford and Fiat tractor ranges remained for several years and the Fiatagri UK headquarters were still at Bury St Edmunds when the four-wheel drive F 100 Winner range was launched in 1991. Six-cylinder 98hp, 110hp, 118hp and 130hp Fiat Iveco 8000 series engines provided the power for the F100, F110, F120 and F130 tractors which had push button operated 540, 750 and 1000rpm power take-off shafts. Other features included electronically controlled front and rear hydraulic linkage and a 32 forward and 16 reverse hi-lo gearbox. A 16 speed shuttle box, a 64 x 32 creep box and an economy 20 forward and 16 reverse Eco Speed gearbox were optional extras. The F115 was added in 1993 and improved engines gave the full Winner range increased torque back-up and reduced fuel consumption. Category II and III three-point linkage and a new air-sprung seat were added at the same time.

107. Pininfarina styled cabs were a feature of the Fiat Winner range launched in 1991.

The two- and four-wheel drive Fiat 94 series, the 55-85 and 60-85 crawlers and the 62-86, 72-86 and 82-96 orchard tractors with 60hp, 70hp and 80hp engines also appeared in 1993. The 65–85hp Fiat 94 series designed with 'the profit conscious farmer of the 1990s' in mind had 3 and 4 cylinder Iveco engines, a synchronised reversing transmission system and a three-speed power take-off with ground speed. The Fiat 'Steering-O-Matic' full-drive system was a new feature on the 55hp and 60hp crawler tractors which were steered with a single joystick, leaving the driver's other hand free to operate the hydraulic system and other controls.

New Holland was the dominant name on blue Ford 70 series and terracotta Fiat G series when two mechanically identical ranges of tractor in the 170–240hp bracket and made on the same production line were launched in 1994.

FORDSON

The first Fordson Model F tractors were made at Dearborn in America in 1917 and production also got under way at Cork in Ireland in 1919. The Model N replaced the F in 1929, production was transferred to Dagenham in 1933 and many thousands had been built by the time the E 27N Fordson Major was launched in 1945. Henry Ford also made the Ford Ferguson 9N for Harry Ferguson in Detroit between 1939 and 1947. The Ford 8N, which replaced the 9N was also made in America until 1952.

The Ford Ferguson 9N, which cost $595, was very similar to the Ferguson TEA 20 but was improved by an access panel in the bonnet for servicing the fuel tanks and radiator. Early 9Ns had a 10 gallon petrol tank and a one gallon reserve but later models were modified to run on paraffin. When America became involved in the Second World War a shortage of materials resulted in the introduction of the Ford Ferguson 2N in 1942. It was an economy version of the 9N on steel wheels with magneto ignition and a starting handle but when rubber became more plentiful American farmers could buy the 2N with pneumatic tyres.

Henry Ford and Harry Ferguson parted company in 1946 and within a year the 9N was replaced by the 35hp grey and red Ford 8N with the Ferguson hydraulic system. The new tractor was similar to the 9N but it

108. Three styles of mudguard were used for the E 27N Fordson Major during its six-year production run.

had gained an extra forward gear and more than half a million had been made when it was discontinued in 1952. The 8N was the subject of a much publicised lawsuit (eventually won by Ferguson) concerning the use of his patented hydraulic system. Ford celebrated their 50th anniversary in 1953 with the launch of the 31hp NAA Golden Jubilee tractor. Known as the Red Tiger it had a wheat sheaf emblem to commemorate the event.

The E27N Fordson Major introduced in 1945 retained the model N's 28½hp petrol and vaporizing oil side-valve engine with cast iron pistons, splash feed lubrication, magneto ignition and starting handle. The model N gearbox was also used but the rest of the transmission was re-designed with a single-plate clutch, crown wheel, differential, spur gear final drive and independent rear wheel drum brakes. The E27N could be supplied with a standard or optional high speed transmission with top speeds of 4.17mph or 7.48mph. Tractors with the low top gear had a green spot painted on the transmission housing and a red spot was used if the tractor had the higher top gear. A swinging drawbar was standard but electric starting, hydraulic lift, power take-off and side-mounted belt pulley were extra. Standard agricultural, rowcrop with adjustable wheel track, land utility and industrial versions of the Fordson Major were made at Dagenham. A factory-fitted Perkins P6 45hp diesel engine option was added in 1948 and the tractor was used for half-track and crawler conversions by County Commercial Cars and Roadless Traction Ltd.

Farmers could choose either a twin-lever Varley hydraulic lift system with a separate control for external services or the single-lever Smith lift. Both systems were self-contained bolt-on units driven by a shaft from the tractor gearbox. Ford could not use the patented Ferguson hydraulic system with its built-in overload safety mechanism but an optional top link with an automatic overload release mechanism was made for the tractor. A hydraulic damper in the top link was connected by a mechanical linkage to the clutch pedal and the increased forward thrust created in the top link when an implement hit an obstruction actuated the linkage and disengaged the clutch. A relief valve in the hydraulic damper could be adjusted to vary the sensitivity of the release mechanism when working with different soil types and implements.

Ransomes made a range of tillage implements for the E27N. Following the purchase of a foundry and factory at Leamington Spa in 1945 the Ford Motor Co produced the Ford Elite two- and three-furrow trailed ploughs, cultivators and ridgers in Warwickshire. A mid-mounted tool bar made by the Martin Cultivator Co, Robot vegetable planters, Allman powder dusters, Compton loaders, Dening saw benches and Bamford mowers were all approved for use with the Fordson Major.

The New Fordson Major E1 ADKN made its debut at the 1951 Smithfield Show. The completely new 40hp tractor had an overhead-valve engine, single-plate clutch, 6 forward and 2 reverse gears and spur gear final drive. Depending on build the same basic engine could run on petrol, vaporising oil or diesel. Three-point linkage and power take-off were optional extras when the tractor was launched but they soon became standard equipment. Power-assisted steering was added to the list of extras a year or so later. The New Fordson Major was used for various conversion including County full tracks, Roadless half tracks, KFD orchard

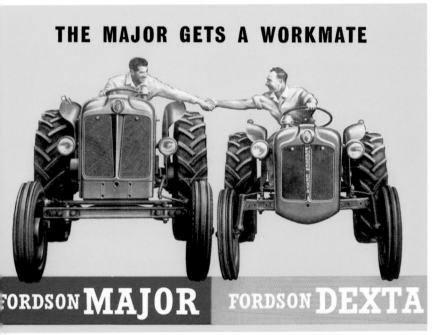

THE MAJOR GETS A WORKMATE

FORDSON MAJOR   FORDSON DEXTA

109. 'The Major gets a workmate'. The Fordson Dexta, launched in 1957 was made alongside the New Fordson Major at Dagenham.

110. The Ford Major 4000 was one of the new 1000 series tractors made at Basildon in 1964.

tractors made for the Kent Ford Dealers and a tricycle-wheeled version made by Roadless Traction was sold in America.

The Dexta, launched in 1957, had a 3 cylinder 30½hp diesel engine, an in-line fuel injection pump and pneumatic governor. It was also the first Fordson tractor with a position and Qualitrol (draft control) hydraulic system. Standard equipment included a 6 forward and 2 reverse gearbox, adjustable wheel track, category I three-point linkage, independent drum brakes, power take-off and a tip-back seat complete with cushion. Optional extras included a dual clutch with live power take-off and hydraulics, an automatic pick-up hitch and power-adjusted rear wheels.

The gearbox and differential were strengthened on the 51.8hp Fordson Power Major when it replaced the New Fordson Major in 1958. The hydraulic lift capacity was increased, rear wheel track adjustment was simplified and the new model had a hand throttle under the steering wheel. Ford had discontinued the paraffin-engined Power Major by the late 1950s when most new tractors were sold with a diesel engine but it was still possible to buy the Power Major with a petrol engine.

The Power Major was replaced by the Super Major in 1960. The Super Major had disc brakes, diff-lock and 'slim line styling' but the most significant improvement was the addition of Qualitrol, position control and a flow control hydraulic system. A more powerful 32hp Dexta with an improved gearbox and hydraulic system was introduced in the same year and Ford added a petrol-engined model for some overseas markets. The orange and blue colour scheme was still current when the 39.5hp Fordson Super Dexta was launched in 1961 but this was replaced by a predominantly blue livery with white wheels and mudguards in 1962. The new colour scheme was also used for the Super Major and Super Dexta with engine power increased to 53.7 and 44½hp respectively but the Dexta remained unchanged at 32hp.

Tractor production at Dagenham came to an end in 1964 when Ford introduced the new 6X or 1000 series tractors. They were made for worldwide sale at Antwerp, Highland Park in America and a new factory at Basildon in Essex. The Dexta 2000, Super Dexta 3000 and Major 4000 with 3 cylinder direct injection Ford engines rated at 37hp, 46hp and 55hp and the 4 cylinder 65hp Super Major 5000 cost £680, £765, £885 and £965 respectively. The 2000 was a basic tractor with a single-plate clutch, 6 forward and 2 reverse gears, drum brakes and category I hydraulic linkage. Independent power take-off, 8 forward and 2 reverse gears, double-acting top link draft control hydraulics and diff-lock were standard on the 2000 de luxe and larger models. The 4000 and 5000 had wet disc brakes but drum brakes were still used on the 3000. There was an optional weather cab and the Select-O-Speed transmission with 4 creeper, 4 field and 2 road speeds was available for the 3000, 4000 and 5000. A single lever was used to select the required gear in the 10 forward and 2 reverse speeds in the clutchless change-on-the-move gearbox. Epicyclic gear units and band brakes engaged the selected gear and an inching pedal gave precise control when manoeuvring in confined spaces and hitching implements. Some drivers called it the 'jerk-o-matic' gearbox as there was a pronounced jump in forward speed when changing up to a higher group of gears or vice versa.

The Dexta and Major names were dropped from the 1000 series tractors in 1968 when engine power was increased to 39hp, 47hp, 62hp and 75hp respectively for the Ford Force 2000, 3000, 4000 and 5000. The Ford Force 5000 engine was used for the Italian-built Mailham 5001 crawler. A few of these tractors with an International Harvester TD9 transmission and Burford running gear were imported in the late 1960s by Gates of Baldock who were a leading Ford tractor dealer in Hertfordshire. The Doe 5100 with a 6 cylinder Ford industrial engine made in the early 1970s was also based on this tractor. The 94hp 7000 introduced in 1971 was the first Ford tractor with a factory-fitted turbocharger. It followed the general design of the Ford 5000 with an 8 forward and two reverse gears, independent power take-off and power- assisted steering.

111. The Ford FW series was made in America by Steiger.

'As spacious, quiet and comfortable as a car' ran the advertising slogan for the new luxury two-door cab on the Ford 600 series launched in 1975. The cab was standard on the seven-tractor 600 series which ranged from the 37hp 2600 to the 97hp 7600. Ford changed from a dynamo to an alternator charging system to provide the extra power required for the improved lighting and in-cab controls. The 5600, 6600 and 7600 were also the first Ford tractors with optional Dual Power transmission and Load Monitor hydraulics. Dual Power doubled the number of gears to give 16 forward and 8 reverse speeds. Load Monitor was an alternative form of draft control which measured changes in torque in the drive shaft between the gearbox and the crown wheel. The system transmitted signals to the hydraulic control valve which raised or lowered the lift arms according to need.

112. The TW 10, TW 20 and TW 30 replaced the Ford 8700 and 9700 in 1979. The 184hp TW 30 was one of the first tractors to have a turbocharged engine with an air-to-air intercooler.

The 6 cylinder 126hp Ford 8600 and 148hp 9600 originally launched in America in 1972 completed the Ford 600 series. Both tractors had a 16 forward and 4 reverse Dual Power transmission, hydrostatic steering, hydraulic disc brakes, lower link sensing hydraulics and a 540/1000rpm power take-off.

Four 700 series models launched in 1976 with new quiet cabs, re-styled exhaust pipes and air cleaner intakes gave Ford a range of eleven two-wheel drive 600 and 700 series tractors in the 37–153hp bracket. The flat floor cab on the 6700, 7700, 8700 and 9700 was a sign of things to come with the pendant pedals and driving controls grouped on the right-hand side of the seat providing an uncluttered floor. The 6600 and 7600 with their original cabs remained in production but the 8600 and 9600 were replaced by the 128hp and 153hp two- and four-wheel 8700 and 9700 with 6 cylinder engines.

The Ford FW30 265hp articulated tractor built by Steiger in America made its UK debut at the 1978 Power in Action event held in Suffolk. The new FW (Four Wheel drive) tractor had a Cummins V8 engine, a 20 forward and 4 reverse constant mesh gearbox and cåtegory 3 hydraulic linkage. The FW60 with a 335hp Cummins engine was also sold in the UK but the 210hp FW20 and the 295hp FW40 were not. An optional 10 speed automatic gearbox for the FW60 was added in 1985. The Ford TW range was made in two-wheel drive format but most of the TW10, TW20 and TW30 tractors sold in Britain were four-wheel drive. The 124hp, 145hp and 184hp tractors had a 16 forward and 4 reverse Dual Power transmission, lower link sensing hydraulics and self-adjusting brakes.

Ford made their five millionth tractor in 1981. They also launched the 10 series based on the earlier 600 and 700 tractors in the same year. The 3 and 4 cylinder re-styled 10 series ranged from the 41hp 2610 to the 98hp 7610 and 7710. The four-wheel drive 6 cylinder 116hp 8210 launched in 1982 superseded the earlier two-wheel drive 115hp 8100 and four-wheel drive 8200. The more significant changes on the 10 series included an 8 forward and 4 reverse change-on-the-move Synchroshift gearbox (with optional Dual Power), an improved hydraulic system and an average 10 per cent power increase across the range compared with the 600 and 700 series. The column gear shift levers on the 2610 to 7610 were not popular and were soon replaced with an H pattern floor change gear lever. Four-wheel drive with a central drive shaft and an automatic diff-lock with a switch operated on-the move drive engagement was a factory fitted option for the 50hp 4110 upwards. A low profile (LP), all-purpose (AP) or de luxe quiet cab could be specified when buying a 10 series tractor.

More new models were launched in 1983 when the TW 15, TW 25 and TW 35 with 132hp, 154hp and 186hp 6 cylinder engines superseded the TW 10, TW 20 and TW 30. The 16hp 1210 and 32hp 1910 compact models replaced the 1100, 1200 and 1900 in the same year. An optional hydro-static transmission for the 1210 and the new 26hp 1710 with optional four-wheel drive were introduced in 1984.

The Ford Force II tractors with Super Q luxury cabs on models from the 6610 to the TW 35 appeared in 1985. The new style low-roof line cab and forward-facing exhaust

113. Some Ford 4610 tractors were sold with four-wheel drive but this option was more popular on the larger 10 series models. It was one of 18 tractors, ranging from the 13hp 1100 compact to the 335hp articulated FW 60, in the 1981 Ford price list.

were the more obvious changes but there was also a more efficient alternator and telescopic stabilisers in place of the old chain and turnbuckle design. Hydrostatic steering was standard on the Force II 5610, 6610 and 7610.

Ford Tractor Operations bought the farm machinery division of New Holland from the Sperry Corporation for a sum in excess of $250m in 1986 and the new company became Ford New Holland. The Basildon factory celebrated 25 years of tractor production in 1989 with a batch of 7610 models with a silver colour scheme. The jubilee was also marked with a special offer of two tractors for the price of one – but the second was a small pewter replica of the real thing!

114. The 40 series SL and SLE with new engines, transmissions and cabs were the first completely re-designed Ford tractors to be made at Basildon for 27 years.

The 20 series compact tractors and high horse power 30 series were launched in 1990. The TW 132hp, 154hp and 186hp engines were used for the new 8630, 8730 and 8830 models, which replaced the TW series. They had an 18 forward and 9 reverse Ford Powershift transmission and an improved hydrostatic steering system. The Powershift gearbox with single-lever clutchless gear changing and shuttle reverse was monitored by a microprocessor designed to prevent engine or transmission overload caused by incorrect gear selection. The two- and four-wheel drive 30 series were multi-purpose tractors suitable for arable and stock farms with four types of transmission, standard and economy power take-off and two designs of cab. The optional economy power take-off gave 540rpm at an engine speed of 1,450rpm or 1,750rpm. A buzzer in the cab warned the driver when the shaft exceeded 630rpm in the economy setting. The Ford Performance Monitor with a radar unit to measure ground speed was standard equipment on the three tractors. The 30 series was extended later in the year when the two- and four-wheel drive 51hp Ford 3930 and the 61hp 4630 replaced the 4110 and 4610. Both models had an 8 speed Synchro Shuttle gearbox or optional 16 forward and 8 reverse Dual Power transmission and a flat floor cab. The 70hp 5030 was added to the range in 1992.

Ford New Holland merged with Fiat Geotech in 1991, the Basildon plant becoming the headquarters for New Holland Geotech. It was stated that both tractor ranges would remain in production. This proved to be true when the Ford 40 Series SL and SLE tractors launched at the 1991 Smithfield Show were advertised as the first completely new models made at Basildon for 27 years. There were 6 two- and four-wheel drive 40 series tractors with 75–120hp PowerStar engines, new transmissions and SuperLux cabs. The 75–100hp SL models had a 12 forward and reverse SynchroShift gearbox with reverse shuttle. The SLE version had the latest Electro-Shift transmission with 16 speeds in forward and reverse. The higher specification of the SLE tractors included the Ford 'ElectroLink' closed centre lower link sensing hydraulics and an Electro-Command electronic instrument panel in a flat floor cab with a passenger seat.

The company name was changed to New Holland in 1993 when the turbocharged 125hp Ford 8340 was added to the 40 Series and a 24 speed Dual Power transmission with an 18 per cent speed reduction in each gear was added to the list of optional extras for SL models. The first New Holland tractors with Ford Blue and Fiat Terracotta colour schemes were launched in 1994.

FOUR-WHEEL TRACTION

Robert Eden Ltd at North Audley Street in London were marketing Italian-built Selene four-wheel drive conversion kits for the Massey Ferguson FE 35, MF 35 and MF 65 from the mid-1950s. Drive to the front wheels was from a transfer box attached to the power take-off shaft via a forward running shaft to the front axle differential housing. The power take-off shaft was extended through the transfer box but as it was necessary to use the ground speed setting to drive the front wheels, the power shaft could only be used at 540rpm with the drive to the front axle disengaged. Similar front-wheel drive kits were also made for the MF 135, 165 and 175 and from the mid-1960s Robert Eden made the strengthened Eden Manuel version under licence for MF tractors. The power take-off driven front axle had obvious disadvantages which were overcome with a new Eden designed transfer box sandwiched be-tween the gearbox and back-end.

Established at North Audley Street in the late 1960s Four Wheel Traction's purpose was to make the transfer box and front axle unit for the Massey Ferguson 135, 165, 175, 178, 185 and 188. The conversion kits with small and equal-size front wheels were made until the late 1970s when Massey Ferguson launched their own four-wheel drive tractors.

A front wheel-drive conversion based on a Leyland 270 with a propeller shaft drive taken from a transfer box behind the main gearbox was sold as the Four Wheel Traction 470 in the mid-1970s. The company continued in business, making components for some UK tractor manufacturers.

115. Power-assisted steering was recommended by Four Wheel Traction Ltd when their front-wheel drive conversion kit was fitted to the Massey Ferguson 178.

FOWLER

The leading steam traction engine manufacturer John Fowler & Co of Leeds was established in the mid-1800s. The company also made the Wyles Motor plough and the Fowler Gyrotiller with contra-rotating tines which could work up to 20 inches deep without bringing up the subsoil. Fowlers turned their attention to building tracklayers in the early 1930s and the first model, called the Diesel 25 and later re-named the 3/30, had a 30hp diesel engine.

The Ministry of Supply took control of John Fowler & Co in 1941. Rotary Hoes Ltd acquired the company in 1945 and within a year they sold it to Marshall, Sons & Co at Gainsborough. Marshalls continued production of the Fowler FD2, originally made by Rotary Hoes for use with the Rotavator, and added the larger FD3 crawler. The Fowler VF crawler (see plate 183 on page 134), which replaced these tractors in 1948 was made until the improved VFA crawler appeared in 1952.

The Challenger III with the choice of a 95hp Meadows or a Leyland engine was the first of a new series of Fowler tracklayers made at Leeds. Launched in 1950 the Challenger III had clutch and brake steering, a single-plate clutch and a 6 forward speed or optional 12 speed gearbox. The Challenger I, introduced in 1951, had an unusual 50hp twin-cylinder two-stroke Marshall E.D.5 diesel engine with five inlet and three exhaust ports in each cylinder. The pressure lubricated 5¼ inch bore and 6 inch stroke engine had a chain-driven blower and a centrifugal pump circulated the water in the cooling system. The engine was started by a 2 cylinder water-cooled donkey petrol engine with a hand-clutch lever to engage drive to the main engine. The donkey engine was left to run until the water in the cooling system, which was also circulated through the main engine, had warmed it up enough to make the diesel easier to start. The Challenger I tractor had four power take-off shafts, one at the rear, another on the side of the

116. The Fowler Challenger I had 6 forward and 2 reverse gears and a top speed of 7mph.

tractor, the front power shaft was an extension of the crankshaft and the fourth shaft also on the side of the engine was driven by the fan pulley. The Challenger I cost £2,300 in 1952 while the Challenger III was £4,045.

The Challenger II with a 65hp 6 cylinder four-stroke Leyland diesel engine appeared in 1952 and the 150hp Challenger IV, mainly used for civil engineering work, was added in 1953. The Challenger I was only made for a short while but the others remained in production until the early 1970s.

Marshall Sons & Co and John Fowler at Leeds became part of the Thomas Ward Group in 1968 and the company name was changed to Marshall Fowler Ltd in 1970. The new owners closed the Leeds factory in 1973 but Marshall tractor production continued at the Britannia Works in Gainsborough.

FRASER

117. The Fraser crawler was exhibited at the 1950 Smithfield Show.

Fraser Tractors of Acton in London made a brief appearance on the agricultural scene in the early 1950s with a 45hp or 60hp crawler tractor which could have a petrol, paraffin or diesel engine with a 24 volt electric or a wind-up inertia starter. The tractor had an automatic centrifugal clutch, 4 forward gears and reverse, steering clutches and Roadless Traction type rubber-jointed tracks. A power take-off and a belt pulley were optional equipment.

There were no foot pedals and the tractor was started from rest by simply opening up the throttle. Returning the engine to tick-over speed automatically disengaged the clutch. Sales literature explained that the automatic clutch enabled the driver to move the tractor in either direction while standing on the ground to hitch an implement. This would undoubtedly be a modern farm safety inspector's nightmare.

GARNER

A number of companies including Garner Mobile Equipment Ltd of London were making small four-wheeled tractors in the late 1940s for small-holders and market gardeners. Many of those using a horse or a two-wheeled garden tractor appreciated the advantage of riding on a 'compact' tractor and, unlike a horse, it did not have to be fed and watered every day of the year. The Garner light tractor, introduced in 1949, had the same 6hp JAP Model 5 air-cooled petrol engine and centrifugal clutch used for the two-wheeled Garner garden tractor. The specification included 3 forward gears and reverse, differential and roller chain drive to the rear wheels. The seat was located in front of the rear-mounted engine and gearbox with the driver having to reach behind his back to change gear. The tractor cost £197.15s on steel wheels while pneumatic tyres added £5 to the price. Optional extras included a belt pulley, power take-off, a plough and various tool bar

118. The Garner light tractor with adjustable wheel track width and steering brakes had a top speed of 10mph.

attachments. A hand lever was used to raise and lower the mid- and rear-mounted tool bars and a single furrow plough. A drawbar was provided for trailed implements.

Sales literature suggested the Garner was the 'leader of light tractors which really could plough'. However, it was rather short of power when the going was tough and this led to the introduction in 1950 of a slightly wider and longer model with a 6/7hp JAP Model 6 air-cooled petrol or paraffin engine. The new model which could also be used with a mid-mounted reversible plough cost £269.15s. The price was rather high when compared with a Ferguson TE 20 and the last Garner light tractors were made in 1955.

GUNSMITH

Farm Facilities Ltd at Maidenhead sold over 200 three-wheeled Mk I and Mk II Gunsmith light tractors between 1948 and 1952. Designed by Frederick Gunn and Harold Smith, the Gunsmith had the same 6hp air-cooled JAP engine as the pedestrian-controlled B.M.B Plow-Mate garden tractor made by Brockhouse Engineering. A few Gunsmith tractors were made with a Briggs & Stratton model ZZ engine. The Plow-Mate's 2 forward and reverse gearbox and rear axle were also used for the Gunsmith. The gearbox provided speeds of 2mph and 3mph which could be increased to 3mph and 5mph by interchanging the engine and gearbox input shaft pulleys. The single front wheel was steered with a tiller handle and a foot pedal controlled an over-centre tensioner pulley which served as a clutch to engage the flat belt drive from the engine to the gearbox. It was claimed that by 'fitting a new belt the clutch could be "re-lined" in a matter of seconds with no

119. Introduced in 1948, the Mk I Gunsmith which could 'plough two acres a day comfortably' cost £178.

mechanical knowledge being required'. Implements could be towed from the drawbar or attached to mid- and rear-mounted tool frames which were raised and lowered with a hand lever.

Solid rear wheel centres were used in place of spoked wheels on the Mk II Gunsmith introduced in 1950. A steering wheel with a geared steering mechanism replaced the tiller handle and the transmission was improved with a system of multiple vee-belt pulleys on the engine and gearbox which provided 4 forward gears and a top speed of 8 mph. Sales literature claimed that the Mk II Gunsmith would 'work as well as any big tractor, often more precisely and always at less cost. Furthermore, youngsters would find it so easy to operate they would delight in doing men's work.' It was also suggested that 'after the Gunsmith had been tried out and it was seen how much work could be done with this amazing little tractor you won't rest until you own one'.

HOWARD

Australian engineer A.C. Howard introduced the 22hp Howard DH22 tractor for use with his rotary cultivator in 1928. The tractor was successful in Australia and was made there for nearly twenty years but little interest was shown when the DH 22 was exhibited at the Royal Agricultural Show of England in the early 1930s.

A.C. Howard, who formed Rotary Hoes Ltd at East Horndon in Essex in 1938, bought John Fowler & Co at Leeds in 1945. Fowler steam engines were known worldwide and the Leeds company was well experienced in crawler tractor production. Rotary Hoes used this expertise to design the FD2 tracklayer with a drive shaft for the Howard Rotavator which they launched in 1946. Within a year Howard made a handsome profit by selling John Fowler & Co to Marshall Sons & Co of Gainsborough, Lincolnshire.

Marshalls made the FD2 for the next year or so and meanwhile Rotary Hoes used the basic design of the FD2 for the new Howard Platypus 28 crawler tractor. About 20 Platypus 28 tractors with a Standard petrol engine, 6 forward and 2 reverse gears, controlled differential steering, 3 power take-off shafts and hydraulic linkage were made by Rotary Hoes at East Horndon. Platypus production was transferred to a factory at Basildon in 1952 and a diesel-engined version appeared in the same year.

The Platypus 30 crawler was introduced in 1952 and many of the 400 or so tractors made in a five-year production run were exported and mainly used for growing sugar cane. The Platypus 30 with a 35hp Perkins P4 (TA) in-direct injection engine, 6 forward and 2 reverse gears and controlled differential steering was advertised as a tractor which 'could pull a four-furrow plough 9 inches deep in third gear'. It had a 540rpm rear power take-off and a two-speed power shaft on each side of the tractor. One of the side shafts was used with an optional belt pulley and the other could be used to drive a Howard Rotavator.

A narrow-tracked Platypus PD2, similar to the Platypus 30, was made in the mid-1950s for rowcrop work. The PD2 was also available with an angle dozer blade or

120. The canopy on the Howard Platypus PD2 Bulloader gave the driver much needed protection from the contents of the loader bucket. Double-acting rams provided the power to fill the bucket at the front and empty it behind the tractor or vice versa.

121. Nineteen Platypus PD4 tractors were made in 1954. Most were exported with a creeper gearbox and used for soil stabilisation work.

a Howard Bulloader overloader shovel. The PD2 Bogmaster with 36 inch wide tracks was used on the Irish peat bogs and a few PD2 Bogwagons with a tipping load platform were sold in Japan.

The Platypus PD4 appeared in 1954 initially with a 51hp Perkins L4 engine but this was replaced at a later stage by a 70hp Perkins R6 power unit. A couple of Platypus PD4 tractors were sold with a Leyland engine and another was made with a 120hp engine and a 34 speed gearbox. The Platypus became unprofitable in the mid-1950s, production ceased in 1956 and the last one was sold in 1957. Trailed Rotavator production was continued at the Basildon factory for a couple of years and was then transferred to East Horndon.

HURLIMANN

Swiss engineer Hans Hurlimann made an 8hp tractor with a single-cylinder engine at Wil near Zurich in 1929 followed by a 10hp model in 1930. Both tractors had a petrol engine and a 3 forward speed and reverse gearbox. A much larger 4 cylinder Hurlimann 4DB85 with a 45hp direct injection diesel engine appeared in 1939. The D series with 45–85hp engines was introduced in 1946; the smallest D-100 with a 45hp diesel engine had a hand and a foot throttle, 5 forward gears and reverse, a two-speed belt pulley and power take-off and a diff-lock. The orange-painted 28–40hp H10, H12, H17 and H19 made from 1951 to 1955 were the last Hurlimann tractors with petrol engines but small-scale production of diesel-engined models continued at Wil for the next 20 years. The D150 and D200 launched in 1969 had a 12 forward and 6 reverse synchromesh gearbox and an independent power take-off. The 155hp D-115 introduced in 1971 was the first turbocharged Hurlimann tractor while an optional hydrostatic transmisson appeared in 1974.

Hurlimann tractors were hand-built to a high standard but the strong sales competition of the early 1970s caused the company serious financial difficulty. The situation improved in 1975 when Hurlimann became the Lamborghini tractor distributor in Switzerland. Earlier discussions with SAME came to nothing but the Italian company bought Hurlimann Traktoren AG in 1978. SAME already owned Lamborghini and with the acquisition of the Swiss company the group became SAME-Lamborghini-Hurlimann in 1979.

A new range of Hurlimann tractors including the H480, H490, H510, H6130 and H6160 with a new green colour scheme appeared in 1979; the H360 and H470 were added later in the year. Turbocharged Hurlimann engines made in Switzerland were fitted to the H480/490 and the H6130/6160; the same power units were also used for some SAME and Lamborghini tractors built in Italy. At least 20 Hurlimann models in the

122. The Hurlimann H-470 was one of a new range of the Swiss-built tractors launched in 1979.

47–165hp bracket were in production in the mid-1980s. Most of them had Swiss-built engines but the H345, H355 and H355F made from 1982 to 1986 had 3 cylinder SAME power units.

A limited range of Hurlimann tractors was imported by W.R. Bridgeman & Son at Newbury in 1980 and the Berkshire company introduced the 110hp 5110 with a 12 forward and 3 reverse gearbox at that year's Royal Show. Publicity material claimed that the four-wheel drive 5 cylinder H 5110 which cost £18,386 had 'the power of six cylinders with the economy of four'. The 4 cylinder 85hp H480 with the 5110 gearbox and the H6130 were also sold in the UK

123. The Hurlimann Elite 6115XB had a 6 cylinder 115hp diesel engine with an electronic governor and a 54 speed forward and reverse gearbox.

in 1980. Within a couple of years W.R. Bridgeman were marketing two- and four-wheel drive 62–160hp Hurlimann tractors. They were advertised as 'hand built' and the 70hp H-470 was typical of the range. It had a direct injection engine with four individual water-cooled cylinders, a dual clutch and a 12 speed synchro-mesh gearbox with 3 reverse gears. The standard specification was impressive with a dual-speed independent power take-off, hydrostatic steering, radial tyres and a tinted glass safety cab with two-speed screen wipers and air conditioning. SAME (UK) at Thirsk took control of Hurlimann tractor distribution in 1983 when the H480, H490 and H5110 rated at 82hp, 95hp and 115hp were advertised in the farming press. The tractors were relatively expensive and although sales were limited they remained on the British market well into the 1980s.

The 1986 Hurlimann price list included six models, from the 62hp H360 to the turbocharged H6170T with a 165hp engine and a 24 speed gearbox.

After a gap of nearly ten years the light green tractors re-appeared in 1995 when Motokov UK Ltd, who imported Zetor tractors, were appointed Hurlimann distributors. The Swiss name was the main link with the past as far as the Italian-built 85–190hp four-wheel drive Hurlimann tractors were concerned. They shared many components with SAME and Lamborghini models but their higher specification included a sophisticated power-shift transmission.

The Hurlimann XT, Elite and Master ranges were advertised in 1997 as 'quality tractors with a long Swiss pedigree but made in Italy'. The four 85–105hp XT models had a 60 speed forward and reverse transmission while the 115hp and 135hp Elite XB and the Master range with 165hp and 190hp engines had a 54 speed forward and reverse electro-hydraulic transmission. An air-conditioned cab, electronic load-sensing hydraulics, four-wheel hydraulic brakes and a trailer braking system were standard equipment. Optional extras include a computerised performance monitor with a radar speed sensor and a remote control rear view telecamera and screen.

Motokov UK relinquished their interest in Hurlimann in 1998.

HYDRAULIC SYSTEMS

Most farm tractors had a three-point hydraulic linkage by the late 1940s. Some had an internal hydraulic system while others had a self-contained bolt-on unit with the pump driven from the gearbox. Examples of bolt-on hydraulic units include the Smith lift and the Varley lift for the E27N Fordson Major (page 78) and the International Harvester Lift-All system on some Farmall tractors.

The Ferguson draft control and weight transfer system was so well protected by patents that other manufacturers were forced to use a basic lift and drop system which required wheels to control the working height or depth of the implement. This prompted engineers to design other ways of controlling implement depth and transferring some of its weight on to the tractor. The Bulwark Cantilever traction attachment made by

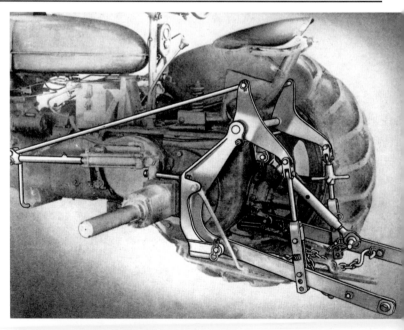

124. The International Harvester Lift-All hydraulic system pump and control valves for the Farmall H were located in a housing in front of the gearbox. The system was introduced in 1940 for use with front-, mid- and rear-mounted toolbars and other three-point linkage implements.

125. Oil for the three-point linkage rams on the Doe tool carrier was provided by the tractor hydraulic system.

Salopian Engineers in 1954 claimed to reduce wheelslip and to save fuel, time and labour by transferring implement weight on to the tractor. According to advertisements the Bulwark Cantilever, designed for the Nuffield Universal, 'only cost £30, could be fitted in 30 minutes and would allow the driver to keep on ploughing, even in the wettest weather'. An adjustable metal block on the transmission housing was used to support the lower-left hand lift arm and with depth wheel fully raised some of the implement's weight would be carried on the tractor. A small hydraulic ram connected to the external services system on the tractor was used to vary implement depth by adjusting the height of the metal block.

TCU (Traction Control Unit), also introduced in 1954, was David Brown's solution to wheelslip. The Meltham publicity department called wheelslip 'the invisible enemy' which they likened to 'the extra time it took a fly to crawl up a wet window compared with the time spent crawling up a dry one'. They explained that the fly's problem 'was much the same as a tractor working in a wet field' but unlike the poor fly, David Brown owners would be able to overcome wheelslip by using TCU. An implement depth wheel was still required when TCU was used to transfer implement weight on to the tractor and overcome wheelslip. Oil pressure in the hydraulic system was restricted by the TCU control unit so that there

126. The SKH Insta-Hitch was designed in Canada.

was insufficient pressure to lift the implement but there was enough to put some of its weight on to the tractor. When wheel-slip occurred the driver engaged TCU and adjusted a valve which varied the oil pressure in the circuit until wheel spin was hopefully eliminated. TCU could also be used with a trailed implement by using a special three-point linkage drawbar hitch which partially lifted the front of the implement and transferred some of its weight on to the tractor.

Draft and position control hydraulic systems were standard on all new wheeled tractors in the early 1960s. Many had live hydraulics provided by an engine mounted pump or a dual clutch. Three-point linkage for crawlers was still in the development stage but Ernest Doe & Sons and Simba were two companies who partly solved the problem with a trailed tool carrier on pneumatic wheels for use with tracklayers and large four-wheel drive tractors including the Doe Triple D. The tool carrier had a category II three-point linkage operated by hydraulic rams connected to the tractor's external services coupling. One Warwickshire farmer, Roger Dowdeswell, found he could not buy a three-point linkage unit for his tracklayer so he built one in his farm workshop! Manufacturing rights were sold to Turner Engineering at Alcester in the late 1960s and fully mounted implements could at last be used on crawler tractors.

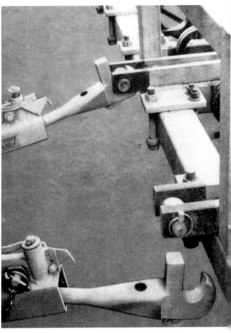

127. The Perry-Jeffes automatic hitching system was invented by a Gloucestershire farmer.

Quick hitches which made it easier and safer to attach an implement to the three-point linkage were already available in the mid-1960s. The Canadian-designed Salopian Kenneth Hudson Insta-Hitch and the German Accord automatic coupler had triangular frames attached to the three-point linkage and to the implement. The triangular frame hitching system was said to complete the task in a matter of seconds. After lowering the linkage careful reversing was needed to align the two frames before raising the lift arms to attach the implement and lock it in position.

Alternative quick hitch systems used various designs of extending lift arm end with hinged claws which were clamped over a ball or bobbin fitted to the lower hitch pins on the implement.

The John Deere quick coupler consisted of a frame with one upper and two lower hook-shaped jaws attached to the three-point linkage. The hooks were located on the implement hitch pins and secured with a spring-loaded locking mechanism. Another system developed by K-H-D in Germany for Deutz tractors also used hook shaped-ends on the lower links which engaged with bobbins on the implement. With the lower links in place, a telescopic mechanism simplified the task of connecting the top link. The Perry-Jeffes hitch sold by Farm Implements Ltd at Stroud in Gloucestershire used extendable hooks on the lower links which engaged with balls fitted to the implement lower link pins. A hook on the implement end of the top link was located on the headstock pin and locked in position with the aid of a rope.

Massey Ferguson's early 1960s Pressure Control system was one of the better-known devices designed to transfer some of the weight of a trailed implement on to the tractor to reduce wheelslip but there were others. The Gale Accord Tracassistor, invented by Wiltshire farmer W.A. Gale, and the Insta-Hitch both achieved the same result. The Tracassistor had four heavy coil springs, connected from the top link position on the Alpha Accord quick hitch frame to a hook welded on the implement drawbar. Weight was transferred on to the tractor when the springs were extended by slightly raising the lower lift arms. The SKH Insta-Hitch was used to transfer trailed implement weight on the tractor, with the aid of a special hitch from the top link position on the hitch frame to the drawbar or pick-up ring hitch.

More advanced hydraulic systems appeared in the 1970s as manufacturers used lower link sensing. By the early 1980s tractor drivers had the facility to use a mix of draft and position control. Electronic draft control systems became standard and the linkage could be raised or lowered with remote control switches on the rear mudguard when hitching heavy mounted implements.

IMT

The Metalski zavodi (factory) established in Belgrade in 1949 grew in size to become Industrija Masina I Tractora (Industrial Motor Tractor) in 1954. The Massey Ferguson connection began in 1956 when the British-built grey and gold FE35 superseded the TE20 series. An agreement with IMT resulted in Massey Ferguson manufacturing the grey Ferguson tractor, badged as the MF 20, at the Belgrade factory from 1956. Approximately 2,000 tractors, including a number with Perkins diesel engines, were made in the first year of production. This arrangement also enabled Massey Ferguson to sell tractors in eastern Europe where restrictive trade tariffs prevented normal export procedures.

The IMT factory was eventually taken over by the Yugoslavian state and in a joint venture with Massey Ferguson the MF35 was also built in Belgrade. Production of the MF35 continued under licence as the IMT 539 and, apart from the use of metric threads, it was very similar to the MF35. Several thousand IMT 539 tractors had been sold when Vowcrest at Stone in Staffordshire introduced the tractor to UK farmers in 1975. The 39hp IMT 539 was still available in Britain in 1998.

128. Apart from a more comfortable seat and power steering, the 1998 version of the IMT 539 had hardly changed since it was first made in 1956.

129. The two- and four-wheel drive IMT 577 was based on a Massey Ferguson tractor. Front-wheel drive on the 577DV engaged automatically when wheel slip occurred.

The 539 was, and still is, by far the best known IMT tractor. An advertisement published in the late 1970s suggested that 'although a dog was a livestock farmer's best friend the introduction of the 539 had put the dog's position in danger'. With 39hp under the bonnet, a dual clutch, ground speed power take-off and a differential lock it was 'a pretty versatile little character, and having been developed over 30 years, the 539's traditional design was 'just as reliable as a dog and cost less to keep'!

The 50hp IMT 555 was introduced in 1963 and other models based on Massey Ferguson tractors were added in the mid-1960s. The agreement with Massey Ferguson ended in 1968 but their influence could be seen in new IMT models introduced in the 1970s. The IMT name was well established in the UK by 1980 and Vowcrest were importing eight models between 39hp and 220hp. They included the new 47hp IMT 547 and the articulated four-wheel drive 207hp 5200. Vowcrest changed their name to IMT Tractors in 1982 when seven models, including the 539, the 110hp 5106, and the IMT 5200 which cost £38,500, were included in the price list. Most of the tractors were shipped to the UK in a semi-finished state and a Perkins or Mercedes engine with Lucas or CAV electrical and fuel injection equipment was added by the importer.

Extra baffles were installed around the IMT 539 engine in 1982 to reduce the noise levels so that the tractor could be sold in Britain with a fold-down safety frame instead of a quiet cab. New models introduced to the UK market in 1983 included the 77hp IMT 577 and four-wheel drive 577DV with 10 forward and 2 reverse gears. The 111hp IMT 5106 and 138hp 5136 could be supplied with various transmission systems ranging from a partly synchronised 10 forward and two reverse unit to a 24 speed synchronised gearbox with a reverser.

A modified range of 39–70hp economy tractors with new cabs was introduced in 1986 and the 549 and 569 were improved with hydrostatic steering and new direct injection engines. An advertisement suggested that by buying an economy range IMT model the days of expensive tractors were numbered and it was time for farmers to 'start ploughing money back where it was needed most – in their pockets'.

IMT Tractors moved to Scunthorpe in Lincolnshire in 1988 when the 539's steel bonnet and mudguards were replaced with fibreglass. The IMT 585 was the top model in the 59–85hp two- and four-wheel drive 5 series announced in 1989. It had an 85hp turbocharged direct injection diesel engine, 10 forward and 2 reverse gears and a heated cab. The basic price of the two-wheel drive 585 was £9,999 and a free pasture topper or post hole digger was thrown in with tractors ordered that year.

IMT Southern at Sturminster Newton in Dorset and IMT Northern at Nantwich in Cheshire were importing the Belgrade-built tractors when the 100hp 6 cylinder IMT 5106 was introduced in 1991. This four-wheel drive model had a 10 forward and 2 reverse mechanical gearbox, hydrostatic steering, wet disc brakes and a two-speed power take-off. There were two hydraulic pumps, one for the electronically controlled hydraulic linkage and the second supplied oil to a bank of three external services spool valves. An improved 539 specification included hydrostatic steering with an optional belt pulley and engine-mounted compressor for air-operated trailer brakes.

There were eight IMT tractors on the UK market in 1992. The 539 was still there and apart from the 43hp two-wheel drive 542 the other models including the flagship IMT 5106 were available with two- and four-wheel drive. Production continued on a small scale during the war in Yugoslavia but trade sanctions imposed in 1993 prevented the export of tractors until 1998 when IMT Southern re-introduced the 539 to the UK market. There were more than twenty models in production in the former Yugoslavia by the end of that year but supplies of these tractors were limited to the 539 in Britain. The range included fruit, high visibility and standard models under 90hp with optional four-wheel drive and a Perkins or an IMR engine built in Yugoslavia under licence from Perkins. Transmission systems ranged from a 6 forward and 2 reverse mechanical gearbox to a 12 speed synchronised box with reverse shuttle. IMR, Mercedes, Perkins and Valmet engines were used for the nine IMT models over 90hp, including the articulated 5360. Transmissions included a semi-synchromesh 10 forward and 2 reverse gearbox and a fully synchronised 24 speed box with reverse shuttle. Front power take-off and linkage, automatic implement hitching and electronic linkage control hydraulics were optional.

130. The IMT 549 introduced in 1986 could be supplied with an air compressor for trailer brakes and inflating tyres.

INTERNATIONAL HARVESTER

The McCormick Harvesting Machine Co, the Deering Harvester Co and three smaller harvest machinery manufacturers merged in 1902 to form the International Harvester Company. The new company made their first farm tractor in 1906 which, in common with other internal combustion engined tractors of the time, looked more like a steam engine than a farm tractor. The 20hp Mogul with an open chain drive to the rear wheels introduced in 1909 followed this trend but the 15-30 first seen in 1921 and the 10-20 launched in 1923 had a more modern appearance. About 6,000 International 10-20s were sold in Britain between 1923 and 1940 and about 300 of those imported after 1938 were fitted with pneumatic tyres, the others had steel wheels. The 22½hp McCormick-Deering Farmall Regular, so called because it was claimed to be the first tractor suitable for all types of farm work, was introduced

131. Thirty-four ball and roller bearings were used on the McCormick-Deering W 30 made between 1932 and 1940.

in 1924. The name was used until the last of the Farmall B 450s were made in 1970.

Farmers were already looking for more powerful tractors in the late 1920s and the Farmall F-30 launched in 1931 and the F-20 in 1932 met this demand. The smaller F-12 made between 1932 and 1938 was one of the most successful rowcrop tractors of the period. The F-14 with a higher engine speed replaced the F-12 in 1938, a power take-off and belt pulley were standard but hydraulic linkage was an optional extra. International Harvester also made a range of ploughing tractors, including the W-12, W-14, W-30, W-40 and WD-40 in the 1930s. The W-12 and W-14 shared engines and a similar 3 forward speed and reverse gearbox with the F-12 and F-14. The 4 cylinder W-30 developed 31 brake hp and 19 drawbar hp and the three gears gave a top speed of 3¾mph. The 6 cylinder W-40 made between 1934 and 1940 was rated at 46¾ belt and 35¼ drawbar hp. The WD-40, also introduced in 1934 and said to be America's first diesel-wheeled tractor, developed 48¾ and 37¼ belt and drawbar hp when tested at Nebraska. McCormick-Deering tractor model letters were self-explanatory: W was for wheeled models, T for tracklayers and D denoted a diesel engine.

132. The TD 6 was the smallest of the four International Harvester TracTracTors. The engine was started on petrol and converted to diesel operation with the flick of a lever.

The first McCormick-Deering tracklayer or crawler tractors were made in 1928. The 10-20 and 15-30 TracTracTors with rear track sprockets larger than those at the front were based on the 10-20 and 15-30 wheeled models. The T-20 crawler introduced in 1931 had a Farmall F-20 engine and a convention-

133. More than 300,000 Farmall Ms were made between 1939 and 1952.

al track layout. The larger T-40 and TD-40 crawlers based on the W-40 and WD-40 were made between 1933 and 1939. More agricultural and industrial crawlers including the T-6/TD-6 , T-9/TD-9, T-14/TD-14, and TD-18 were launched in America during 1938 and 1939. The TD-14A and TD-18A replaced the previous models in 1949. The TD-6 and TD-9 were started on petrol and had 5 forward and 2 reverse gears, clutch and brake steering, power take-off and optional belt pulley. The 85hp TD-18 which weighed just over 10 tons and used more than 6 gallons of fuel per hour was more than three times heavier than the TD-6 with a full tank of diesel fuel.

The Farmall F series was superseded by the Farmall A, B, H and M launched in America in 1939. The A and B were described as 'one plow tractors', the 26hp H was a 'two-plow model' and the 'three plow' Farmall M had a 36hp engine. The same 18hp paraffin engine was used for the Farmall A and B but the A had a 40 to 68 inch wheel track adjustment compared with 64 to 92 inches on the Farmall B. The seat and driving controls were off-set and this design, called 'Cultivision', gave the driver an unobstructed view of rowcrops. The Farmall A and B were made with tricycle or standard front axles and the high clearance Farmall AV had larger diameter wheels with extended front axle stubs. The Super A with 4 forward gears, a top speed of 10mph, electric lights, electric starting and Touch-Control hydraulics replaced the Farmall A in 1947.

The Farmall M was one of the most popular International tractors in Britain and America. Many of these tractors made during the war had steel wheels and the top speed was reduced to under 6mph by blanking-off the fifth gear. Most Farmall H and M tractors, including the high clearance HV and MV rowcrop models with tricycle front wheels, had pneumatic tyres by the mid-1940s. Optional equipment for the Farmall M and H included power take-off, belt pulley, the Lift-All hydraulic system, electric starter and lights. The diesel-engined Farmall MD launched in 1941 was replaced by the Super MD in 1952 and this tractor was made until 1954.

134. The McCormick-Deering W-6 Standard was a three-plow tractor.

The high ground clearance Farmall H and M were well suited to rowcrop work while the McCormick Deering W-4, W-6 and W-9 made between 1940 and 1953 were ideal ploughing tractors. The W-4 had the same engine as the Farmall H and the Farmall M and MD engines were used for the W-6 and WD-6. The W-9 and the WD-9 were both rated at 52hp and the Farmall MD start-up system, which automatically switched from petrol to diesel operation after the engine had run for about 900 revolutions, was used for the diesel engined WD-9. The W-4 and W-6 had 5 forward gears and a top speed of 14mph, the W-9 was 1mph faster in top gear and, like the Farmall, fifth gear was blanked off on tractors with steel wheels. Specialist versions of the W series tractors were also made. Heavy cast iron wheel centres were used for the industrial ID-4, ID-6 and ID-9 versions, the O-4 and O-6 orchard tractors had a down-swept exhaust, relocated air cleaner, guards over the rear wheels prevented tree damage and a shield over the steering wheel gave the driver some protection. The cheaper OS-4 was similar but did not have tree guards over the rear wheels and steering wheel.

Construction of a new factory at Doncaster for International Harvester was started in 1939 but the onset of war delayed tractor production until September 1949 when the first British-built Farmall M was driven off the assembly line. The Doncaster-built 37hp paraffin-engined tractor was known as the Farmall BM to denote it was made in Britain. Meanwhile, the Farmall M and H were still being made in America. The BMD with a 38hp British-built diesel engine was added in 1952; both tractors were improved in 1953 and became the Super BM and Super BMD respectively.

The Super BM had a 50½hp petrol or a 42¼hp vaporising oil engine. The 50½hp Super BMD with an indirect injection diesel engine had a heater (glow plug) in each cylinder for cold starting. A maximum 88 inch rear wheel track setting was achieved by sliding the wheels in or out on their axles and by reversing the centre discs. The front track width could be adjusted in 4 inch steps from 51 to 81 inches. Live hydraulics with an engine-mounted pump was an innovation on the Super Farmall models. A constant supply of oil was pumped from a separate reservoir to the control valves and an external double acting ram raised and lowered the lift arms. The ram was also used to alter the height of the drawbar which was a useful aid when hitching trailed equipment.

The Doncaster factory was in full production by 1954 when the new Farmall 100, 200, 300 and 400 tractors with 20–50hp engines were launched in America. Most of the tractors sold in Britain were diesels when the Doncaster built 50½hp Super BWD-6 was launched in 1954. The Super BW-6 with a vaporising oil engine was

135. The Farmall Super BM and Super BMD had a live double-acting hydraulic system. A control lever under the seat enabled the driver to regulate the rate of implement lift and drop.

added in 1955 but very few were sold. The new tractors had Super BM and Super BMD engines, 5 forward gears and reverse, live 'Liftall' hydraulics, a 540rpm power take-off and a belt pulley. The BW-6 and BWD-6 were ploughing tractors and the heavy cast iron rear wheel centres limited track width adjustment to 56, 60 and 64 inches. Power take-off shaft speeds were at last falling into line with international standards and Super BWD-6 sales literature pointed out that a safety shield was provided for the power shaft which conformed with current SAE and BSI standard speeds. The Super BWD-6 and BW-6 were discontinued in 1958.

The B250, made at the old Jowett car factory in Bradford and

136. A driver's eye view of the Super BWD 6. The driving controls were: 1. starter switch. 2. light switch. 3. oil pressure gauge. 4. indicator light for the glow plug heaters. 5. throttle. 6. belt pulley lever. 7. gear lever. 8. clutch pedal. 9. brake pedals.

launched at the 1955 Smithfield Show, was the first British-built medium-powered International Harvester tractor. It had a 30hp 4 cylinder indirect injection diesel engine with glow plug cold starting, a 5 forward and reverse gearbox, live dual category hydraulics with an engine mounted pump and automatic pick-up hitch. It was one of the first wheeled tractors to have disc brakes and a diff-lock. Standard and high-clearance versions of the more powerful B275 with a 35hp diesel engine and an 8 forward and 2 reverse gearbox were added to the British-built tractor range in 1958. Otherwise the B275 was similar to the B250 which remained in production until 1961 and the International B275 was discontinued in 1968.

The Farmall B450 also launched in 1958 was a re-styled version of the BWD 6. It had a 4 cylinder 55hp indirect injection engine with a pneumatic governor, 5 forward speeds and reverse,

137. The tricycle-wheeled Farmall B 450 was the rowcrop version of the BWD 6.

diff-lock and self-energising disc brakes. 'Thin oil which gave instant all-weather response' stored in a separate reservoir was supplied by an engine-mounted pump to the live category II hydraulic system. The B450 had a new two-stage response control designed to improve traction in tough conditions. The first two thirds of movement with the control lever progressively transferred implement weight on to the tractor and the final third was used to raise it from work.

Power take-off and hydraulic linkage were still optional equipment on International Harvester tractors in 1959. The B 250 cost £510 and the B 275 £540, power take-off and hydraulic linkage added £57 and £78 respectively and, although it appears rather mean, £2.13s was added to the bill for an hour meter. The Farmall B 450 cost £795 plus £90 for power take-off and hydraulics but the hour meter was included in the price!

The British-built International Harvester BTD6 and BT6 crawlers launched at the 1953 Royal Show in

138. Vary Touch draft control hydraulics with an engine-mounted pump were standard on the B 414.

Blackpool were similar to the American TD6 which had been available in the UK for several years. The BTD6 had a modified 38hp Farmall BMD indirect injection engine with electric starting, 5 forward gears and reverse, clutch and brake steering and an hour meter. The Farmall BM vaporising oil engine was used for the BT6 crawler.

Improved versions of the BTD6 and BT6 with 50½hp engines, a strengthened transmission system and a spiral bevel crown wheel and pinion instead of the earlier straight-toothed gears appeared in 1955. The 42hp BTD640 announced in 1957 was a modified BTD6 with lighter agricultural tracks and cost £1,500. The 40hp BTD5 was added to the International crawler range in 1964. The BTD5, also based on the BTD6, was designed for agricultural work and an optional offset frame for the hydraulic linkage made it possible to run both tracks to run on level ground when ploughing.

139. The International 523 was made in France.

Sales literature described the McCormick International B414 launched in 1961 as 'the tractor with everything you've wanted most'. Farmers were consulted, a report was written, and International Harvester then 'went ahead and actually built the tractor'. Things that farmers wanted and got on the new tractor included a 36hp diesel engine, 8 forward and 2 reverse gears, a diff-lock, Vary-Touch automatic draft control hydraulics, self-energising disc brakes and a more comfortable seat. There was also a petrol-engined B414 and a narrow model for orchard work. The 60hp B614 launched in 1964 was similar to the earlier B450 with live hydraulics and an independent 540rpm and 1,000rpm power take-off with multi-plate clutch. Two power take-off stub shafts with 6 and 21 splines were supplied with the tractor and the required shaft was bolted on to a hub at the back of the tractor.

The International 706 and 806, with 89hp and 110hp engines respectively, launched in America in 1963 were introduced to British farmers a year or two later. Petrol- and diesel-engined versions were made and they were among the first tractors to have hydrostatic steering. The 806 had a torque amplifier giving 16 forward speeds, twin disc hydraulic brakes and a torsion bar sensing system was used for the lower link draft control hydraulics. It had 3 hydraulic pumps: one was used for hydrostatic steering and brakes, another for the power take-off clutch and the third serviced the hydraulic system. The 806 was also one of the first tractors to have a dry element air cleaner with an automatic dust unloader. The 706 and 806 were discontinued in 1967.

Standard, high-clearance and narrow versions of the B 434 replaced the B 414 in 1966. Improved styling, better access for servicing and another 4hp under the bonnet were the more obvious changes on the petrol and diesel versions of the B 434. The German-built 52 SAE hp 3 cylinder International 523 cost £3,400 when it was launched in 1967. An 8 forward and 2 reverse gearbox was standard and the optional Agrio-matic-S transmission with a clutchless change in each gear doubled the number of speeds.

The National Institute of Agricultural Engineering at Silsoe had developed an experimental hydrostatic trans-mission in the early 1960s but the International Harvester 656, first seen in America in 1967, was the first pro-duction model with this type of transmission. The 656 had an engine-driven hydraulic motor which transmitted power through a mechanical final drive system to the rear wheels. There were two speed ranges and a control lever provided maximum stepless forward speeds of 8mph and 20mph. The reverse speeds were limited to 4mph and 9mph and a Foot-N-Inch pedal, as well as serving as an emergency clutch, gave precise control in confined spaces.

More new International tractors including the 354 and 374 with 35hp engines and the 42hp 444, appeared in 1971. The 'no frills' 374 had an 8 forward and 2 reverse gearbox, live category I and II hydraulics and a two-door cab. The 354 and 444 were similar with an optional independent power take-off. The 454, 474, 574 and 674 with 50–71hp engines were added to the range in 1972. An optional hydrostatic transmission controlled with a single lever on the dashboard was also available for the 474 and 574.

High horse power two-wheel drive tractors were popular in America in the 1970s and the 6 cylinder 106hp International

140. The International 1046 was made between 1975 and 1978. The cab was mounted on rubber blocks and the suspension seat could be adjusted to suit the driver's height and weight.

Harvester 966 Farmall launched there in 1971 was a typical example. The 966 which arrived in Britain the following year had an 8 forward and 4 reverse gearbox, hydrostatic steering, hydraulic brakes and optional hydrostatic transmission. There were separate hydraulic pumps for the power steering and brakes, the power take-off clutch and for the category II lower link sensing hydraulic system. The rear wheels could be moved along on their axles to give track widths from 73 inches to 102 inches and the cab, built around a safety frame, could be tilted backwards for servicing the transmission. Many features of the 966 were retained when it was replaced by the 946 and 1046 in 1975 but the new models had 6 cylinder 90hp and 100hp engines and a 12 forward and 5 reverse synchromesh gearbox.

141. The 77hp International 785XL had a 4 cylinder direct injection engine, a synchromesh gearbox, hydrostatic steering and oil-immersed disc brakes.

International Harvester had a nine-model range when the 84 Series High-Performers was launched at the 1977 Smithfield Show. The two-wheel drive 35hp 374 which cost £4,100 was the smallest and the four-wheel drive 136 gross hp 1246 with a £16,400 price tag was the largest and most expensive model in the range. Five new 84 series tractors, together with the 955 and 1055 which replaced the 946 and 1046, completed the list.

The 374 and 384 were the only tractors without the option of four-wheel drive and their standard specifications did not include a synchromesh gearbox, hydrostatic steering and an independent dual speed power take-off. The 77hp Hydro 84 had an infinitely variable hydrostatic transmission, the other 84 series had 8 forward and 4 reverse synchromesh gearbox with an optional torque amplifier to double the number of speeds and a 12 forward and 5 reverse synchromesh gearbox was standard on the 1246.

Five Fieldforce 85 series tractors ranging from the 52hp 485L to the 82hp 885XL, made at Doncaster between 1981 and 1985, were improved versions of the 84 series. Publicity material explained that other tractors had a cab but the 85 series was different with its 'new XL control centre with glass from the floor to the roof' which had cost £28m to develop. A full synchromesh gearbox with 8 forward and 4 reverse speeds was standard and an optional change-on-the-move torque amplifier doubled the gear range. Four-wheel drive was available for the 69hp, 77hp and 82hp tractors, including the 77hp Hydro 85 with hydrostatic transmission which replaced the Hydro 84. The 45hp 385L was added to the 85 series in 1984.

International Harvester were also marketing a range of 90–170hp tractors in the UK in 1981. The two- and four-wheel drive, 6 cylinder 55 series launched in 1977 were improved with new XL cabs. The 955XL, 1055XL and 1255XL had 90hp, 100hp and 125hp engines and a 145hp turbocharged power unit was used for the

142. The International Harvester 'Snoopy' tractors were made in America.

flagship 1455XL. Turbo clutches, 20 forward and 9 reverse gears and a 'buddy seat' were standard equipment for the German-built 1255XL and 1455XL.

The three articulated four-wheel drive International 'Snoopy' tractors launched in America in 1979 did not arrive in the UK until 1981. Classed as rowcrop tractors in America the 6 cylinder 3388, 3588 and 3788 rated at 130hp, 150hp and 170hp had a rear-mounted control centre (cab) and a torque amplifier which doubled the number of gears in the basic 8 forward and 4 reverse mechanical gearbox.

Tenneco, who already owned Case and David Brown, widened their product range in 1985 with the acquisition of the agricultural division of International Harvester. Manufacture of the 85 series continued at Doncaster, the David Brown Case 94 series were still in production at Meltham and the big Case 4694 and 4894 tractors with 250hp and 291hp engines were made in America. The International 85 series tractors remained in production until the late 1980s when they were replaced by the Case IH Magnum and Maxxum series.

ISEKI

The Iseki Agricultural Machinery Manufacturing Co was established in Japan in 1926 but Iseki tractors did not appear in Great Britain until the mid-1970s. Farm tractors had become more powerful over the years and the stage was reached where they were no longer suitable for smaller farms. This situation

143. The Iseki TX 4510 from Japan cost £7,600 with a roll bar in 1982. A quiet cab added £475 to the price.

144. Power steering and wet multi-disc brakes were features of the Iseki SX 65 and SX 95.

provided an opening for a number of Japanese tractor manufacturers, including Iseki and Kubota, to enter the British market.

Following a visit to Japan in 1976, Mr. L.E. Tuckwell, a John Deere dealer in Suffolk, started a company called L.E. Toshi Ltd at Ipswich to import the two- and four-wheel drive 13hp and 15hp Iseki TS and TX tractors with Mitsubishi 2 cylinder water-cooled engines. The TS2810 and TS3510 with Isuzu water-cooled engines were soon added to the UK range. An 8 forward and 2 reverse gearbox, live hydraulics, a four-speed power take-off and a safety start mechanism in the clutch pedal linkage were features of these 28hp and 35hp tractors.

The same models were imported in 1979 when Iseki established a partnership with Lely at St. Neots. This arrangement continued until 1986 when Iseki started their own import business near Huntingdon which eventually moved to Bourn in Cambridgeshire. More powerful Iseki models appeared in Britain in 1982 but they were still classed as compact tractors. The 1.5m wide two- and four-wheel drive TS4510 had a 45hp 3 cylinder water-cooled engine with special combustion chambers claimed to improve fuel economy. The 8 forward and 2 reverse gearbox gave a top speed of 13mph and the tractor could be supplied with a roll-bar or a quiet cab. The 65hp four-wheel drive Iseki TX 6500 had a similar specification to the TX4510.

Iseki entered the big-power league in 1986 when they launched four new SX models with 50–95hp engines. They had a 12 forward and 4 reverse or a 24 forward and 8 reverse gearbox with Super-Shift transmission. Other Iseki models on the British market in 1986 included the 3 cylinder 16hp TX 2140 and 18hp TX 2160 together with five TE models in the 24–48hp bracket. The TX 2160 had closed centre hydraulics and optional hydrostatic transmission. The four-wheel drive TA series with 25hp, 33hp, 40hp and 48hp engines introduced in 1989 had a 16 forward and reverse speed mechanical gearbox and power-assisted steering.

Massey Ferguson signed an agreement with Iseki in 1993 to supply 88–125hp MF 3000 and 3100 tractors with crystal blue paintwork for sale in Japan and 25–48hp Iseki TA models with the MF colour scheme were sold in Britain. This arrangement remained in place until 1997 when Iseki TF and TM tractors were added to the Jacobsen (part of the American Textron Group) product range. The TF models had 20hp, 25hp and 30hp engines and the TM models with 15hp and 17hp 3 cylinder water-cooled engines had a mechanical or optional hydrostatic transmission. When Ransomes were taken over by Textron the Iseki range was distributed from Ipswich.

J C B

Bamfords of Uttoxeter were a leading manufacturer of farm machinery in the early 1900s but Joe Bamford left the family business in 1945 to establish his own agricultural engineering company. Early products included tipping trailers and front-end loaders for the E27N Fordson Major and Nuffield tractors. Half-track conversions with slatted rubber tracks and the single arm Si-Draulic front-end loader came next and by the mid-1950s the product range had been widened to include loader shovels and the first JCB digger-loaders.

Field trials of a prototype JCB High Mobility Vehicle started in 1987 and the pre-production HMV or Fastrac unveiled at the 1990 Smithfield Show was probably one of the worst-kept secrets in the history of farm tractors. The initial image of the 'Fastrac' which eventually went on sale in the summer of 1991 was that of a fast transport tractor unsuited to ploughing and heavy field work. Important innovations on Fastrac, advertised as 'the world's first genuine high speed tractor', included coil spring front suspension, self-levelling hydro-pneumatic rear suspension, air-operated disc brakes on the four equal-size wheels and an air-conditioned two-seater cab. The tractor could have a naturally aspirated 125hp or a turbocharged 145hp Perkins diesel engine; other features included an 18 forward and 6 reverse gearbox, front and rear power take-off shafts and hydraulic linkage with the Bosch Hitch-Tronic draft control system.

145. The first JCB High Mobility Vehicle made its debut at the 1990 Smithfield Show.

146. The JCB Fastrac 145T.65 with a top speed of 40mph was launched at the 1992 Smithfield Show.

The improved Fastrac 125.65 and 145T.65 were announced by JCB Landpower Ltd at the 1992 Smithfield Show. Different wheel equipment and gearing gave the tractor a 40mph top speed, the hydraulic linkage was re-designed as a full category III unit and there was a choice of a light or heavy duty rear load platform.

There were three Fastrac models in 1993: the 125 remained in production, the 135hp Fastrac 135 was added to the range and the new 150hp Fastrac 155 replaced the 145T.65. The improved transmission had a 36 forward and 12 reverse Powersplit change-on-the-move gearbox and an optional pre-select Selectronic system with a column-mounted change lever which provided rapid changes of speed and direction. An even more powerful Fastrac 185 with a 6 cylinder turbocharged 170hp Cummins engine made its debut at the 1994 Royal Show. The new model had an improved transmission and rear axle with the choice of a 65kph or 75kph gearbox. The diff-lock was automatically disengaged when the hydraulic linkage was raised and the optional field area meter stopped measuring at the same time.

The smaller and lighter Fastrac 1115 with a 115hp Perkins engine replaced the Fastrac 125 in 1995 and the similar 135hp 1135 was added to the compact range later in the year. The larger 130hp, 150hp and 170hp Fastracs had four-wheel hydraulic power braking and twin-line air braking system for trailers.

Changes in 1996 included a new engine for the 1115 which became the 1115S, the addition of the 125hp Fastrac 1125 and also the 1135 which completed the 1000 series. They were all available in two- and four-wheel drive and a new air-over hydraulic braking system replaced the previous hydraulic power brakes. A Quadtronic four-wheel steer option also introduced in 1996 gave JCB their first fully suspended all-wheel-steer fast tractor with a much reduced turning circle.

The Fastrac was well established by 1997 with six models with 6 cylinder engines in the 115–170hp bracket. The 1000 series met the demand for a smaller high speed tractor and the 100 series provided more power for heavier work. The 100 series consisted of the 135 and 155 with Perkins 135hp and 150hp engines and the 185 with a 170hp Cummins turbocharged engine. With the weight evenly distributed over the four wheels, a full suspension system and air-operated disc brakes made the 1000 series tractors legal for use on the road at speeds of up to 50kph (31mph).

The Fastrac 100 and 1000 tractors were improved, re-styled and re-badged in 1998 as the 3000 and 2000 series with a 54 forward and 18 reverse transmission system. The 155 and 185 became 3155 and the 3185 and four 2000 series tractors in the 115–148hp bracket included the new Fastrac 2150. The 148hp Fastrac 2150 was added to the range to meet the needs of existing 1135 owners who wanted the power of the 3155 with the compactness and manoeuvrability of the previous 1000 series tractors.

147. The JCB Fastrac 1135 had a 135hp turbocharged Perkins 1000 series engine.

148. Re-styled 3000 and 2000 Fastracs replaced the 100 and 1000 series in 1998.

JOHN DEERE

With his engineering apprenticeship completed, John Deere started a blacksmithing business in the small town of Grand Detour, Illinois in 1836. He made his first plough with steel mouldboards in 1837, plough production was moved to Moline, Illinois in 1859 and the leaping deer trademark appeared in 1876. The company showed some interest in tractors in 1892 but little else happened until they acquired the Waterloo Gasoline Tractor Co at Waterloo in Iowa in 1918.

The Waterloo Boy Model N tractor sold in Britain as the Overtime Model N was made until 1923 when it was replaced by the two-speed John Deere Model D. North America was the main market for the Model D which had a horizontal 2 cylinder engine and roller chain final drive but a considerable number were sold in Europe between the two world wars and many of them were still being used in the late 1940s. An improved 30–41hp Model D with a three-speed gearbox was made from 1935 until 1953. Tractor horse power figures at the time indicated drawbar and belt hp in that order. The 19–25hp Model C rowcrop tractor launched in 1927 was a serious competitor for the Farmall F series tractors. A pedal-operated tool bar lifting mechanism, a power take-off shaft and belt pulley were added to the Model C in 1928 when it was re-named the John Deere GP.

The tricycled-wheeled 18–24hp Model A rowcrop tractor introduced in 1934 had a hydraulic system and pneumatic tyres. It was also an early example of a tractor with rear wheels which could be moved in or out on their axles to adjust the track width. The smaller 12–16hp Model B introduced in 1935 was advertised as a tractor 'able to do as much work as two horses'. Styled versions of the Model A and Model B with a new 4 speed gearbox were introduced in 1938 and a two-lever 6 forward speed gearbox was used from 1941. So-called styled tractors had a sheet metal bonnet and radiator grille giving a more modern look compared to earlier models where the engine, radiator and steering mechanism were exposed. The 'three-plow'

149. Two-cylinder John Deere tractors including the 8–14hp Model H were hand started with the external fly-wheel. Life became easier in 1947 when an electric starter was added to the list of optional equipment.

150. A twin-cylinder horizontally-opposed donkey petrol engine with an electric starter was used to start the 49hp 5 forward speed Model R. It was the first John Deere tractor to have optional live power take-off and hydraulics.

31–41hp Model D was the biggest John Deere tractor in 1935 when the AR and BR were introduced to meet a demand for smaller tractors. The 'two-plow' AR and BR, with steel wheels or pneumatic tyres, were general purpose versions of the A and B. The BR was discontinued in 1947 but the AR was made until 1953. Other versions of the Model A and B included the narrow rowcrop AN and BN, the wide rowcrop AW and BW, the AO and BO orchard tractors and the AV and BV for vineyard work. F.A.Standen Ltd of Ely in Cambridgeshire, who became a leading sugar beet machinery manufacturer, sold a number of high-clearance tricycle-wheeled Model A tractors to fen farmers in the mid-1930s.

The John Deere Model L was introduced in 1937 to replace the horse on small American farms. It had a 2 cylinder 9–10 1/2hp Hercules engine, a 3 forward and reverse gearbox and an off-set seat which provided good visibility of rowcrops. A 10hp John Deere engine replaced the Hercules power unit in 1942. The 35hp Model G rowcrop tractor with 4 forward gears and reverse appeared in 1938 and the 13–15hp Model H rowcrop tractor with the same gear range launched in 1939 had a very modern foot throttle. The 12hp LA rowcrop model, also with an offset driving seat, was added to the range in 1941.

Horizontal 2 cylinder petrol engines were still being used in 1947 when John Deere introduced the 20hp Model M with power take-off, electric starting and lights. The new Touch-o-Matic three-point linkage on the Model M was used with a range of John Deere mounted implements and raised or lowered the drawbar. The Model M, the MT tricycle-wheeled rowcrop tractor and the MC crawler introduced in 1949 were discontinued in 1952.

The twin-cylinder Model R, introduced in 1949, was the first John Deere tractor with a diesel engine. It had a 5 forward speed and reverse gearbox, power take-off and an improved Power-trol hydraulic system controlled from an 'armchair driving seat'. An independent power take-off and live hydraulic system were optional for the Model R which was the last of the letter series of John Deere tractors. Model numbers were used when the 31hp and 41hp John Deere 50 and 60 replaced the Model A and Model B in 1952. Rear wheel track widths on the Model 50 were adjusted with a ratchet mechanism which moved the wheels along the axles on a very coarse thread.

The standard, rowcrop and high-clear versions of the Model G were rated at 39hp when they became the Model 70 in 1953. The Model M was re-named the Model 40 at the same time. The Model 70 had a 43hp all-fuel (kerosene) or a 50hp petrol engine while a 50hp diesel model was added in 1954. The diesel tractor was started with a petrol donkey engine and a de-compressor to help it get the diesel engine up to the required starting speed. The Model R was superseded by the 2 cylinder 67hp Model 80 diesel tractor in 1954. It had 6 forward gears and reverse, live hydraulics and was started with a donkey engine (usually called a 'pony' engine in America).

John Deere 2 cylinder 20 series tractors were introduced in 1956. The 25hp Model 40 renamed the 320 was the smallest and the new 29hp 5 forward speed 420 made in standard, rowcrop, tricycle rowcrop, high-clear and tracklayer format was next in line. The petrol-engined John Deere 520, 620 and 720 were rated at 38, 48 and 59 belt hp; slightly more powerful liquefied petroleum gas (LPG) engines were also available for these tractors but LPG was not available in all parts of America. Power steering was standard on the 520, 620 and 720. The 67hp diesel-engined Model 80, also with power steering, became the 820 in 1956 and with engine change in the following year the 820 was rated at 75hp. Standard features on the 20 series tractors included draft control hydraulics, a pedal to engage drive to the power take-off, a more comfortable driver's seat and a new colour scheme with yellow flashes added to the familiar green paintwork. A re-styled 20 series with the

151. The 93hp John Deere 4010 'rowcrop' tractor was marketed in the UK by Lundell (GB) Ltd.

same engines and improved driving controls and operator comfort became the John Deere 30 series made between 1958 and 1960. The John Deere 435, which had a 32hp G M Detroit 2 cylinder diesel engine in the late 1950s was otherwise very similar to the 29hp petrol-engined 430 and this version of the 435 was the last of the long line of John Deere tractors with 2 cylinder engines.

John Deere was the only major North American tractor manufacturer without a factory in Europe until they acquired a major share in Lanz in 1956 and then purchased their Mannheim factory in Germany in 1960. The Lanz Bulldog tractor was discontinued after a 35-year production run at Mannheim and following a huge investment in the factory the first multi-cylinder John Deere-Lanz 300 and 500 tractors appeared in 1961. Meanwhile, in America the first of the new 10 series tractors which gradually replaced the 30 series was launched in 1960. Wheeled and crawler versions of the John Deere 1010 and 2010 came first, the 3010 and 4010 were added in 1961, followed by the 125hp 5010 in 1963. Most British farmers were buying new diesel tractors by the early 1960s but John Deere were still making petrol and LPG engined models for the North American market.

F.A. Standen & Sons, H. Leverton & Co and Jack Olding imported John Deere tractors in the 1950s but it was all change in 1962 when Lundell (Great Britain) Ltd at Edenbridge in Kent became part of the John Deere organisation. Ford and Massey Ferguson had the lion's share of UK tractor sales in the early 1960s so it was difficult for Lundell, who had been selling forage harvesters and some John Deere machinery for about six years, to break into the British tractor market. A supply of 4010 tractors imported in 1964 in wooden packing cases was dispatched to some of Lundell's dealers, including Drake & Fletcher in Kent, Ben Burgess at Norwich and L.E. Tuckwell in Suffolk. The big green 4010 with its 93hp 6 cylinder engine was viewed with some apprehension by many British farmers and, apart from a John Deere mounted reversible plough, there were very few implements big enough to make full use of this new-found power.

John Deere replaced the 10 series with the 47–143hp 20 series tractors over a three-year period. The 3020 and 4020 were launched in 1964, the 1020 and 2020 appeared the following year and the 1120 and 5020 completed the range in 1966. The 4020 accounted for almost half of John Deere's worldwide tractor sales by 1966 when they opened their own distribution centre depot at Langar in Nottinghamshire. Technically well ahead of its time, the 100hp 6 cylinder 4020 had power-steering and a two speed power take-off with separate 540rpm and 1,000rpm shafts. An optional hydraulically operated diff-lock cost £35 and the new 8 forward and 4 reverse Power Shift transmission with a top speed of 20mph was an extra £171. The 4020 was the first John Deere tractor with a ROPS (roll-over protective structure) safety frame. It was also the first tractor on the British market with optional powershift transmission and, like the Ford Select-O-Speed, an inching pedal was provided for implement hitching and emergency stops. The Power Shift transmission was also optional on the 3020 with an 82hp 4 cylinder diesel engine. Petrol-engined versions of the 20 series with the 3020 LPG engine for the 3020 were available in America.

The Mannheim-built 1020, 1120 and 2020 medium-powered tractors with at least 1,000 interchangeable parts did not join the 4020 and 5020 on the UK market until 1967. The 47hp 1020 had a 3 cylinder direct injection engine, the 53hp 1120 and 64hp

152. *Made at Mannheim and launched in 1966 the 56hp John Deere 710 had a 1,000rpm power take-off on one side of the engine. Many farmers in continental Europe used this for a mid-mounted mower and so it was usually left on the tractor.*

153. The articulated 8630 and 8430 were the flagships of the John Deere 30 series made in the early 1970s.

2020 had four cylinders and with many common features the basic prices were £899, £990.5s and £1,115.15s respectively. Closed centre hydraulics with lower link sensing, a hand and foot operated diff-lock, hydraulic disc brakes, front-mounted fuel tank and foot throttle were standard. Optional extras included a dual speed power take-off, a Hi-Lo change-on-the-move speed reduction in any gear and power steering. The driving controls were grouped conveniently around the standard seat or an optional fully adjustable sprung version which added £9 to the price of the 1020. The 20 series was enlarged with the launch of the 2520 and the 4520 in 1969 and these tractors were made until the 30 series appeared in 1972. The 53hp 1120 was retained until the mid-1970s when it was replaced by the 1130, which was also rated at 53hp.

The John Deere 710 was a direct competitor for the Ford 4000 and Massey Ferguson 165. The specification included a 10 forward and 3 reverse synchromesh gearbox, a live power shaft drive on one side of the engine for a mid-mounted mower and two shafts at the rear, power-steering and live top link sensing hydraulics.

The 2030 with a petrol or diesel engine launched in 1971 was the first of the new John Deere 30 series made in Germany and America. The 30 series eventually ranged from the 71hp 2030 to the 215hp 8430 and 275hp 8630. Hydraulic trailer braking kits were offered for the 1130 to 3130 models and hydrostatic

154. A change-on-the-move 16 forward and 8 reverse speed Power Synchron transmission was optional on the 88hp turbocharged John Deere 2850 and other 50 series tractors made at Mannheim.

front-wheel drive was optional on the 4230 and 4430. The 53–97hp tractors had tilt-back safety cabs and the 122hp 6 cylinder 4230, also available in the UK, had 16 forward and 6 reverse gears, power steering and a safety roll bar. A re-styled and refined 30 series with an 'operator protection unit' or quiet cab claimed to surpass all safety and noise level regulations in force at the time was advertised in 1976. The articulated four-wheel drive 8430 and optional hydrostatic front-wheel drive for the 2130 and 3130 were introduced to British farmers in the same year.

The seven 'Schedule Masters' 40 series tractors, ranging from the 50hp 1040 to the 97hp 3140 launched in 1979 were made at the Deere factory in Moline, Illinois with an 8 speed synchromesh gearbox or optional change-on-the-move Power-Synchro high-low transmission. Other features included hydrostatic steering and mechanical front-wheel drive controlled with a switch on the instrument panel. A diff-lock which automatically engaged when the wheels started to slip was standard on the larger 40 series tractors.

New models came thick and fast in the early 1980s. Five new 50–82hp tractors in the LP series for livestock farmers and the XE 40 economy range appeared in 1983. The 352hp 8850 with a V-8 turbocharged and inter-cooled power unit was launched in the same year along with the 115hp 4040S and 132hp 4240S with a 16 speed Quad Range transmission.

John Deere introduced five high horse power 50 series tractors in 1985. When the range was completed the following year sixteen 50 series 44–352hp tractors had replaced the 40 series. There were four conventional four-wheel drive models, starting with the 140hp John Deere 4350, and two articulated four-wheel drive tractors, including the flagship 8850 with a touch-control digital monitoring system in the cab. The smaller 50 series made at Mannheim and introduced to British farmers in 1986 was claimed to be between 10 and 20 per cent more fuel efficient than the equivalent 40 series tractors. The 3 cylinder 44hp 1550 was the only two-wheel drive model while the 50hp 1750 to the 6 cylinder 100hp 3350 were in two- and four-wheel drive format and those with even more power were four-wheel drive only. An automatic eco-viscous drive radiator cooling fan and 16 speed Power Synchron 40kph transmission were standard on 6 cylinder models and optional on the other four-wheel drive tractors.

Six-cylinder turbocharged engines and a 15 speed powershift transmission were standard on the American built four-wheel drive 128hp 4050 and 144hp 4250 introduced to British farmers in 1987. With a hydro-cushion seat and stereo radio in the cab, category II and III linkage and prices approaching £40,000 they were advertised as the first tractors in the UK to have a full power shift transmission with clutch-less control in forward and reverse.

155. John Deere returned to a full frame chassis in 1992 when they launched the 6000 and 7000 series with sophisticated TechCenter cabs.

Five new 55 series four-wheel drive 'rowcrop tractors' with 128–228hp 6 cylinder engines and a 15 forward and 4 reverse powershift transmission were launched in 1990. They had the John Deere 'Intellitrak Monitoring System' which not only monitored tractor performance and field operation but was also used by service engineers for diagnostic checks to locate faults.

John Deere's rack and pinion rear axle adjustment for quick track width changes was re-introduced on the smaller 60 series in 1991 and the more powerful 8560 and 8760 were improved with the addition of an electronic engine governor.

The unitary construction principle used for the best part of forty years was dropped when John Deere returned to a full frame chassis to support the engine and transmission system for the 6000 and 7000 series launched in 1992. The four 6000 tractors had 75–100hp 4 cylinder engines and 130hp, 150hp and 170hp 6 cylinder power units were used for the three 7000 models. SynchroPlus or PowerQuad shift-under-load transmissions were optional on the 6000 series. A 19 forward and 7 reverse speed powershift with an electronically controlled shifting was available at extra cost for the 7000 range. The improved hydraulic system had a pressure and flow compensating system (PFC) with a low standby pressure to reduce fuel consumption. The 1993 John Deere range included the new 6000 and 7000 series seven 50–88hp 50 series tractors and the 6 cylinder 4755 and 4955 rated at 190hp and 228hp.

The 185–260hp 8000 series launched in 1995 had the driving controls, including those for the computerised headland management system, located on the Command arm rest attached to the swivel seat in the TechCentre cab. Other features included a 16 speed electro-hydraulically controlled powershift transmission with field cruise control and load sensing hydraulics. Three 7010 series tractors with 140hp, 155hp and 175hp engines replaced the 7000 series in 1996 when 84hp and 100hp models were added to the 6000 series. There was also a 55–85hp 3000 series with an 18 forward and reverse speed transmission for the smaller farm.

Standard versions of the 55hp and 70hp 5300 and 5400 in the new 5000 series assembled by Carraro in Italy for John Deere's European market were launched in 1997. The two- and four-wheel drive 50 series included the narrow 5300N, 5400N and the 80hp 5500 N orchard tractors.

156. This rubber-tracked John Deere 8000T series tractor was one of four models with 185–260hp engines launched in 1997. The transmission system had an electro-hydraulically engaged planetary final drive system and the steering wheel was used to vary the power transmitted to each of the friction-driven tracks when changing direction.

The 6100 series introduced at the 1997 Smithfeld Show with new engines and an improved cab with storage space for the farm laptop computer. Four- and six-cylinder engines were used for the 75hp 6010 to the 135hp 6910 and the John Deere triple-link front axle suspension system was optional on the 100hp 6310 and larger models.

KUBOTA

Large numbers of Japanese mini-tractors were already being sold in America when the tractor division of the Marubeni Corporation established an outlet at Whitley Bridge in Yorkshire to sell Kubota tractors. The 24hp 3 cylinder L 225, the two-cylinder 17hp L 175 and 12½hp B6000 with water-cooled diesel engines arrived in the UK in 1975. The three Kubota tractors had 8 forward and 2 reverse gears, three-point linkage, front and rear power take-off and independent brakes. The 24hp four-wheel drive L 245 was added in 1977 and the 3 cylinder 16hp B 7100 with 6 forward and 2 reverse gears followed in 1978.

Compact tractor horse power gradually increased as the years passed. The four-wheel drive 34hp Kubota L 345DT launched in 1980 was the most powerful of a ten-model range. It had a dual clutch, 8 forward and 2 reverse speeds, power-steering, front and rear power take-off and wet disc brakes. Having outgrown the Yorkshire premises Kubota moved to Thame in Oxfordshire in 1982. Various models were added over the

157. The Kubota L 225 with a safety-start mechanism built into the clutch pedal was introduced to the British market in 1975.

158. The four-wheel drive L 5450, shown with an LA 1150 loader attached, was the most powerful Kubota tractor on the British market in 1990. Kubota L 3250 and L 2250 tractors are in the background.

159. High ground clearance is a feature of the four-wheel drive 44hp Kubota Grandel L 4200.

years, including the two- and four-wheel drive 19hp B 8200 and B 8200HST with hydrostatic transmission launched in 1983.

Kubota Tractors in Canada made the two- and four-wheel drive M series tractors for the North American market in the 1980s. The series included the M 5950 and M 7950 with 62hp and 84hp water cooled engines, 16 forward and 8 reverse gears, hydraulic clutch, wet disc brakes and an independent power take-off with ground speed.

The four-wheel drive L 5450 introduced in 1990 with a 54hp 5 cylinder engine, wet clutch, power steering and hydraulic shuttle transmission was the most powerful Kubota tractor yet seen in the UK. The 2 cylinder 12½hp four-wheel drive B 4200 was the smallest model in the 1993 range which included the 29½hp L 2550 GST with a Glide Shift Transmission providing 8 clutchless changes in speed and direction.

Three new L series Grandel compact tractors launched in 1994 had 16 forward and reverse speeds in a synchromesh gearbox, a creep speed box and a hydraulic shuttle reverser. Indirect injection Kubota water-cooled 34hp, 37hp and 44hp engines provided the power for the Grandel series with hydrostatic steering and wet disc brakes.

The 1997 Kubota catalogue included the 12½–24hp B series, the 34–43hp Grandel L models and the 29hp four-wheel drive ST 30 with hydrostatic transmission. The B series with water-cooled engines had a 6 forward and 2 reverse gearbox or hydrostatic transmission, mid and rear power take-off and optional safety frame or cab. The optional bi-speed turn on the four-wheel drive models was designed to increase the front wheel speed by about 60 per cent over the rear wheels to give a much smaller turning circle.

LAMBORGHINI

Ferruccio Lamborghini made his first tractor in 1948 but within 20 years this Italian engineer was famous for his high-performance sports cars. The 39hp 3 cylinder, diesel-engined 5C crawler introduced in the early 1960s was the first Lamborghini tractor to attract any serious interest outside Italy. It had a very unusual track design with three pneumatic tyred transport wheels which were used to raise the tracks off the ground when travelling on the public highway. The two rear wheels, driven by the track sprockets, were skid steered with the steering levers and a front castor wheel enabled the tractor to make relatively sharp turns. A narrow vineyard version of the 5C had a standard clockwise power take-off shaft and a second shaft ran anti-clockwise at 2,000rpm.

Lamborghini sold his tractor business to SAME in 1972 and the Maulden Engineering Co at Flitwick in Bedfordshire introduced a range of 38–105hp Lamborghini tractors, including the new 67hp 654 offered to British farmers in the mid-1970s. Competition for sales was fierce by the late 1970s and there were some good deals around. A Vauxhall Cavalier car was offered as a free gift with the first three Lamborghini tractors bought and paid for in full at the 1980 Royal Show. The car, which cost just under £4,600, was equivalent to a 30 per cent discount.

Maulden Engineering listed eight Lamborghini two- and four-wheel drive tractors in the 1980 Smithfield Show catalogue. The 105hp and 125hp 6 cylinder 1056DT and 1256DT were the most powerful, followed by the 92hp 5 cylinder R955DT. The 4 cylinder 62hp, 72hp and 82hp models had air-cooled engines and a 12 speed synchromesh gearbox. The range was completed by the 3 cylinder 53hp R 503 and 62hp R603 with roll bars and three crawlers with 38hp, 59hp and 60hp engines.

The 1356 and turbocharged 1556 were launched in 1981 and with water-cooled engines rated at 135hp and 155hp they departed from the traditional air-cooled power units on Lamborghini tractors. However, the 75hp C 754L crawler based on the 854 wheeled model and 115hp 1156 wheeled tractor launched at the same time had 4 and 6 cylinder air-cooled engines.

Universal Tractors, based at Brough in Yorkshire, who later became Linx Agriculture, were appointed concessionaires for Lamborghini tractors in 1983. The 60–155hp two- and four-wheel drive Italian tractors had a pedal-operated hydraulic trailer braking system and oil-immersed front disc brakes were standard on four-wheel drive models over 110hp. Distribution of the Italian tractors in the UK was taken over by SAME-Lamborghini at Barby in Warwickshire in 1986. There were nine two- and four-wheel drive models with water-cooled engines ranging from the new 60hp 660 to the established 165hp Lamborghini 1706. Lamborghini and

160. The Lamborghini R 503DT was the smallest of the Italian-built tractors imported by Maulden Engineering in the early 1980s. Two-wheel drive and narrow versions of the tractors were available.

SAME tractors were very similar apart from their colour and the air-/oil-cooled engines used for the SAME range.

'Drive by wire' was the 1989 advertising slogan for the new four-wheel drive Lamborghini Grand Prix 674-70, 774-80 and turbocharged 874-90 with more than a hint of motor racing in their name. They were advertised as the first tractors with an individual electronically governed injection pump for each of the four cylinders. The 70hp, 80hp and 90hp Grand Prix tractors had push button control of the four-speed power take-off and the 90hp model had a 40 speed gearbox. Lamborghini sports car stylists had some influence in the design of the bonnet and cab on the Formula

161. The 3 cylinder air-cooled 53hp Lamborghini 583DT marketed by Linx Agriculture in the early 1980s had 12 forward and 3 reverse gears and a new low-profile cab.

115 and 135 tractors launched in 1990. The 6 cylinder 115hp and 132hp tractors had an electronic engine monitoring system and a 36 forward and reverse speed gearbox.

The Lamborghini Racing 165 introduced in 1992 with electronic control of engine governing, hydraulic linkage and a clutchless 27 speed powershift gearbox was, except for its 165hp water-cooled engine, very

162. The two- and four-wheel drive 1356 with a 135hp water-cooled engine was added to the Lamborghini range in the UK in 1981.

similar to the SAME Titan 160. The Racing 190 with a turbocharged 6 cylinder engine launched later that year gave Lamborghini a range of models from the 25hp Runner 250 to the 189hp Racing 90. The 150hp Lamborghini Racing 150 launched in 1994 had the SAME clutchless transmission with 9 powershift speeds in each of three ranges selected electronically with a push button switch on the joystick control lever.

An agreement with AGCO resulted in some Lamborghini tractors with silver and black paintwork being sold in America in the early 1990s under the White brand name. Power take-off horse power was an important factor for American farmers when buying a tractor. The 60–105 pto hp Lamborghini models in White livery complimented the more powerful American White tractors in the 120–200 pto hp bracket made by AGCO at Independence, Missouri.

The 85–105hp Lamborghini Premium models launched at the 1994 Smithfield Show had electronic engine speed control. An electronic engine governor was standard on the 6 cylinder 1060 and optional on the other models. There was a choice of a mechanical or an electronic 20 forward and reverse powershift transmission and

163. A Twin System reverse drive facility incorporating a front power take-off and hydraulic linkage was introduced in 1989 as an option for Lamborghini models such as the 775-F Plus orchard tractor.

SAME-Lamborghini's electronic linkage control with the lower link sensing hydraulic system.

Twenty-three Lamborghini models, from the 25hp Runner 250 to the flagship Racing 190 with a 6 cylinder and a 27 forward and reverse speed transmission, were marketed by SAME Deutz-Fahr in the UK in 1998. The Champion 120, 130 and 150 launched at that year's Smithfield Show were more sophisticated versions of the medium-powered SAME Rubin models.

164. An electro-hydraulic clutch control system was an optional extra for the 132hp Lamborghini Formula 135 introduced in 1997.

LANDINI

Steam engines and vineyard machinery were being made by Giovanni Landini at Fabbrico in Italy in 1884 but by 1910 he was making single-cylinder two-stroke 'hot bulb' semi-diesel engines. This type of engine was used by a number of manufacturers including Deutz, Lanz and Munktell for the next 40 years or so.

Landini died in 1924 but his three sons carried on the business. The first Landini tractor with a horizontal 30hp semi-diesel two-stroke engine was made in 1925. A 40hp model appeared in 1930 and the 50hp single-cylinder water cooled Super Landini with 3 forward gears and reverse introduced in 1934 was made until the outbreak of war in 1939. The 30hp Velite was added in 1935, followed by the Buffalo to give Landini three models with semi-diesel engines by the late 1930s.

Semi-diesel engines were still being used when tractor production was re-started in 1950 with the launch of the 25hp Landini L 25. The 45hp L 45 with 6 forward gears and reverse appeared in 1952 and the L 55 with optional half tracks was added in 1955. The Landinetta launched in 1957 with the engine and transmission off-set in the style of the Allis Chalmers Model B was the last new model to be made at Fabbrico with a semi-diesel engine.

An agreement made in 1957 allowed Landini to make Perkins engines under licence in Italy. A 3 cylinder 30hp full diesel engine was used for the Landini R 35 launched in the same year and for the C35 crawler introduced in 1958. A 4 cylinder 50hp Perkins engine provided the power for the 6 forward and 2 reverse speed R50 with optional four-wheel drive. The Landinetta was made until 1959 when it was replaced by the R 25 with a 28hp Perkins engine which became the R 3000 in 1960. Massey Ferguson, who also owned Perkins, bought the Fabbrico factory in the same year and the last Landini tractor with a semi-diesel engine was made in 1961.

Landini tractor design moved forward under Massey Ferguson and from the early 1960s to the present day blue Landini and red Massey Ferguson tractors have been made on the same production line. The 4 cylinder Landini R 4500 based on the Massey Ferguson 65 and introduced in 1962 was the first model made at Fabbrico under the new regime and the 45hp Landini C4500 crawler was added in 1963. The Massey Ferguson influence became more obvious in 1967 with the launch of the 80hp two-wheel drive R 8000 and the four-wheel drive DT 8000. The DT (Dual Traction) version with a Selene front axle was designed as a four-wheel drive tractor rather than as a two-wheel drive with a live front axle added at a later stage. Four Wheel Traction Ltd marketed similar Selene front-wheel drive conversion kits for Massey Ferguson 165, 175 ánd 185 tractors.

A new range of Landini crawlers appeared in 1975, including the 41hp 3 cylinder C6500 with 8 forward and 4 reverse gears was made with standard width and narrow tracks. The C6500 appeared in the Massey Ferguson colours at the 1976 Royal Show as the MF 134C. The 47hp and 61hp MF 154C and 174C crawlers

165. The 1992 Landini 7880 Viewmaster had a 12 speed shuttle transmission with an optional 12 forward speed creep box or overdrive unit.

122

were also made by Landini. The four-wheel drive 14500 DT with a 107hp Perkins A 6.354 launched the same year was the first Landini tractor with more than 100hp under the bonnet.

Landini were still a wholly owned subsidiary of Massey Ferguson when they made their first specialist fruit tractors in 1982. The letter V denoted a narrow vineyard model, F was used for standard orchard tractors and L for wider orchard models.

Almost half of the 12,000 or so tractors made at Fabricco in 1989 were painted in Massey Ferguson colours but when the Varity Corporation sold Massey Ferguson to AGCO in 1990 Landini were at last able to sell their blue tractors in Britain. A Luxembourg company owned the majority share in the new company but Massey Ferguson retained an interest in the business. The 1990 Landini range included the 80 and 10,000 series wheeled tractors and 47–80hp crawlers. The two- and four-wheel drive 80 series

166. Brakes on all four wheels were a feature of the 47hp, 56hp and 63hp Landini Globus models.

included the 62hp, 71hp, 80hp and 93hp Landini 6880, 7880, 8880 and 9880 with 4 cylinder Perkins engines and a 24 forward and 12 reverse synchromesh gearbox with an optional 10 forward speed creeper box. Hydraulic inboard multi-disc brakes and diff-lock were standard. Optional Landtronic electronic draft control and performance monitor were added later that year. The 10,000 series had 103hp, 110hp and 132hp Perkins engines with the 80 series transmission system and lower link sensing hydraulics.

Watveare Ltd, who were still based in Wiltshire and importing Deutz-Fahr tractors, became the Landini distributor for the UK in 1991. They introduced a limited range of the Landini 80 and 10,000 series at a time when British farmers were already faced with a choice of more than 500 different models of tractor from 30 manufacturers and importers.

High clearance versions of the four-wheel drive Landini 8880 and 9880 with equal-size wheels and disc brakes on all four wheels and the Viewmaster 7880 and 8880 with sloping bonnets appeared in 1992. The first of the two- and four-wheel drive Blizzard tractors with 62hp, 71hp and 80hp engines and a 12 forward and reverse speed gearbox designed for stock and mixed farms were launched in the same year. Forward control versions of the 8880 and 9880 with a rear platform for a sprayer or fertiliser spreader were added in 1993. Landini AMS at Bury St Edmunds in Suffolk became the UK distributor for the light blue Italian tractors in 1994. The 110hp and 123hp Legend DT 115 and DT 130 were launched in the same year but were not available in the UK until 1996. Some components on the 6 cylinder Perkins-engined Landini Legend tractors were supplied by the Massey Ferguson factory in France. The standard 36 speed change-on-the-move transmission had a splitter and reverse shuttle while an optional creep speed box doubled the ratios to give 72 gears in each direction. The turbocharged 90hp Blizzard DT 95 with a 24 forward and 12 reverse 40kph transmission and disc brakes on all four wheels was added in 1995. A 60 degree steering angle combined with a fast-run front axle which increased front wheel speed when turning on the headland was a new feature on the four-wheel drive Globus 50, 60 and 65 tractors introduced in northern Europe in 1996. The Globus had a four-speed power take-off with reverse drive and optional 12, 15 or 25 speed reverse shuttle transmissions.

Since the change of ownership in the early 1990s, Landini, distributors of Massey Ferguson equipment in Italy and makers of MF crawlers and fruit tractors, widened their activities to include production of the Globus series for Iseki, who have a shareholding in the Italian company.

Landini were still making specialist tractors for Massey Ferguson when three models of the 'Trekker' crawler with 71hp, 85hp and 95hp Perkins engines were introduced in 1996. Features include a 16 forward and 8 reverse overdrive transmission, a hydraulic track tensioning system and category II hydraulic linkage.

Motokov UK were appointed Landini tractor distributors for the British Isles in 1998 and the Kings Lynn company imported 47–100hp models. The 56hp and 66hp Globus four-wheel drive models with a 15 or 25 speed shuttle gearbox were added to the Italian tractor range at that year's Smithfield Show.

167. The Landini Trekker crawler range was launched in 1996.

168. The 138hp Legend DT 145 with a 36 speed shuttle transmission was the most powerful tractor made by Landini when it appeared at the 1996 Smithfield Show.

LANZ

Heinrich Lanz founded an engineering company at Mannheim in Germany in 1859 and within a few years he was also selling British-built Clayton & Shuttleworth threshing machines. Chaff cutters and barn machinery were being made by 1867 and Lanz products in the early 1880s included threshing machines and steam engines. The Lanz Landbaumotor with a four-stroke 80ps engine had a chain-driven rear-mounted rotary cultivator. It was probably the first agricultural machine with a crude form of hydraulic lift and the rotary cultivator could be removed to leave the tractor free for other work.

The first Bulldog or HL Landbaumotor (Heinrich Lanz agricultural engine) made in 1921 had a 12hp single-cylinder, horizontal two-stroke semi-diesel engine. It was known as the Bulldog throughout its 40-year production run because the front of the tractor with a hot bulb on the cylinder head vaguely resembled

169. This vintage 12hp Lanz Bulldog was made at Mannheim in Germany in 1921. The John Deere 6900 came from the same factory 75 years later.

the face of the British bulldog. The tractor was started by heating the hot bulb with a blowlamp before cranking the engine with the steering wheel inserted in the centre of the flywheel. The Bulldog engine ran at 420rpm and the direct chain drive from the flywheel to the rear wheels was engaged with a lever-operated clutch. The tractor had a top speed of 3.5mph and could only be reversed by stopping the engine and re-starting it again with the flywheel turning in the opposite direction.

Several Bulldog models appeared in the 1920s and 1930s. A 15hp version of the HL Bulldog had the same engine with its speed increased to 500rpm and the four-wheel drive Bulldog HP based on the HL with the front wheels larger than those at the rear appeared in 1923. The HP was an early example of a steel-wheeled articulated tractor but it was too expensive and was only made for three years. The more powerful 22–30hp HR2 made for about four years was discontinued in 1929. It had 4 forward and 4 reverse speeds but like the HL the engine had to be stopped and re-started backwards to put the tractor into gear. A radiator and cooling fan, pedal-operated clutch and a 3 forward speed and reverse gearbox were some of

170. The bracket under the cylinder head of this 1935 Lanz Bulldog supported the blowlamp used to heat the hot bulb before starting the engine.

the advanced features on the 15–30hp Lanz HR 5 made between 1929 and 1935. A rowcrop version was made and tractors with optional pneumatic tyres had higher top speed. Like earlier Bulldogs the engine had a dry crankcase with oil pump lubrication and the bearings had to be lubricated by hand before it was started if the tractor had not been used for two days. The Bulldog 38, which had a six speed gearbox and sprung front axle and was made until 1934, was a variant of the HR 5. The engine could be set to run at 540rpm or 630rpm, the higher speed providing an additional 8hp.

The D 8500 and D 9500 also introduced in 1934 had the same engine which ran at 540rpm and 630rpm and developed 35hp and 54hp respectively on the two tractors. Other models of the D series appeared from time to time, including the D 1560 crawler version of the Bulldog. It was steered with levers and a steering wheel on a shaft stowed at the back of the tractor was used to start the engine.

The semi-diesel engined Bulldog 06 series were made at Mannheim from the mid-1930s and more than 100,000 Bulldog tractors had been manufactured when the factory was virtually destroyed in the early part of the Second World War. Some of the Bulldog D 7006 and D 9006 tractors made during the early part of the war ran on wood gas produced by a generator mounted on the tractor. Lanz struggled to survive in the immediate post-war years and although the more powerful 06 series tractors re-appeared in the late 1940s but the smaller models did not return until 1950. The first two figures of the 06 series model numbers indicated maximum horse power and alternative speeds of 850rpm, 950rpm and 1,050rpm enabled the driver to vary engine power according to need. The D 1706, D 1906 and D 2206 had a 130mm bore and a 170mm stroke engine while a 150mm bore and 210mm stroke engine was used for the D 2806, D 3206 and D 3606. A 6 forward and 2 reverse speed gearbox and pneumatic tyres were standard features of Lanz 06 series tractors.

171. Most Lanz Bulldogs were painted blue during their final years of production and the last hot bulb engined models were made in the early 1950s.

The Bulldog D 5506 introduced in 1950 was the first new model made at Mannheim factory after the war. The hot bulb had been moved to the left-hand side of the engine, a blowlamp was still an important part of the tool kit but an optional electric starter made life easier for the driver. The hot bulb was dispensed with in 1952 when a flat-topped cylinder head with an ignition chamber was used for the semi-diesel engine on the D 5506. The single-cylinder Bulldog breed finally disappeared in 1955 when Lanz launched the D 1616 and D 2016 tractors with full diesel engines.

The Lanz Alldog tool carrier had a 12hp air-cooled single-cylinder diesel engine, a 5 forward and

172. A top speed approaching 12mph was a feature of the first Lanz Alldog tool carriers made in 1951.

reverse gearbox and final drive housing at the rear of an open tool frame. About 2,000 Alldogs had already been sold when it was demonstrated for the first time in Britain by H. Leverton & Co of Spalding in Lincolnshire at the 1952 sugar beet harvester event. Features of the Alldog included a power take-off shaft and hydraulic linkage at both ends, rear-mounted belt pulley and independent brakes. An advertisement for the Alldog claimed that the driver 'could attach a wide range of front, mid- and rear-mounted implements without difficulty'. The tractor was front wheel-steered but the rear axle, connected to the tool frame by a single pivot pin, could be steered independently to reduce side-slip when working across slopes.

John Deere who had been looking for manufacturing facilities in Europe bought a majority share holding of Heinrich Lanz AG in 1956 and then acquired the company in 1960. The 11hp single-cylinder two-stroke diesel-engined Lanz D 1106 'Bulli' with a 6 forward and 2 reverse gearbox was made between 1956 and 1958. The blue tractor with red wheels was very much the traditional Bulldog but it did not enjoy the same success. The Bulldog type tractors now with green paintwork were made on a limited scale at Mannheim and a 3 cylinder John Deere-Lanz crawler was introduced in 1959.

The 4 cylinder 28hp and 36hp John Deere-Lanz 300 and 500 tractors made at Mannheim were unveiled in 1961. The new green tractors with yellow wheels had independent coil spring suspension on the front axle, disc brakes and three-point linkage. The Lanz 300 and 500 had 540 and 1,000 power take-off shafts placed side by side at the rear and a side power shaft for a mid-mounted mower. The Lanz name disappeared when production of the John Deere 1020, 1120 and 2020 started at Mannheim in 1965.

173. The John Deere Lanz 300 and 500 tractors launched in 1961 had a 10 forward and 3 reverse speed gearbox.

LEYLAND

The Leyland Motor Co and British Motor Holdings who made Nuffield Tractors at Bathgate in Scotland merged in 1967 and the British Leyland Motors Tractor Group was formed in 1968. Leyland continued tractor production at Bathgate and three 'new' two-tone blue Leyland tractors were introduced at the 1969 Smithfield Show. The Leyland 154, 344 and 384, advertised as 'three new tractors for the seventies' had a new colour scheme but were otherwise very similar to the Nuffield 4/25, 3/45 and 4/65 they had replaced.

The 154 was retained when Leyland announced the 245, 255, 270, 285/485 and 2100/4100 in 1972. The first digit in the model number denoted two- or four-wheel drive and the remaining figures indicated horse power. The 85 and 100hp models were well equipped for the time with a 6

174. The 485 and 4100 were the four-wheel drive versions of the 85hp and 100hp Leyland 285 and 2100.

cylinder engine, 10 forward and 2 reverse gears with a top speed of 21mph, live hydraulics, dual speed independent power take-off, hydrostatic steering and multi-plate wet disc brakes. The medium-powered trac-tors had 4 cylinder engines, 10 forward and 2 reverse gears, independent power take-off and dry disc brakes. Power-steering was an optional extra.

The 262 and 272 replaced the 255 and 270 in 1976 and apart from the 154, hydrostatic power steering and quiet cabs became standard on Leyland tractors. Prices were in an upward spiral in the mid-1970s when the Leyland 154 cost £2,392, compared with the £585 price tag for the similar BMC Mini-tractor when it was launched in 1965. Leyland also broke the £10,000 barrier in 1976 when they advertised the four- wheel drive 4100 at £10,178. The Leyland 272H added to the range in 1977 was a variant of the standard tractor with a high ratio final drive giving a 27 per cent speed increase in all forward gears.

The Leyland Synchro range which included the 245, 262/462 and 272/472, all with a new 9 forward and 3 reverse synchromesh gearbox, was launched in 1978. The 272 and 472 engines were turbocharged in 1979 and with an extra 10hp these tractors became the 282 and 482. The 9 forward and 3 reverse synchromesh gearbox was also used on the Leyland 285 from 1979. The 154 had been made for ten years when it was replaced in 1979 by the Leyland 235 manufactured in Turkey. Similar to the 154 it had a more powerful engine and an improved hydraulic system.

Harvest gold and black were the colours for a new range of two- and four-wheel drive Leylands launched at the 1980 Smithfield Show. The first two figures in the model number were a rough guide to horse power and the 2 or 4 denoted the number of driven wheels. The 4 cylinder indirect injection engined 302 and the 502 with a 3 cylinder direct injection engine had a 9 forward and 3 reverse synchromesh gearbox and disc brakes. The 602/604, 702/704 and turbocharged 802/804 had the same gearbox with a dual clutch, live hydraulics and two-speed power take-off. Depending on the price paid the driver could sit in the standard QM cab or optional Explorer cab with windscreen wiper and indicator switches on the steering column. According to publicity material the new Explorer cab 'provided a luxurious environment which was second to none'.

The 92hp 904 XL with a 15 forward and 5 reverse gearbox was added to the range in 1981 and this gearbox became optional on the 62hp, 72hp and 82hp tractors. Leyland reported a 45 per cent increase in sales of the new tractors compared with the previous range and the 302, which superseded the 235, was seen as Leyland's answer to the growing numbers of Japanese compact tractors on the UK market. The quiet cab on the 302 could be lifted off after removing four bolts when working in low buildings or orchards and the bonnet tipped forward for engine maintenance purposes.

175. The 82hp Leyland 282 had 9 forward and 3 reverse synchromesh gears in three ranges.

The state-owned British Leyland was one of the first companies privatised by Mrs Thatcher's government in 1982. Marshall, Sons and Co Ltd bought Leyland tractors and production continued at Bathgate in Scotland. The completed tractors, now with a Marshall badge, were taken to their factory at Gainsborough for a thorough pre-delivery inspection.

176. The 604 was one of the first Leyland tractors with the new harvest gold and black colour scheme. Publicity material described it as a 'real workhorse that simply out-performs many machines that others call a big tractor'.

LELY

Founded in 1948, implement makers Lely Industries at Maasland in Holland entered the tractor market in 1970 with the Hydro 90. The 6 cylinder MWM direct injection diesel-engined tractor had a hydrostatic transmission with a stepless variable forward speed from 0 to 12½mph and from 0 to 7½mph in reverse. Planetary final drive reduction gears transmitted the power to the wheels. The Lely Hydro 90 had a diff-lock, rear drum brakes and a parking brake was automatically applied when the transmission was in neutral. Other features included hydrostatic steering, ZF hydraulic linkage and an 80hp hydraulically driven dual-speed power take-off.

The Lely Hydro 150, with a 152hp Ford engine, a high/low ratio hydrostatic transmission and steering, hydraulic brakes and category II hydraulic linkage, was also made in the early 1970s. It was an early version of the modern systems tractor with reversible driving controls

177 Two- and four-wheel drive versions of the 87hp Lely 90 Hydro were made in the early 1970s.

and seat which could be 'driven with equal ease in either direction'.

Lely also made a prototype forward control tractor in 1972. The 178hp Supertrac had a Perkins diesel engine, 10 forward gears, a rear load carrying platform and hydraulic linkage. A set of matched implements were planned but the project did not progress and Lely concentrated on the development of other products.

Lely returned to the tractor scene in 1979 when they established a partnership with Iseki to market 13–35hp Japanese TS and TX compact tractors in the UK. This arrangement continued until 1986 when Iseki established their own distribution company in Cambridgeshire.

178. The Lely Hydro 150 had a dual range hydrostatic transmission with top speeds of 8mph and 20mph.

LOYD

Tracked military vehicles were made by Vivian Loyd & Co Ltd at Camberley in Surrey during the war years and they used this expertise in the late 1940s to manufacture agricultural tracklayers. The 33hp DP with a water-cooled Turner V4 diesel engine and the 50hp D with a Ford V8 engine were the first Loyd crawlers. Both tractors had differential brake steering, a 4 forward speed and reverse gearbox and military type carrier tracks. Another version with a Dorman diesel engine was made for a short while before the Loyd Dragon with conventional four bottom roller tracks was launched at the 1950 Smithfield Show.

Publicity material announced that the Dragon had been put through a series of tests including a trial on an army tank track where potential distributors from the UK and overseas had 'never before seen a tractor subjected to such a destructive test'!

A Turner V4 or a Dorman-Ricardo in-line diesel engine, both rated at 36½hp, was used on the Dragon which had a 4 forward and reverse gearbox, multi-plate clutch and brake steering and power take-off. A maximum pull of 7,000lbs at the drawbar and 6psi ground pressure was claimed for the Dragon which weighed in at 8,200lbs. The Model 1071 with a Dorman engine had heavy duty tracks and the Turner-engined Model 1079 had lighter track-running gear.

179. It was anticipated that the Loyd Dragon would cost £1,450 ex-works before it was announced in 1950.

MANN

J. Mann & Son, who introduced the Claas combine harvester to British farmers in 1947, made the Gazelle low ground pressure vehicle in 1980 and 1981. A 6 cylinder 108hp Ford 2715E industrial engine provided the power for the Gazelle's hydrostatically driven 12 inch wide flat steel tracks with rubber road pads. Basically a contractor's machine with a top speed of 18mph it was steered with a joystick from a large air-conditioned cab. The rear load carrying platform was used for a 300 gallon Tecnoma sprayer or a one ton capacity fertiliser distributor with a Vicon pendulum spreading mechanism driven by a hydraulic motor. The Gazelle tracks had a ground pressure of approximately 3psi when the machine was fully loaded.

180. The Mann Gazelle low ground pressure vehicle was designed for fertiliser spreading or spraying with a 40ft or 80ft spraybar.

MARSHALL

The Britannia Works at Gainsborough in Lincolnshire founded by William Marshall in 1848 were the home of Marshall portable steam engines, traction engines and threshing machines for many years. The first Colonial 'oil-engined' tractor, which ran on petrol and paraffin, was made at Gainsborough in 1908 and like other tractors of the day it had chain drive to the rear wheels. Marshalls also made a 70hp Model F Colonial oil-engined tractor which was almost as big as a traction engine.

The 15/30 introduced in 1930 weighed over three tons and was the first Marshall diesel tractor. It was based on the Lanz Bulldog design and had a single-cylinder, two-stroke, 550rpm horizontal engine with an 8 inch bore and a 10 inch stroke. The 18/30 made between 1932 and 1934 was an improved version of the 15/30. Customers were able to specify the colour of their new Marshall tractor but by the mid-1930s they were all painted green.

Marshalls acquired Clayton & Shutleworth in 1930 and this led to an early example of 'badge engineering' with a number of Marshall tractors sold in Belgium and Greece as the Clayton 18/30.

Norfolk farmer Ben Burgess became a Marshall tractor dealer in 1931 when the 18/30 cost £333.6s.8d. He recalls that one customer told him that his horses walked at 3mph and he considered the 18/30's top speed of 3½mph was too fast for satisfactory ploughing!

British farming was sliding into a deep depression when the Marshall 12/20, still with the Lanz Bulldog influence, was introduced in 1935. The depression seriously reduced tractor sales and

Marshalls became associated with Thomas Ward Ltd of Sheffield in 1936. An improved 12/20 became the Model M in 1938. Engine speed had gradually increased over the years: the 15/30 ran at 550rpm, the 12/20 was flat out at 680rpm and the engine on the Model M had a top speed of 700rpm. A few Model M tractors were made during the war years when Marshall's contribution to the war effort included production of midget submarines.

Tractor production resumed in 1945 with the launch of the new Field Marshall Series I which had the same single-cylinder diesel engine as the Model M but the speed was increased to 750rpm and the Field Marshall engine was rated at 40hp. The tractor had 3 forward gears and reverse, a diff-lock, transmission brake and there was a choice of steel or pneumatic tyred wheels. The Field Marshall had a large external flywheel at one end of the crankshaft and a belt pulley combined with the cone clutch and its housing at the other end. An off-set power take-off shaft and a winch were available at extra cost. There were two versions of the Series I tractor: the Mk I with a top speed of 6mph was intended for farm work and the Mk II with more efficient brakes and a top speed of 9mph was mainly used by threshing contractors.

The Field Marshall was hand-started with the aid of a de-compression mechanism operated by a disc running in a groove on the flywheel. A smouldering paper wick on a metal rod screwed into the cylinder head provided some heat to help start the engine. On very cold days the engine could be started with a special cartridge placed in a holder above the piston and fired with a suitable blunt instrument.

An advertisement claimed the Field Marshall would 'run for one-sixth of the cost of a petrol tractor and plough one acre in an hour on one gallon of diesel fuel'. It was also pointed out that the tractor had 'only 66 working parts compared with an average of 194 on a petrol tractor and would therefore only 'go wrong' a third as often'! Low-cost maintenance was claimed as another plus and 'in return for its labour the tractor required de-carbonising once or twice each year and the simple design of the engine enabled unskilled labour to complete this task in three hours'. Other publicity material explained that 'tests had shown that cylinder wear was only fifteen thousandths of an inch after three years' service and when necessary it was cheap and easy to have a new cylinder block fitted and start all over again'.

John Fowler of Leeds, like Marshall Sons & Co, became associated with Thomas Ward Ltd in 1946 and both companies eventually became part of the Thomas Ward Group in 1968. An improved Series II Field Marshall replaced the Series I in 1947. The new model did not have a diff-lock but the transmission was strengthened, it had a larger clutch combined with the belt pulley, new internal or expanding shoe brakes, wider rear tyres and a more comfortable seat.

181. The Series II Mk I Field Marshall was the agricultural model while the Mk II with a higher top speed was mainly used by threshing contractors who replaced their traction engines with these single-cylinder diesel tractors.

182. Most of the Series IIIA Field Marshalls had orange paintwork.

There was a Series II Mk I version for farmers and the Mk II had a higher top speed for threshing contractors. Materials were still in short supply in 1947 and Marshall advertisements apologised to farmers because 'a shortage of supplies meant that the waiting period for delivery of a new tractor was longer than they would wish it to be'.

Engine rotation was changed to anti-clockwise on the 40 belt hp Series III Field Marshall launched in 1949. The power take-off shaft was no longer off-set and the tractor had a dual range 6 forward and 2 reverse speed gearbox. Engine performance was improved on the Series IIIA, made from 1952 to 1957. Some Series IIIA tractors were sold with the familiar green livery but

183. The multi-plate engine clutch was combined with the belt pulley on the Fowler VF and VFA crawlers.

most had a new orange colour scheme with silver trimmings. The Series IIIA was also the first Field Marshall tractor with optional electric starting and a bolt-on hydraulic lift system made by the Adrolic Engineering Co.

The 40hp Fowler Mark VF crawler, based on the single-cylinder Field Marshall, was introduced in 1948 with a 6 forward and 2 reverse gearbox, controlled differential steering and power take-off. An improved Mark VFA based on the Series IIIA Field Marshall replaced the earlier model in 1952 and like the wheeled tractors most of them were painted orange.

The Track Marshall 50 with a 48hp Perkins L4 engine and transmission system similar to the VFA appeared in 1956. The re-styled bonnet gave it a very different appearance to the previous model and optional extras included a rear belt pulley, electric lighting and a weather cab. An improved Track Marshall 55 with a 55hp Perkins 4-270 engine appeared a couple of years later. The Fowler side of the Marshall organisation at Leeds introduced the first of four Challenger crawlers in 1950 (page 85). The

184. The 70hp Marshall MP6 is considered by enthusiasts to be the last true Marshall wheeled tractor.

185. A 6 cylinder 70hp Perkins engine provided the power for the Track-Marshall 70C crawler with controlled differential steering and a top speed of 6 mph.

50hp Challenger I was only made for a short while but the 65hp Challenger I, 80hp Challenger II and 150hp Challenger III remained in production until the factory closed in 1973.

Marshall designers were working on a replacement for the Field Marshall in order to match their competitors who had already used multi-cylinder diesel engines for several years. Their efforts resulted in the introduction of the Marshall MP6 at the 1954 Smithfield Show. The new tractor had a 6 cylinder, four-stroke, 70hp Leyland diesel engine instead of the traditional single-cylinder power unit used for Marshall tractors since the 1930s. The MP6 with a 6 forward and 2 reverse gearbox was provisionally priced at £1,400 and optional extras included a belt pulley, power take-off, cast iron wheel weights and a 12 volt lighting set. The new orange tractor with silver trim found little favour with British farmers and although manufacture was due to start in 1955 none were made until 1956. Fewer than 200 had been built, and most of them were exported, when the last MP6 was made in 1960.

The Track-Marshall 55's model number indicated the horse power of its Perkins L4 engine and so the Track-Marshall 70 launched in 1961 had a 70hp 6 cylinder Perkins power unit and manually operated steering mechanism. Hydraulically controlled steering was introduced for the 70hp crawler in 1962; tractors with hydraulic steering became Track-Marshall 70H and the 70C was the standard model. The Track-Marshall orange colour scheme was changed to bright yellow in 1964.

When the Thomas Ward group acquired Marshall Sons & Co and John Fowler in 1968 the 55 and 70 were replaced by the slightly more powerful 56 and 75C and the Track Marshall 90 was added to the range. Weather cabs and hydraulic linkage were optional equipment and low-ground pressure versions of the 56hp and 75hp models designated the 56W and 75W with wide tracks were also available.

The Ward group bought Bristol Tractors and changed the company name to Marshall-Fowler Ltd in 1970. They closed the Fowler works at Leeds in 1973 and then sold Marshall-Fowler to British Leyland Special

186. Publicity material for Marshall tractors suggested owners would agree that the 804 was one of the finest of its type available at a price which offered excellent value with electro-static paintwork, quartz halogen ploughing lamps and radial tyres.

187. The 115hp four-wheel drive Marshall 115 was launched in 1984.

Products group in 1975. The new owners used the Aveling-Marshall name for the 56, 75C and 90 tractors and later models until Lincolnshire farmer Charles Nickerson bought the company in 1979. He revived the original Track-Marshall name and the A-M crawler range remained in production as the Track-Marshall 100, 105, 120 and 140. The Track-Marshall TM 135 with a 136hp 6 cylinder Perkins engine, an air-conditioned cab and running track with sealed lubrication was launched in 1980. The 70hp Britannia was added to the Track-Marshall range in 1982. Named after the Gainsborough works, the Britannia had a 4 cylinder Perkins engine, hydraulic clutch and brake steering, power take-off and Marshall's own three-point linkage. Track-Marshall, who were making the Britannia, TM 110, TM 120 and TM 135 at Gainsborough, were the only British manufacturer of crawler tractors when Charles Nickerson bought the Leyland wheeled tractor business in 1982.

The Marshall name re-appeared on wheeled tractors after a gap of 24 years when the revived Marshall, Sons & Co Ltd introduced the harvest gold and black 502, 602/604, 702/704 and 802/804. Production was continued at the old Leyland truck factory at Bathgate and the completed tractors were taken to Gainsborough for a thorough pre-delivery inspection.

The Nickerson era was short lived but the company was able to improve the 62hp, 72hp and 82hp wheeled tractors and launch the new Marshall 115, 100 and 904XL before the 1984 Smithfield Show. There were ten different models on the stand and the Field Marshall name and baton logo decorated the front grille of the angular styled Marshall 100 and 115. The 103hp Marshall 100 with the choice of two- and four-wheel drive and the 115hp four-wheel drive Marshall 115, advertised as a brand new supremo for the Marshall army, had 6 cylinder Leyland engines. Both models were equipped with a 20 forward and 9 reverse gearbox and an optional creep speed box, electronic linkage control hydraulics with remote switches on the rear mudguards and a flat floor Explorer cab. The turbocharged 92hp 904XL was an improved version of the 804 with a 15 forward and 5 reverse synchromesh transmission. The same 15 speed gearbox and a slightly longer wheelbase were the main changes on the improved two- and four-wheel drive 602/604, 702/704 and 802/804XL tractors.

188. A 90hp water-cooled 4 cylinder Steyr engine provided the power for the Marshall D944 made by Steyr in Austria and sold in the UK by Marshall-Daimler Ltd of Scunthorpe.

Marshall Sons & Co Ltd went into receivership in 1985. The wheeled tractor operation was rescued by Bentall-Simplex Industries who, trading as Marshall Tractors Ltd, moved to Scunthorpe. The tracklayer side of the business changed hands yet again, this time bought by Herbert Flatters and re-named Track Marshall of Gainsborough Ltd.

With no space available at the 1986 Smithfield Show Marshall Tractors introduced the lightweight two-wheel drive Marshall 132 to the farming public at a nearby hotel. The tractor was assembled at Scunthorpe with a 35hp engine based on a Perkins power unit, a transmission made in Yugoslavia, a Duncan cab and category I hydraulic linkage. The 154, 184 and 264 four-wheel drive compact models with 'light touch but firm tread' completed Marshall's light tractor range. Two-cylinder 18hp and 26hp Ruggerini or Lombardini air-cooled diesel engines were used for the Marshall compact models.

Nine new Field Marshalls with 75hp, 85hp and 95hp Perkins engines and the original baton logo on the radiator grille were announced in 1987. The 752/754X and 852/854X had 9 forward and 3 reverse synchromesh gearboxes while the XL versions and the four-wheel drive 954XL had 15 forward gears and 5 in reverse. The Marshall Explorer cab was retained but unlike earlier cabs it had separate heating and ventilating systems and an easily serviced dust filter.

Sales did not come up to expectations and the Marshall range gradually disappeared but new heart was put into the company in 1989 when they signed an agreement with Steyr Daimler Puch to sell Steyr tractors in Marshall livery in the UK. Later that year Marshall-Daimler Ltd at Scunthorpe launched a range of 64–150hp two- and four-wheel drive Steyr D series tractors with harvest gold and black paintwork and the Field Marshall

189. The Track Marshall TM 200 had a hand-operated hydraulic ram to tilt the cab for servicing. Later models had a twin-speed range hydrostatic transmission and a motor to drive each track.

baton logo. Marshall-Daimler predicted the D series with a 12 forward and 4 reverse gearbox and the proven Explorer 2 control centre (cab) would take them to fifth place in the UK tractor sales league table within three years. Optional equipment for the D series from 72hp upwards included electronic load sensing hydraulics, D-matic 36 forward and 12 reverse change-on-the-move transmission and the Marshall-Daimler Informat computerised driver information system. Informat monitored engine performance, recommended the most efficient engine speed and gear ratio for maximum fuel economy and automatically controlled D-matic transmission gear selection. Originally marketed in Britain as the Steyr D series the same tractors were still sold elsewhere in the world as Steyrs with a red and white colour scheme.

The Marshall S series, also made by Steyr, was launched in 1990. The 6 cylinder S-542/S-544 and S-624/S-644 two- and four-wheel drive tractors had 56hp and 64hp engines. The four-wheel drive 72hp S-744 had a 16 forward and 8 reverse gearbox, live hydraulics and two-speed power take-off. However, the relationship with Steyr was short lived and the company re-emerged as Marshall Tractors, this time selling spare parts and re-built tractors from the Scunthorpe factory.

Meanwhile production of Track Marshall crawlers, including the new 155hp TM 155, continued at Britannia Works. There was another change of ownership in 1987 when Tom Walkinshaw Racing (TWR) bought the Gainsborough company. The 70hp Britannia was discontinued but plans were in hand for the new rubber-tracked Track Marshall. The TM 200, which made its debut at the 1990 Royal Show, was the first real competitor for the Caterpillar Challenger. About 1,000 of the rubber-tracked American crawlers had already been sold worldwide since its launch in 1988. The TM 200 had a 210hp turbocharged Cummins engine and early models had a 16 forward and 2 reverse hydro power shaft transmission. The steering wheel operated a control valve which slowed the inner track when changing direction. The Australian designed rubber tracks had lugs on the underside which engaged with the rear driving sprockets and a wheeled tractor type pivoting front axle was linked to a pneumatic suspension system. The TM 200 did not prove to be a big seller and it was phased out in 1994. The TM 155 was only made to order until production finally ceased in 1996.

MARTIN MARKHAM

190. Sales literature described the Martin Markham Colt as a 'small tractor with great performance and the most practical and versatile machine in its class'.

Martin Markham, who manufactured a range of farm machinery at Stamford in Lincolnshire, made about 200 standard and de-luxe Colt tractors between 1960 and 1968. The standard tractor had a 7hp air-cooled Kohler engine with a recoil starter. A 12 volt electric starting system with a dynamo and battery was an optional extra. The Colt was equipped with a single-plate dry clutch, a 3 forward and reverse gearbox and a single foot brake with a parking latch. The rear wheel track could be adjusted in 4 inch steps from 32 to 40 inches and the front track was adjustable from 29 to 37 inches. A gear pump with an output of 4 pints per minute supplied oil to the four-point hydraulic linkage ram cylinder and to an external ram connection used for the Martin Markham front-loader and tipping trailer. The Colt had three power take-off shafts, the one at the rear turned at 280rpm while the front power shaft with a vee-belt pulley and a central shaft with a flat belt pulley ran at approximately half engine speed.

The de-luxe Colt was similar to the standard model but with a 10hp Kohler engine and electric starter. Additional standard equipment included a 6 forward and 2 reverse gearbox, independent foot brakes which could be locked together when driving on the road and a hand brake. A sales leaflet explained that the 'light automotive steering, simple gear change and finger-tip hydraulics made the Colt de-luxe so easy to control that anyone could learn to drive it in a matter of minutes'.

MASKELL

191. The optional hydraulic motor on the left-hand side of the Maskell rowcrop tractor could be used to drive seeder units and other equipment attached to anywhere on the tool frame.

The 3 forward speed and reverse Maskell rowcrop tractor with a 21½hp Enfield 100 twin-cylinder air-cooled diesel engine and electric starting was made at Wilstead near Bedford in the late 1950s. The rear-mounted engine, clutch, gearbox and differential reduction unit were attached to a hollow rectangular section steel frame above the chain-driven rear wheels. The Maskell had independent steering brakes and a tiller handle was used to steer the single or optional double front wheels. Hydraulic linkage and an on-board hydraulic motor which could be attached at various points on the tool frame were optional extras. The Maskell, which used less than one gallon of fuel per hour, had a minimum ground clearance of 17 inches and a top speed of 8.5mph. Barfords of Belton in Lincolnshire, who were part of the Aveling-Barford Group, made the re-named Barford-Maskell rowcrop tractor in the early 1960s.

MASSEY FERGUSON

192. The Massey Ferguson 65 had a live power take-off and hydraulic system with category I and II ball ends for the three-point linkage.

Nearly 360,000 Ferguson TE 20 tractors had been made at Coventry when Massey-Harris and Ferguson amalgamated in 1953 but no immediate changes were made to either company's product range. The grey and gold Ferguson FE 35 with a 4 cylinder Standard petrol, paraffin, diesel or 29hp lamp oil engine replaced the TE 20 in 1956. The Massey Ferguson badge did not appear on Coventry built tractors until the MF 35 replaced the FE 35 in 1957. The change to the red and grey Massey Ferguson colour scheme was the only difference between the two tractors. The petrol- and diesel-engined MF 35 were rated at 37hp and the paraffin model at 30hp. The de-luxe version had a dual clutch with live power take-off and hydraulics.

193. The 3 cylinder Massey Ferguson 35 was launched in 1959.

The MF 35 gained a big brother when the Mk I MF 65 was announced in 1957. The publicity department celebrated the event by advertising that 'together the 35 and 65 tractors made 100 per cent Ferguson farming available to all'. The 50½hp 4 cylinder Perkins diesel-engined MF 65 had many of the features found on the MF 35, together with inboard disc brakes and epicyclic final drive reduction units. A diff-lock and power-steering were optional extras.

Massey Ferguson bought the Banner Lane factory from the Standard Motor Co and also Perkins Engines Ltd of Peterborough in 1959. The 39.9hp MF 35 tractor with a 3 cylinder Perkins engine was launched in the same year and tractor drivers who had struggled to start the previous 4 cylinder Standard-built diesel engine on a cold morning welcomed the change. In praise of the new MF 35, a sales brochure suggested it 'had a place on every farm and would give its owner extra energy to tackle fresh work and bring profit from every single acre'.

MF 65 tractors were not at their best with trailed implements so Massey Ferguson introduced the Multi-Pull hitch in 1960. It was the forerunner of Pressure Control and had a heavy chain attached to a three-point linkage frame which was wrapped around a trailed implement drawbar. Partially raising the hydraulic lift arms transferred some of the implement weight on to the back of tractor and improved wheel grip.

The 56.8hp Mk II MF 65 with a diff-lock and optional road lights was introduced at the 1960 Smithfield Show. The engine developed a maximum of 58.3hp when the tractor was tested by the National Institute of Agricultural Engineering at Silsoe and Massey Ferguson heavily promoted the extra power. An optional factory-fitted 12 forward and 4 reverse speed Multi-Power gearbox was announced in 1962. The new change-on-the-move system which cost £70 had a hydraulic clutch controlled by a switch on the instrument panel which gave a 30 per cent speed increase or decrease in each gear. The list of optional equipment for the MF 35 widened in 1962 to include a diff-lock and power-adjusted rear wheels (PAVT) but Multi-power was not available until later that year when the 44½hp MF 35X made its debut at the Smithfield Show. Although most tractors were sold with a diesel engine in the early 1960s it was still possible to buy the MF 35 with a petrol or vaporising oil engine but the 35X was limited to the Perkins diesel engine.

194. The American-built Massey Ferguson Super 90 was exhibited at various agricultural shows in Britain in 1963 to test farmer reaction. It was expected to cost about £1,980 but in the end it was not sold in the UK.

The 77hp diesel-engined Super 90 was another new tractor on the Massey Ferguson stand at the 1962 Smithfield Show. Standard equipment included an 8 forward and 2 reverse gearbox, power-adjusted rear wheels, disc brakes and power steering. The hydraulic system pump located in the gearbox used transmission oil cooled by a radiator at the front of the tractor. The Super 90 had a lower link sensing draft control system with a heavy duty double-acting assister spring. A switch on the instrument panel was used to adjust the level of response made by the hydraulic system to changes in the load on the lower links.

The 'Red Giant' 100 series with square shaped bonnets and lights built into the radiator grille replaced the 35 and 65 in December 1964. Flat top wings were used for the 165, 175 and the 135 when it was supplied with a weather cab but round mudguards were used on the 130 Economy and the cab-less 135.

The 30hp French-built MF 130 Economy model had a 4 cylinder, indirect injection diesel engine. The standard specification included 8 forward and 2 reverse gears with synchromesh on 3rd to 4th and 7th to 8th, disc brakes, diff-lock and a mechanical linkage lock to hold implements in the raised position for transport. The de-luxe 130 had a dual clutch and a centre power take-off shaft for mid-mounted implements.

The 135 and 165 were very similar to the MF 35 and Mk II 65. A slightly more powerful MF 35X engine on the 135 was rated at 45½hp. The MF 175 with a 66hp 4 cylinder Perkins engine with heavy cast iron wheel centres, PAVT rear wheels and power steering was similar in other respects to the 165. Pressure Control, which replaced the earlier Multi-Pull hitch system, was optional on the 165 and 175 but within a few months it was standard. Pressure Control could be used to transfer up to a ton of trailed implement weight on to the back of the tractor but without suitable strengthening the implement drawbar was likely to bend and sometimes did. Optional extras for the 135, 165 and 175 included multi-power transmission, hydraulic spool valves, weather cab, foot throttle, spring suspension seat and a cigarette lighter.

Various improvements were made to the Red Giants during their 12-year production run. The 165's engine power was increased to 60hp and the 66hp 175 became the 72½hp MF 178 in 1968. Other changes in the early 1970s included the addition of dry element air cleaners, oil-cooled brakes, improved hydraulics and independent power take-off. Flat top wings were standard across the range from 1970 when all MF tractors sold in Britain had a safety cab in order to meet government regulations.

195. Massey Ferguson claimed that the 1100 had the world's most comfortable and efficient driving platform. It had an adjustable steering column and a padded seat 'suspended on a cushion of air and oil to iron out jolts and bumps over the roughest terrain'.

The 96hp Massey Ferguson 1100 described as 'the biggest red giant of them all' originally made at Detroit in 1965 was the most powerful Massey Ferguson tractor available in the UK when it was introduced to British farmers at the 1967 Smithfield Show. The 1100 had a 6 cylinder Perkins engine, a twin plate transmission clutch, a 12 forward and 4 reverse Multi-Power transmission and hydrostatic steering. Other features included a two-speed independent power take-off, two fuel tanks, PAVT rear wheels and a safety start mechanism in the clutch pedal linkage. Two hydraulic pumps with an oil cooler provided oil pressure for the three-point linkage, auxiliary service rams, power steering, brakes, power take-off clutch and hydraulically suspended seat. Pressure Control was standard and the 1100 was one of the first tractors with the facility to mix the operation of the position and draft control systems.

The 90hp two-wheel drive French-built MF 1080 launched in the UK in 1969 was similar to the earlier American MF 180. The specification included a 12 forward and 4 reverse Multi-power transmission, hydrostatic steering with an adjustable steering column, dry disc brakes, cast iron wheel centres, PAVT rear wheels and an optional 1,000rpm power shaft. A package of 17 changes on the 92hp Mk II 1080 compared with the previous model included a much quieter cab, inboard oil-cooled brakes and the 1,000rpm power take-off shaft was standard. Some manufacturers provided a pair of ear defenders to overcome the problem of high noise levels in safety cabs. This prompted MF to improve the sound insulation on the Mk II 1080 cab and a sound deadening kit which cost £16 was introduced for the earlier Mk I cab.

Four-wheel drive was becoming popular by the late 1960s and Four-Wheel Traction Ltd marketed Selene conversion kits from Italy for the Massey Ferguson 100 series tractors. The same period also saw the introduction of turbochargers which were said to increase engine power by about 20 per cent.

An 8 forward speed gearbox and longer wheelbase were features of the new high specification 148, 168 and 188 '8' line tractors introduced in 1971. The 6 speed '5' line 135 and 165 were retained while the 185

196. The 1200 articulated four-wheel drive tractor was made by Massey Ferguson between 1972 and 1980.

replaced the 178. Engine power was on its inevitable upward trend with the 135 and 148 rated at 47hp and 49hp respectively, the 165 and 168 at 62hp and 69hp and the 185 and 188 with an identical 75hp under the bonnet.

The MF 130 was discontinued in 1972 and the four-wheel drive Massey Ferguson 1200 introduced to British farmers in the same year was by far the biggest MF tractor yet seen in the UK. The 105hp MF 1200 had a 12 forward and 4 reverse speed Multi-power transmission, equal-sized wheels and centre-pivot articulated steering with double-acting hydraulic rams.

Opico and other companies offered turbocharger kits for existing MF 185, 188 and 1200 tractors. The 1,000rpm power take-off shaft on the turbocharged MF 1200 developed 106hp compared with 87 pto hp on the standard model.

The 88hp MF 595, which superseded the 1080 in 1974, was the first of the new square-front Massey Ferguson 500 series designed to replace the popular 100 series tractors. The two- and four-wheel drive 595 had a single-plate dry clutch

197. The 47hp MF 154C crawler was one of a range made in Italy by Landini in the mid-1970s.

and the usual 12 forward and 4 reverse Multi-power transmission with a top speed of 20.4mph. The drive shaft to the front-axle was under the engine and a switch engaged and disengaged drive on-the-move. The flat floor cab, isolated from the chassis on anti-vibration rubber mountings, had full instrumentation, large areas of glass and a spring suspension seat. Sales literature described it as 'a super comfort, pressurised cab with heating and ventilation system approaching motor car standards'.

The two-wheel drive MF 1135 with a turbocharged 6 cylinder 135hp Perkins engine and the MF 1155 with a 155hp Perkins V8 engine, launched at the 1975 Smithfield Show, had similar specifications to the 1080. The 'roomy super comfort cab' which provided 'a dust free, low noise level working environment' could be tipped backwards to service the gearbox and rear axle. The 1155 was made until 1977 while the 1135 was phased out in 1979.

The MF 550, 565, 575 and 590 with 47hp, 60hp, 66hp and 75hp Perkins engines launched in 1976 had increased hydraulic pump capacity and a second gear pump was used to supply oil to the auxiliary circuits. Optional equipment for the 500 series included an 8 speed manual or 12 speed Multi-power transmission and an independent power take-off or a live power shaft with a dual clutch. Prices ranged from £4,100 for the most basic MF 550 to £5,578 for a top specification 590 with Multi-power transmission.

The standard version of the 135 was discontinued in 1976 when the MF 500 series was widened to five models but the orchard, vineyard and crawler versions of the 135 were made until 1982. The French-built vineyard and the QD versions had a 45hp Perkins AD 3.152 diesel engine. A quick-detach safety cab was standard on the 135QD orchard model and an easily removed safety frame was supplied with the vineyard tractor. A special three-point linkage (category V) with cranked lower links for the vineyard model was introduced in 1976. The 135 engine was de-rated to 41hp on the 134C tracklayer built in Italy by Landini who also made the 47 and 61hp Perkins-engined MF 154C and MF 174C crawler tractors, for which an optional dealer-fitted British cab was available.

The most powerful articulated four-wheel drive Massey Ferguson tractor yet seen in the UK appeared in 1977. The MF 1505 with a 180hp direct injection Caterpillar V8 diesel engine had an air-conditioned cab on

146

rubber mountings, Category III hydraulic linkage and a 1,000rpm power take-off rated at 160hp.

The 45hp MF 240 and the 60hp MF 265 launched in 1979 were the first of the new MF 200 series. These relatively basic tractors had an 8 speed transmission, drum brakes, manual steering and a quick detach cab. Optional extras included Multi-power, power-assisted steering, automatic pick-up hitch and pressure control. The cab was equipped with lifting eyes and could be removed in less than ten minutes. The 200 series was extended in 1981 with the intro-duction of the MF 290 with a 4 cylinder 75hp Perkins engine

198. The MF 240 was one of the first 200 series tractors made at the Banner Lane factory in Coventry.

and detachable Duncan cab. The MF 290 could be supplied with an 8 forward and 2 reverse, a 12 forward and 4 reverse synchromesh gearbox or a 12 speed Multi-power transmission. The MF 250 added in 1982 had the 3 cylinder 47hp engine and 8 speed manual gearbox used for the MF 550 and optional Multi-power transmission. The 250 was the first MF 200 series tractor to have power steering and oil-cooled brakes. The two- and four-wheel drive 66hp MF 275 and 88hp 298 with 12 forward and 4 reverse gears appeared in 1985. The 275 had a low-profile cab and the higher specification MF 298 had hydrostatic steering, hydraulic wet disc brakes and a two-speed independent power take-off. A sales drive at the 1985 Smithfield Show offered 500 gallons of free fuel with every top of the range 200 series tractor bought at the show.

199. The 93hp MF 2620 was one of the 2000 series tractors made at Beauvais in France from 1979.

Massey Ferguson launched the 2000, 400 and 600 series during the late 1970s and early 1980s. The French-built 2000 series two- and four-wheel drive MF 2640 and MF 2680 rated at 104hp and 120hp were intro-duced in 1979. The 130hp MF 2720 and the 93hp MF 2620 were added a year or two later when the power rating of the earlier models was increased to 110hp and 130hp respectively. The 1200 was discontinued in 1980 but not before the articu-lated 112hp MF 1250 with an improved transmission and hydraulic system had been added to the Massey Ferguson range.

The 2000 series had a 16 forward and 12 reverse Speedshift transmission with

200. A Cummins V8 engine provided the power for the Massey Ferguson 4880 which made its British debut in 1982.

shuttle reverse, inboard disc brakes and a hydraulically engaged diff-lock. The lower link sensing hydraulic system had external lift rams and the driving controls were located on the right-hand side of a spring suspension seat in a high visibility cab.

Following an evaluation exercise in eastern England the articulated four-wheel drive Massey Ferguson 4840 was introduced to the British market in 1980, coincidentally exactly 50 years after the first four-wheel drive Massey-Harris General Purpose tractor appeared in 1930. The MF 4840 was made in North America with a 260hp Cummins V8 engine. It had an oil-cooled multi-disc clutch and an 18 forward and 6 reverse gearbox with three changes on-the-move in each of the six gear ratios. It was also the first tractor in the world to have an electronically controlled hydraulic linkage. A series of induction coils were used to sense changes in the load on the tractor and transmit electrical signals to a solenoid unit linked to the hydraulic control valve. The driver enjoyed the comfort of an upholstered, swivelling seat in an air-conditioned cab which

201. The turbocharged Massey Ferguson 698T had a 4 cylinder direct injection Perkins engine. Like the other 600 series models the re-styled bonnet and cab were the usual red colour but the new MF charcoal grey paint was used for the rest of the tractor.

148

occasionally had to be left to fill the 160 gallon fuel tank. The 225hp MF 4800 and the 315hp MF 4880 were also made in North America in the early 1980s.

The two- and four-wheel drive, 4 cylinder MF 675, 690 and 698 rated at 66hp, 77hp and 88hp launched in 1981 were the first 600 series tractors. They had a 12 forward and 4 reverse synchromesh gearbox or optional Multi-power transmission, hydraulic brakes, hydrostatic steering and a flat floor cab. The 6 cylinder 98hp MF 699 was added to the 600 series in 1984 when the 90hp MF 698T with a waste-gate turbocharger replaced the MF 698. A wastegate turbocharger gives a high power boost at low engine speeds and a spring-loaded dump valve (or waste-gate) prevents an excessive power surge when the engine approaches its maximum speed.

At the other end of the power scale Massey Ferguson were still marketing special purpose tractors which had started with the vineyard model of the TE 20 in the early 1950s and continued with

202. Ear defenders were included in the tool kit for the MF 158F fruit tractor which had power steering and a quick-detach safety frame.

narrow versions of the FE 35, MF 35 and MF 135. The 33hp MF 230 introduced in 1981 was a basic two-wheel drive 200 series tractor with an 8 speed gearbox and safety frame.

The Italian-built MF 145 vineyard and MF 158F fruit tractor replaced the long-serving specialist 135 models in 1982. The 48 inch wide MF 145 had a 45hp 3 cylinder Perkins engine and the 59 inch wide MF 158 had a 4 cylinder 55hp Perkins power unit. The Massey Ferguson 135 square-shaped bonnet was used for both tractors; it had an 8 speed synchromesh gearbox and 'zero-leak' hydraulic ram which acted as a lock for the three-point linkages when the engine was stopped.

203. The 73hp Massey Ferguson 294C was the largest of five Italian-built crawlers announced in 1983. The 45 inch wide 45hp 234C, the 47hp 254C, the 53hp 264C and 62hp 474C completed the range.

Massey Ferguson tested customer reaction to a range of small Japanese tractors at the 1983 Royal Show and a favourable response brought about the launch of the MF 1010, 1020 and 1030 compacts in 1984. The two- and four-wheel drive 16hp, 21hp and 27hp diesel models cost from £3,790 for the two-wheel drive MF 1010 to £5,650 for the four-wheel drive MF 1030 which had more horse power under its bonnet than the original Ferguson 20.

The improved MF 2005 series replaced the 2000 tractors in 1985. Improvements such as a new two-door cab with a roof hatch, increased hydraulic capacity and engine power were the result of a questionnaire sent to 4,000 farmers. However, electronic linkage control (elc) with sensor pins to measure draft forces in the lower links was the most significant new feature on the MF 2645, 2685 and 2725 which had 6 cylinder engines rated at 110hp, 130hp and 147hp respectively.

204. The 93hp MF 3070 was the mid-range model of five French-built 3000 series two- and four-wheel drive tractors launched in 1986.

The MF 3000 series with the new computerised Autotronic and Datatronic systems was introduced in 1986. Dubbed the intelligent tractors they could be programmed to think out the most cost-effective way of maintaining peak performance and productivity with maximum economy. The Autotronic computer gave automatic control of a variety of driving functions. The more sophisticated and expensive Datatronic system controlled wheelslip and provided information on the tractor's performance to help the driver achieve maximum efficiency. The 3000 series ranged from the 4 cylinder 68hp MF 3050 to the 107hp MF 3090 with a 6 cylinder engine. The standard specification included a hydraulic self-adjusting clutch, a 16 forward and reverse synchromesh gearbox with two 'H' gate levers and electronic linkage control hydraulics.

Seven 47–97hp MF 300 series tractors with improved transmissions, hydraulics, steering and cabs went into production in 1986. They replaced the top five 200 series tractors but the MF 230 and 240 were retained to provide relatively basic tractors at the lower end of the power range. There were five gearbox options for the two- and four-wheel drive 300 series and the 4 cylinder 90hp MF 399 was the first Banner Lane tractor with a turbocharged engine. The 58hp MF 360 replaced the 355 in 1987 and the 90hp turbocharged 390 T was added in 1989. An optional low-profile cab was available for all models except the 399 from 1988 and a Hi-Line flat floor cab was introduced for the 78–110hp tractors in the same year. An earlier offer of 500 gallons of free fuel with some of the 200 series tractors was repeated in metric form in 1989 when a bait of 2,000 litres of free diesel was offered to farmers buying specified MF 300 and the 3000 models. The two- and four-wheel drive 59hp MF 362 with 8 forward and 2 reverse gears or an optional 8 speed shuttle transmission, hydrostatic steering and hydraulically engaged power take-off was added in 1990.

There were more changes to the 300 series in 1991 when a 12 speed synchromesh reverse shuttle transmission became standard on the Hi-Line cabbed 300 series, starting with the 71hp MF 375. A new 104hp 6 cylinder Perkins Quadram engine was used on the 399 and a 40kph 12 speed transmission was an added option for the larger four-wheel drive models.

The more powerful 3600 series was added to the 3000 series in 1987. Described as the 'thinking tractors with power to spare' the 113hp, 133hp and 150hp MF 3610, 3630 and 3650 Datatronic and Autotronic models had a 16 speed synchromesh reverse shuttle gearbox, improved lower link sensing elc hydraulics and oil cooled disc brakes.

Changes came thick and fast in the early 1990s. A key-operated engine stop control was introduced in 1990 for some 3000/3600 tractors which were also the first to have the facility to download performance and field data from the Datatronic monitoring system to the farm computer. The 3600 models, which had 16 speed reverse shuttle gearboxes, included the 142hp 3645 and 155hp 3655 with Perkins engines but 170hp, 180hp and 190hp Valmet engines were used for the 3670, 3680 and 3690.

Massey Ferguson's optional Active Transport Control (ATC)

205. The radiator header tank was re-positioned to accommodate the sloping bonnet on the Massey Ferguson 3065 HV High Visibility tractor.

206. The 240hp MF 9240 introduced in 1995 was based on a White tractor made by AGCO in America. It had a 6 cylinder Cummins engine and an 18 forward and 9 reverse speed shuttle transmission. The rear axle was made by David Brown Transaxles in Yorkshire.

system designed to improve driver safety and comfort on the 3000, 3100 and 3600 series was introduced in 1991. ATC used a nitrogen accumulator in the hydraulic circuit to smooth out shock loads caused by implement bounce during transport.

The Dynashift transmission and the MF 3065 HV sloping bonnet line achieved by moving the radiator header tank to the rear of the engine compartment were Massey Ferguson's innovations for 1992. The 32 forward and reverse speed Dynashift system with 24 clutchless powershift changes was standard on the 132–190hp MF 3600 series.

The turbocharged 120hp MF 3120 replaced the 3115 in 1992 and the Perkins Dual Zone torque engine for the MF 3100 and 3600 series appeared in the same year. Precise control of the fuel injection system on the Dual Zone engines provided separate torque ranges for light and heavy work. This enabled the engine to respond quickly to an increasing load when ploughing or provide an economical power output for lighter work. Massey Ferguson were supplying four models from the 3000 and 3100 ranges with 88–125hp engines and crystal blue paintwork to Iseki in the early 1990s and similar arrangements were made with Landini, Steyr and Valmet.

The Allis Gleaner Corporation (AGCO), formed in 1990 at Atlanta in Georgia, were MF tractor and machinery distributors in North America when they bought Massey Ferguson from the Varity Corporation in 1994. The acquisition added the Massey Ferguson product range to their existing brand names which included Allis, Gleaner, White and Hesston. AGCO were marketing a combined total of about 70 models of tractor in the 13–425hp bracket in 1995. There were Allis models from 40–215hp, White tractors with 60–215hp engines, articulated four-wheel drive 350hp and 425hp AGCO star models and the full MF range. AGCO were also selling 12 specialist SAME models and a range of 51 Landini tractors in North America. The Varity Corporation retained the Perkins engine business while the industrial equipment division was bought by a management team. Trading as Fermec International, the new owners sold the Massey Ferguson industrial range for a while but the business was eventually acquired by Case IH.

207. The 80hp MF 6120 was the smallest of the five 6000 series tractors launched in 1995.

The 6000 and 8000 series replaced the 80–190hp 3000 and 3600 series in 1995. The smallest MF 6100 matched the 80hp 3060 and the flagship 8160 had a 200hp 6 cylinder turbocharged Perkins 1000 series engine. The specification included a multi-plate oil-cooled clutch, a 32 forward and reverse Dynashift pressure lubricated gearbox, digital electronic hydraulic linkage control and a new generation of the MF Autotronic and Datatronic management systems.

Massey Ferguson made their three millionth tractor, a 66hp MF 375E, at Banner Lane on 15 October 1996. Tractors were being made at Coventry for AGCO, White, Iseki, Valmet, and Landini when the new MF 4200 series was launched in 1997. The new Coventry-built tractors were introduced to farmers in 30 European countries in a four-minute spot on satellite televison. The sequence was seen by farmers attending the breakfast time launch at their local dealership. Features of the Lo-Profile, Standard and Hi-Visibility versions of the 52–110hp 4200 tractors included a raised central drive shaft to the front wheels on four-wheel drive models and automatic engagement of the front diff-lock when using the rear diff-lock.

The most powerful Massey Ferguson yet made in Europe made its debut at the 1998 Smithfield Show. Standard features of the 260hp MF 8180 included a 6 cylinder turbocharged and intercooled Valmet engine and an 18 speed powershift transmission.

208. When the MF 8170 with a 230hp Valmet engine was launched in 1998 Massey Ferguson were making a range of tractors, from the 38hp MF 230 to the 240hp MF 9240. The list included the 200, 4200, 6100 and 8100 series, together with the narrow 300 series tractors made by Landini.

MASSEY-HARRIS

The Massey Manufacturing Co and A. Harris & Son who made various farm machines including knife mowers, reapers and threshers merged in 1891 to form Massey-Harris. Daniel Massey started work in his Ontario workshop in 1847 and ten years later his eventual partner Alanson Harris established his business at Beamsville (also in Canada). The new Massey-Harris company was not involved with tractors until 1917 when they introduced the American-built Bull tractors to Canadian farmers. When the Bull Tractor Co failed in 1919 Massey-Harris sold tractors based on Parrett designs made in Chicago. The Wallis 20-30 made by the J.I. Case Plow Co at Racine, Wisconsin, was the next tractor marketed by Massey-Harris. They bought the Racine factory in 1928 and sold the J.I. Case Plow Co name to the J.I. Case Threshing Machine Co in the same year.

Massey-Harris opened factories in France and Germany between the two world wars and acquired a major interest in H.V. McKay Co of Sunshine near Melbourne, Australia,

209. Introduced in 1936 the 17–27hp Pacemaker had a U-shaped frame design first used by Massey-Harris in 1913. The frame provided a rigid structure to support the engine and gearbox. Chassis frames went out of use in the early 1940s and it was 50 years before they re-appeared on farm tractors.

in 1930. Wallis tractors, now with a Massey-Harris name plate, appeared in the early 1930s. Other new models included the four-wheel drive 15-22 General Purpose, the Pacemaker and the Challenger followed by the Massey-Harris 80, 100 and 200 series.

The four-wheel drive Massey-Harris 15-22 or General Purpose tractor had a 25hp 4 cylinder Hercules side valve engine with a 3 forward and reverse gearbox and a top speed of 4mph. The arrangement of the final reduction gears and large equal-sized wheels gave a ground clearance of 30 inches and the wheels could be adjusted to give a 48–76 inch track widths.

The 17–27hp Massey-Harris Pacemaker introduced in 1936 had a 4 cylinder water-cooled, overhead-valve paraffin engine with a tubular radiator, 16 inch cooling fan, centrifugal water pump and a mix of splash and force feed lubrication. One farming magazine considered the 4 speed gearbox with a top speed of 8.5mph to be 'very useful when moving the tractor from field to field'. The Pacemaker with power take-off, belt pulley and spade lug wheels cost £260 when delivered to the 'nearest railway station'. Dunlop low-pressure pneumatic tyres in place of steel wheels added £45 to the price.

Standard, rowcrop and tricycle wheeled versions of the 39–45hp Massey-Harris 44 and the 52–59hp Massey-Harris 55, with the choice of petrol and diesel engines, were introduced to Canadian farmers in 1946. The 'one-plow' Massey-Harris Pony tractor availiable in the UK was added in 1947 to compete with the Allis-Chalmers Model B, Farmall A and Ferguson 20.

Small-scale production of Massey-Harris mowers and hay machinery began at Trafford Park, Manchester in 1946. The company also sold the Canadian-built 44 and 55 tractors in the UK until the Massey-Harris 744

PD went into limited production at Manchester in 1948. The prefix '7' was used to indicate British manufacture. The 46hp 744PD with a 6 cylinder Perkins P6 engine, electric starter and Ki-gass cold starting system cost £854.10s ex-works. The specification included a 5 forward and reverse gearbox, independent brakes, belt pulley, power take-off and wheel weights. Category II hydraulic linkage with a pump driven from the engine crank-shaft was an optional extra. The tractor became the 744D when production moved to Kilmarnock in 1949 and about 200 of them, including a Hi-Arch high clearance rowcrop version were made each month. The two-part cast iron chassis used for the Canadian 44 tractor was also shipped to the UK for the 744D. One part of the chassis supported the Perkins P6 engine and the other section housed the transmission. The 5 forward and 2 reverse gearbox had a top speed of 12mph and the final drive included a spiral bevel crown wheel, spur tooth reduction gears and shoe brakes on the differential shafts.

210. The first Massey-Harris 744 PD tractors were made at Manchester in 1948.

The Massey-Harris 745 with a 44.6hp 4 cylinder L4 Perkins diesel engine and 5 forward speed transmission replaced the 744D in 1954. The standard model, which cost £699, had a Hardy Spicer coupling from the clutch to the gearbox to facilitate clutch repairs. The rear wheels were fixed on the standard tractor but track width could be adjusted on the rowcrop model by sliding the rear wheels along on their axle shafts and reversing the wheel centres. Optional equipment included the new 'instant action' hydraulic three-point linkage with the pump driven by the engine timing gears and twin-wheel or Hi-arch rowcrop adjustable front axles. The 'Velvet Ride' seat in lieu of the standard spring leaf version and an hour meter were both listed at £3.10s while the optional power take-off shaft cost £10. Sales literature described the 745 as 'a genuine all-purpose four-furrow tractor, strong and versatile, with plenty of power for the heaviest work but equally efficient and economic for the smaller jobs around the farm'.

The amalgamation of Massey-Harris and Ferguson in 1953 meant the 745 was the last Massey-Harris tractor but the Kilmarnock factory was forced to make one last change when the Canadian-built 44 tractor was discontinued in 1957. The 44 chassis castings were no longer available from Canada so a steel-framed chassis was used for the modified 745S. The last 745S tractors were made in 1958 when the Massey-Harris-Ferguson name was shortened to Massey Ferguson.

211. The Scottish Aviation cab for the Massey-Harris 744 D cost £34, carriage paid to the nearest railway station, in 1950. A roll-up curtain with a plastic window cost an extra £2.5s.

MATBRO

The Matthew brothers started a general engineering business in Surrey in the late 1940s where they made forklift trucks and mechanical handling equipment. Matbro entered the tractor market in 1962 with a modified four-wheel drive articulated loader called the Mastiff 6/100MT which cost about £2,500. The Mastiff had a 6 cylinder 100hp Ford diesel engine, two Fordson Super Major transmission systems and rear axle units linked by a central pivot and a diff-lock on both axles. The

212. The Matbro Mastiff 6/100 MT was made at Horley in Surrey in the early 1960s.

engine was located above the front transmission unit and separate drive shafts transmitted power to both axles locked in permanent four-wheel drive. A high capacity engine-mounted hydraulic pump provided oil pressure for the double acting steering rams and live Super Major hydraulic linkage.

About 20 Matbro Mastiff 6/100 MT tractors were made before the articulated Mk II Mastiff with a 128hp Ford industrial engine was seen at several farm machinery field demonstrations in 1967. The Mk II tractor had a Ford 5000 gearbox to transmit drive through a transfer box to two opposing Ford 5000 rear axle units. The Mk II Mastiff with centre-pivot steering and hydraulic lift was priced at £3,495 but it failed to sell. The design concept re-appeared in 1972 when Massey Ferguson launched the articulated four-wheel drive MF 1200. Although Matbro enjoyed little success with tractors, production of mechanical handling equipment has continued to the present day.

213. This articulated Mk II Matbro Mastiff was demonstrated to British farmers in 1967 but it did not sell and finished its working days at Rotterdam docks.

MERCEDES-BENZ

The Mercedes-Benz name was not used by Daimler-Benz until the mid-1920s. The company name was derived from Karl Benz and Gottlied Daimler who were pioneers of the motor car and had engineering works in different parts of Germany. Benz founded his business in 1871 while the Daimler established his company in 1882 after working with Nicolaus Otto who developed the four-stroke cycle engine. Mercedes was the daughter of an important Daimler dealer in Germany and her name was used on a Daimler-Benz car which took part in a 1901 motor race but the name was not used for Daimler-Benz vehicles until the mid-1920s.

The first Daimler-Benz tractor with a 50hp engine, sprung front axle and

214. The Mercedes-Benz MB-trac 65/70 made its debut at the 1972 German Agricultural Trade Fair.

canopy to protect the driver was made in 1919 but the four-wheel drive Mercedes-Benz MB-trac did not appear until the early 1970s. The MB-trac 95/105 specifically designed for agricultural use with front and rear power take-offs and provision to attach implements at both ends was introduced in 1974. The MB-trac 1100 and 1300 were added in 1976. The 10,000th MB-trac was made in 1979 and the 150hp 1500 first appeared in 1980.

The early 1980s MB-tracs in the 65–150hp bracket were designed to have even weight distribution on the four equal-size wheels. Standard features included a diff-lock on both axles and a 12 forward and reverse gearbox with a top speed of 25mph. Meanwhile, with a top speed of 50mph the Unimog was able to show its more sophisticated relation a clean pair of rear wheels. The 95hp MB-trac 1000 was added in 1984 and by 1986 Mercedes-Benz (UK) Ltd at Milton Keynes were offering British farmers five models, from the 75hp MB-trac 800 to the 150hp MB-trac 1500.

Daimler-Benz and KHD formed Trac-technic in 1987 and this led to Watveare Ltd taking over distribution of the hand-built four-wheel drive MB-trac in the UK. A new 110hp model announced in 1987 increased the range to seven models, from the 75hp MB-trac 800 to the 156hp 1600. The engines were improved and a new fast response electronic hydraulic draft control system with

215. The 125hp MB-trac 1300 was the largest of four two-directional MB-tracs in production in the mid-1970s. They had three implement mounting points, hydrostatic steering and a diff-lock on both axles.

216. The bi-directional 1500 (right) was the most powerful MB-trac in the early 1980s. It had coil spring front axle suspension, category III hydraulic linkage and a rear load-carrying platform. Sales literature explained that the 90hp MB-trac 1000 (with a trailer) had 'easy to use controls in a spacious cab with plenty of room for the driver and co-driver'.

greater sensitivity to soil conditions was an additional option for the 125hp and 150hp MB-trac 1300 and 1500.

The seven MB-tracs on the UK market in 1990 had 80–160hp engines, the smaller models had a 16 forward and 8 reverse gearbox which included 6 creep speeds and the 1300, 1400 and 1600 had a 16 speed synchromesh gearbox with a reverse shuttle and 8 creep speeds. An electronically operated weight transfer system controlled from the cab, also introduced in 1990, transferred front- or rear-mounted implement weight on to the front or rear wheels to reduce wheelslip and improve fuel economy.

A new flagship MB-trac 1800 with a turbocharged and intercooled 6 cylinder 180hp engine was launched at the 1990 Royal Show in a smart metallic light green livery. A reverse console in the cab made it possible to use the 1800 with a rear-mounted forage harvester in the same way as a conventional self-propelled machine. The last MB-tracs were made in 1991.

MINNEAPOLIS-MOLINE

Three separate tractor and farm equipment makers joined forces in 1924 to form the Minneapolis-Moline Power Implement Company who made various models of Twin City tractors until 1938. The two-three plow Minneapolis-Moline Z launched in 1937 was 'vision lined' with a tapered bonnet; the fuel tank and the steering wheel were off-set to give the driver a clear view when working in rowcrops. Unlike modern glossy brochures Minneapolis-Moline sales literature often gave very detailed information. The model Z leaflet provided illustrations of many engine and transmission components, including a valve spring, rocker gear, camshaft and so on. In common with many other American tractors there were several variants of the Model Z. The ZTS was the standard version, the rowcrop ZTU had vee-front wheels, the ZTN had a single front wheel and the XZTI was the industrial model.

Sale Tilney & Co at Wokingham in Berkshire imported their first Minneapolis-Moline tractors in time for the 1939 Royal Show, having previously introduced other MM products at the 1938 Smithfield Show. Early models sold in the UK included the GT which was the largest MM tractor at the time, the RT with disc brakes, the UDLX with a comfort cab complete with radio and clock, and the ZTS standard model. The GT, with a 4 forward and reverse gearbox and 36hp at the drawbar, was made from 1938 until it was replaced by the GTA in 1942. The new model was basically the same as the GT with steel wheels but an enclosed flywheel and a channel section engine chassis replaced the earlier heavy cast iron framework.

With the war at an end Sale Tilney and Minneapolis-Moline formed MM (England) Ltd in 1946, in order to manufacture Minneapolis-Moline products including combine harvesters, saw benches, winches and hammer mills. The UDS tractor was also assembled at Wokingham; some of the parts were made there with the remainder brought in from America. It had a 46hp Dorman or a 66hp Meadows engine with a 24 volt starting system. Otherwise this tractor had the same 5 forward speed and reverse transmission, expanding shoe brakes, power take-off and belt pulley unit used for the UT series.

MM (England) Ltd went into receivership in 1949 but American-built tractors were imported by Sale Tilney until the early 1950s when the distinctive yellow tractors disappeared from the British market. Sale Tilney were also importing New Holland balers and this arrangement continued until 1955 when the franchise was taken over by Western Machinery of Devon.

The Cleveland Tractor Co, who made Cletrac rowcrop tractors, was acquired by B.F. Avery & Sons of Louisville, Kentucky in the early 1940s. The new company was taken over by Minneapolis-Moline in 1951. The Avery Model R and Model V were being made at the time and the 4 cylinder side-valve engined Model R with a 4 forward and reverse gearbox became the Minneapolis-Moline Model BF. Although Minneapolis-Moline tractors had disappeared from the British market they were still produced in America and by 1953 there were six basic models, ranging from the 60hp 4–5 plow Model G to the one-plow Model V previously made by B.F. Avery. According to information given in a 1953 advertisement, the price of a tractor was 'equivalent to the market price of nine beef cattle in 1940 but in 1953 farmers could

217. The Minneapolis-Moline Standard Vision-lined model was described in sales literature as 'a two-three plow tractor for general all-around use.'

get a much better (Minneapolis-Moline) tractor for less than the market price of four beef cattle'. A similar comparison in the late 1990s would be difficult to imagine. A testimonial from the same advertisement declared 'I'm farming with an MM because I've found out just how much money it can make for me.' These words were obviously uttered by an American farmer as most of his British counterparts would never admit to making a profit!

Minneapolis-Moline made high-power tractors for Massey Ferguson from 1958 to the early 1960s and the White Motor Co, who already owned Oliver and Cockshutt, bought MM in 1963. The White Motor Co continued the production of tractors under the three brand names until 1974 when Oliver, Cockshutt and MM were dropped and their tractors were all sold under the White brand name.

218. Rubber was in short supply when the MM GTA was introduced in 1942. Early models were sold on steel wheels.

MOFFETT

219. The Moffett Multi-Functional Tractor (MFT) introduced in 1991 was built around a Massey Ferguson skid unit.

The Moffett Engineering Co was already established as a fork lift truck manufacturer at Dundalk in Ireland when the first Moffett Multi-Function Tractor (MFT) based on a Massey Ferguson skid unit with a 90hp Perkins engine appeared in 1991. The bi-directional MFT was a four-wheel drive tractor combined with a rear-mounted two ton capacity industrial loader. It had a Massey Ferguson 12 speed gearbox with a reverse shuttle, an optional four-speed torque converter and wet disc brakes on the rear axle. Three-point linkage and two-speed power take-off were standard and an optional front linkage was available. The driving seat and controls, which could be reversed in a matter of seconds, gave equal visibility in both directions. The 120hp MFT with an improved cab, also based on a Massey Ferguson skid unit, replaced the original model in 1994. It had a 12 speed reverse shuttle gearbox and was designed for ploughing, forage harvesting and other heavy work.

The MFT 7840 with a 100hp 6 cylinder New Holland engine superseded the MF-based tractor in 1996. The 7840 with a de-mountable parallel linkage rear loader had a 24 speed synchroshift gearbox with Dual Power and a clutchless reverse shuttle. Standard features included top link sensing rear hydraulic linkage and two-speed power take-off.

220. The driving position of the bi-directional Moffett MFT 7840 could be reversed in seconds. The tractor had two steering columns with a quick-release steering wheel, a reversible driving seat and foot pedals at the front and rear of the cab.

MOROOKA

Yuasa Warwick Machinery introduced a range of 80–325hp Morooka rubber-tracked crawlers to British farmers in 1996. The Japanese company, which also makes earth moving machinery, fork trucks and loaders, was formed in 1958. Robert H. Crawford & Son of Boston, appointed Morooka distributors in 1997, included 8 models from 65–325hp with hydrostatically driven reinforced rubber tracks steered with two levers in their price list. Komatsu diesel engines provide the power but Cummins power units have been used for some of the larger models since 1997. Standard features included category II hydraulic linkage, twin-speed range hydrostatic transmission and dual-speed power take-off. Exceptions to the standard specification included category III linkage on the 250hp and 325hp models and a 1,000rpm power take-off on the largest model in the range.

221. The Japanese Morooka rubber track crawlers were first seen in the UK in 1996.

MUIR-HILL

Mr Muir and Mr Hill were making shunting engines for railway trucks in Manchester in the early 1920s. They were based on Fordson tractors and by the end of the decade Muir-Hill were also using the Fordson power unit for dumper trucks. Winget, who were well known for their concrete mixers, bought Muir-Hill in 1959 and they made dumper trucks and loader shovels at Manchester until the early 1960s.

Production had been transferred to Gloucester when the four-wheel drive Muir-Hill 101 with a Ford industrial engine and four equal-size wheels designed for agricultural and industrial use was launched in 1966. A low-speed contractor's model for drainage and forestry work was added in 1967. The Muir-Hill 101 cost less than £3,000 and like many of its competitors had a Ford 5000 gearbox with 8 forward gears and a top speed of 20mph. Transmission and hydraulic systems were also supplied by Ford but Muir-Hill made their own transfer box and front axle drive shaft. The front and rear wheel track was adjustable from 64 to 80 inches and drive to the front axle could be disengaged when necessary. Other features included oil-immersed disc brakes on both axles, power-assisted steering and an independent hand-lever operated power take-off clutch. Winget, and Muir-Hill, became part of the Babcock and Wilcox group in 1968.

The Muir-Hill 110 with a 6 cylinder 110hp Perkins engine and the 161 with a 163hp V8 Perkins engine were launched in 1969. With a 10 speed gearbox, hydrostatic steering and detachable cab the 161 was the most powerful farm tractor on the British market at the time. An improved Muir-Hill 101 with a 120hp Ford engine and full hydrostatic steering appeared in 1971 but within 12 months the series II Muir-Hill 111, 121 and 161 had been launched with improved flat floor cabs. The Muir-Hill 111, still with a 110hp Perkins engine, superseded the 110 and the Muir-Hill 121 with the same 120hp Ford engine and gearbox replaced the 101.

The series II 161 with twin exhaust pipes remained in production until 1975 when it was replaced by the 171 with a 170hp

222. A 6 cylinder 101 Din hp Ford diesel engine provided the power for the Muir-Hill 101.

223. The Muir-Hill 111 had a 110hp Perkins engine but otherwise was similar to the M-H 121.

V8 Perkins engine, lower link sensing hydraulics and a new cab.

The Series III Muir-Hill 111, 121, 141 and 171 announced in 1978 were similar to previous models except for a new sound insulated Spacecab with a tinted glass windscreen. The new cab with an opening rear window had a push button radio with a fibreglass aerial while the heating and ventilation system was said to give five air changes per minute. The Muir-Hill 141 with a 6 cylinder turbocharged 143hp Ford or a 132hp Perkins engine was a new addition to the series III range. In 1978 the Ford 8 forward and 2 reverse gearbox with optional Dual-power was still used for the 111, 121 and 141 but the 8 cylinder 171, now with 170hp under the bonnet, had a 10 forward and 2 reverse gearbox, hydrostatic steering and self-adjusting oil-cooled disc brakes on both axles.

Muir-Hill tractor production came to an end when Babcock sold its construction equipment division in 1982. Following a period under various ownerships including Sanderson Forklifts and Aveling-Barford the business was acquired by Lloyd Loaders at Mytholm in Yorkshire. The new owners introduced the Myth-Holm 131 in 1989 and this tractor remained in small-scale production for about six years. Very similar to its Muir-Hill ancestors it had a 6 cylinder 130hp Ford engine, Dual Power transmission and an air-conditioned cab.

224. The series III Muir Hill 121 with a 6 cylinder 132hp Ford engine had equal weight distribution on the front and rear axles when ploughing.

NEW HOLLAND

A farm implement repair business started by Abram Zimmerman at New Holland, Pennsylvania in 1895 was manufacturing barn equipment by the end of that century. Stationary engines were being made in the early 1900s and the New Holland Machine Co were making automatic twine-tying pick-up balers in the late 1930s. The Sperry Corporation purchased New Holland in 1947 and by the mid-1950s the company was making a wide range of farm equipment, including balers, bale loaders, forage harvesters and manure spreaders. Combine harvesters were added to the product range when New Holland bought the Clayson works in Belgium in 1964.

The New Holland farm machinery business was acquired by the Ford Motor Co in 1986 and Ford New Holland bought Versatile Manufacturing Ltd of Canada in 1987. The next change came in 1991 when Fiat bought Ford New Holland and the headquarters of New Holland Geotech were established at Basildon in Essex. Fiatagri made their range of tractors in Italy and Ford tractor production continued at Highland Park in America, Antwerp and Basildon until the first mechanically identical blue New Holland Ford 70 series and terra cotta New Holland Fiatagri G series tractors were launched in 1994. The model numbers of the Fiatagri G 170, G 190, G 210 and G 240 indicated the horse power of the turbocharged power units and the same engines were used for the Ford 8670, 8770, 8870 and 8970. An 18 forward and 9 reverse electro-hydraulic Powershift transmission with microprocessor controls was standard on the four-wheel drive tractors. The Super-steer front axle with a 65 degree steering angle compared with the usual 50 per cent angle was an optional extra. The Fiat G series and Ford 70 Series were the last new models with the Fiatagri and the Ford oval badges and within a year the New Holland blue leaf logo had appeared on the bonnet of the terra cotta and the blue tractors.

New Holland launched the 65–90hp Ford 35 series and Fiat L Series together with the 100–160hp Ford 65 series and Fiat M Series tractors in 1996. Farmers needing even more power could order a 360hp Versatile 9682 in New Holland blue livery. The 9682 was one of a range of four high horse power tractors made at the Versatile factory in Canada.

225. The New Holland Ford 8970 had the Super-Steer front axle.

New Holland announced the medium-powered TS 90, 100 and 110 and three TNF fruit tractors in 1997. The 80hp, 90hp and 100hp TS tractors with a 24 speed forward and reverse transmission replaced some of the previous 40 series models but the popular 7840 and 8340 remained in production. The New Holland Super-Steer front axle with an improved 76 degree steering angle was a feature of the new narrow 65hp, 76hp and 88hp TNF fruit tractors.

The TS range was extended with the launch of the 6 cylinder TS 115 at the 1998 Smithfield Show. The new model with a 24 speed reverse shuttle transmission replaced the 100hp 7840.

226. The Fiatagri G 240 was made on the same production line as the New Holland Ford 70 series tractors.

NEWMAN

Newman Industries at Bristol introduced the tricycle-wheeled Newman tractor with a 10.5hp or optional 12hp Coventry Victor air-cooled petrol engine in 1948. An improved three-wheeled Newman WD 2 with a Coventry Victor water-cooled single-cylinder diesel engine appeared in 1949. The WD 2 had a single-plate dry clutch, a conventional transmission with 3 forward gears and reverse with a top speed of just under 9mph and independent brakes. The basic tractor cost £330 but the optional power take-off, belt pulley and hydraulic linkage increased the price to £410.12s. This was considerably more than the price of £335 for the Ferguson TED 20.

The four-wheeeled Newman Model E2 with a 12hp twin-

227. High ground clearance and a mid-mounted toolbar made the Newman an ideal tractor for rowcrop work.

cylinder Petter water-cooled diesel engine and a 4 forward and reverse gearbox appeared in 1951. The engine was started by hand with the aid of a decompressor and a fuel priming lever. The basic model with adjustable wheel track with settings from 42 inches to 54 inches at the front and up to 72 inches at the rear cost £430. Optional extras included a rear-mounted belt pulley for £10, a 1 1/8 inch diameter power take-off shaft for £18 while a hydraulic system with a gear pump in the transmission housing added another £46.10s to give a total price of £504.10s. A swinging drawbar was standard and the tractor could be used with front, mid-mounted or rear tool bars raised and lowered with a hand lever or optional hydaulic system.

NORTHROP

The Chaseside company, based in Middlesex, who built loading shovels and railway shunters based on Fordson tractors, merged with British Northrop of Blackburn in the late 1950s. British Northrop were making machinery for the weaving industry so it was the Chaseside expertise which led to the introduction of the equal-size four-wheel drive Northrop 5004 in 1965. Built mainly with Ford 5000 parts it had a 67hp 4 cylinder engine, 8 speed gearbox or optional Select-O-Speed box and a central drive shaft from a transfer box to the front axle.

Northrop Tractors had moved to Ware in Hertfordshire when they added a turbocharger to the 5004 engine which increased its rated power to 85hp. The Northrop 5006 launched in 1967 was also based on the Ford 5000 tractor with a 6 cylinder 90hp Ford diesel engine and an 8 forward and 2 reverse gearbox with a top speed of 20mph. It had epicyclic reduction gears, diff-locks and hydraulically operated disc brakes on both axles. Track width was adjustable from 56 inches to 80 inches. The 5006, complete with category II hydraulic linkage and power take-off, cost £2,900 but with only a handful made the tractor went out of production in 1967. Within twelve months British Northrop had sold the Chaseside business to JCB.

228. Ford 5000 components were used for the Northrop 5006.

NUFFIELD

William Morris, who later became Lord Nuffield, gave his name to the Morris motor car and Nuffield tractor. The Morris Motors Agricultural Division launched the Nuffield Universal M4 and tricycle-wheeled M3 with vaporising oil engines and the petrol-engined PM4 at the 1948 Smithfield Show. The 40.8hp petrol engine and 38hp vaporising oil engine were based on a 4 cylinder Morris Commercial side-valve power unit and the relatively advanced Nuffield design included a 5 forward speed and reverse gearbox, electric starting and adjustable wheel track width. Prices started at £495 for the M4 and £487.10s for the M3 but hydraulic linkage with two auxiliary service points and power take-off added another £80 to the bill. The optional single front wheel, mainly for the North American market, was an unusual feature for a British-built tractor; a single front wheel conversion kit for the M4 cost £37 and a similar kit to convert from M3 to M4 was £46.10s.

Sales literature described the Nuffield as 'the newest aid to power farming' and explained that 'much thought had been given to driver comfort which was shown by the provision of a rubber sprung, deep cushioned seat, good vision of work, light steering, conveniently grouped controls, and a low floor with an easy driving or standing position.'

The first diesel-engined Nuffield Universal appeared in 1950. The DM4 with a 48hp Perkins P4 (TA) engine cost just under £670, compared with £550 for the M4 with a paraffin engine. Morris Motors became part of the British Motor Corporation in 1952 but the Perkins engine was retained until 1954 when it was replaced by a new 45hp BMC diesel engine. The re-numbered Nuffield 4 DM was advertised as a tractor with 'greater fuel economy,' smoother running, easier starting and better cooling at a very reasonable price.' An optional independent power take-off and hydraulic system with a dual clutch was introduced in 1956. The transmission clutch was controlled with a pedal and a hand clutch was used for the power take-off.

The Nuffield 4DM became the Unversal Four when the 37hp Universal Three with a 3 cylinder BMC direct injection diesel engine and a 5 forward speed and reverse gearbox appeared in 1957. Both tractors had conventional dished rear wheel centres for rear track width adjustment but the earlier sliding hub arrangement on the rear axle was optional on the Universal Four. A rather sparse specification required a long list of optional extras to make the Universal Three a serious competitor for the Massey Ferguson 35

229. The Nuffield Universal M4 was one of the first British-built tractors with five forward gears. The rear wheel track was adjusted by sliding the wheels along on their axles.

or Fordson Dexta. However, electric starting, steering brakes and a parking brake, a swinging drawbar, lubricating oil and a licence holder were included in the basic price of £555. Optional Category I and II hydraulic linkage and independent power take-off cost £122.10s but the diff-lock only added £5 to the bill. Electric lighting, horn and number plates cost ten guineas and the extra comfort provided by a de-luxe seat with a cushion added another £3. 2s. 6d. For a relatively low basic price of £610 the Nuffield Universal Four had a BMC diesel engine and a 5 forward and reverse gearbox but an independent power take-off and hydraulic system were among numerous extras required to match the competition.

Technical information published in the late 1950s concerning tractor horse power could be confusing

230. The Nuffield Universal Three was introduced in an attempt to break into the lower power range market which was dominated in the late 1950s by Ford and Massey Ferguson.

231. The Nuffield 10/42 and the more powerful 10/60 made between 1964 and 1967 were claimed by BMC to be the first British-built tractors with 10 forward gears.

and sales literature for the Nuffield Universal Four which gave six different horse power ratings was typical. The list started with a maximum of 56 SAE bhp (bare engine brake hp measured at the flywheel); with the fan belt replaced the Din bhp was reduced to 53hp at 2,000rpm and 39.6hp at 1,400rpm. Drawbar power was given as 45.8hp and 34.8hp at 2,000 and 1,400rpm respectively and the belt pulley developed 52.1hp when running at the standard belt speed of 3,100ft/min.

The Universal name was dropped when the Nuffield 342 and 460 replaced the Universal Three and Four in 1961. The first figure related to the number of cylinders and the other two indicated engine horse power. Even at this stage the basic price of £595 excluded hydraulic linkage and power take-off, the standard 460 with hydraulics and a power shaft cost £650 while the de-luxe model priced at £810 had an independent power take-off and depth control hydraulics. Tractor production was transferred from Birmingham to a new BMC truck factory at Bathgate in Scotland in 1962.

The 10 series announced in 1964 were the first Nuffield tractors to have the power take-off and hydraulic linkage with interchangeable dual category lower link ball ends as standard equipment. The de-luxe models had an independent power-take-off shaft. The 60hp 10/60 with 10 forward speeds was faithful to its model number but the 10/42 also with 10 forward gears was rated at 45hp. Disc brakes were a new feature on these tractors which BMC literature explained were just as efficient as expanding shoe brakes. Power-assisted steering and a rear-mounted power take-off driven belt pulley were optional extras for both tractors and the original Nuffield Universal sliding rear wheel hubs which gave stepless wheel track adjustment could be specified for the 10/60.

A 'new era in farming economy' was forecast by BMC when they launched a 15hp Mini-Tractor at the 1965 Smithfield Show. Advertisements explained that the 'light, compact, ultra-manoeuvrable and ultra-economical BMC Mini-Tractor was capable of all but the heaviest tasks and it would start a new era of Mini-mechanisation'. The 'entirely new and ingenious prime mover' with its own range of implements would 'cut farm economics down to size and stem the growing trend towards bigger and bigger tractors'. In reality the BMC Mini, made by Nuffield but without their name, had some similarity to the Ferguson TE 20 introduced some 20 years earlier. A 4 cylinder indirect injection engine with a CAV rotary type fuel injection pump and a heater coil in each cylinder for cold starting provided the power for a 9 forward and 3 reverse gearbox with a top speed of just under 13mph. The basic tractor with disc brakes, diff-lock, parking latch, electric starter and tractor meter cost £512.10s. The HPU model with hydraulic linkage, a front loader kit and lights was another £62.10s. The BMC Mini-Tractor was not a great success so it was re-launched in 1968 as the Nuffield 4/25 with a more powerful 4 cylinder, indirect injection 25hp diesel or optional 25hp petrol engine.

Improved and re-styled 3/45 and 4/65 tractors replaced the Nuffield 10/42 and 10/60 in 1967. The same engines were used but a higher engine speed on the 10/60 increased power output to 65hp and the hydraulic system was improved with a double-acting top link. The tractor had two hydraulic pumps; one supplied oil to the lift cylinder and external rams and a smaller pump was used to operate the draft control system. The 10/42 and 10/60 gearboxes with a top speed approaching 20mph were retained but power-steering, still considered a luxury item, was an optional extra. The

232. The BMC Mini-Tractor had 9 forward and 3 reverse gears provided by a three speed constant mesh box combined with a high, medium, low and reverse range gearbox.

drag link was put inside the main frame to tidy the steering linkage and keep it away from side-mounted equipment. Prices ranged from £765 for the standard 3/45 with hydraulics to £1,044.10s for the de-luxe 4/65 with independent power take-off. Four-wheel drive conversions of Ford tractors were popular by the late 1960s and Bray Construction Equipment Ltd followed the trend with four-wheel drive versions of the 4/65 and the earlier 10/60.

The BMC Nuffield tractor operation became part of British Leyland in the late 1960s but the Nuffield name was retained until 1969 when the poppy red 4/25, 3/45 and 4/65 became the Leyland 154, 344 and 384 with a new two-tone blue colour scheme.

233. Cosmetic changes to the Nuffield 4/65 when it replaced the 4/60 in 1967 included wide top wings and a re-styled bonnet. An access panel was provided for battery maintenance and the 15 gallon fuel tank was located in front of the radiator.

ON-TOP

Two- and four-wheel drive fast tractors designed to pull up to 24 tons at speeds of 30 to 45mph have been made since the early 1990s by On-Top Tractors at Balgowan near Perth in Scotland. A combination of new and reconditioned components, including a 230hp 6 cylinder turbocharged Leyland diesel engine were used for the two-wheel drive On-Top 800 series Cruiser tractors. Other features included a 10 forward and 8 reverse gearbox with a top speed of up to 45mph, an Albion six ton capacity front axle, auxiliary hydraulics and split circuit air brakes. The On-Top tractor was primarily designed to pull large trailers and it could be equipped with a ground speed power take-off

234. The two-wheel drive 230hp 800 series On-Top Cruiser fast tractor had a top speed of 45mph.

suitable for use with power-driven trailer axles and optional ball hitch or fifth wheel coupling for the On-Top gripmaster powered-axle trailer.

A combination of new and recycled ex-military running equipment used for the two- and four-wheel drive On-Top Trekker included a 205hp turbocharged Bedford diesel engine, a twin range gearbox with 12 forward gears, power-assisted steering and air-operated brakes with a trailer braking system. The Trekker and Cruiser could be supplied with a dual speed power take-off, live hydraulic system and a pick-up hitch.

OTA

The name of the OTA tricycle-wheeled tractor, cast in large letters on the radiator grille, was derived from the initials of Oak Tree Appliances at Coventry. The OTA was launched at the 1949 Smithfield Show following an earlier appearance at a local agricultural show. The first tractors were red and yellow but most of them had blue paintwork. The OTA cost £246.10s with an electric starter and hydraulic linkage. A Beccles vaporising oil conversion kit cost £10.10s, a four-speed power take-off shaft with a 10 inch belt pulley was £22.10s and a pair of wheel strakes were an extra £11. 6s. 8d.

The OTA had a 10hp water-cooled, side valve Ford industrial engine with coil ignition and electric starter. There was a starting handle dog on the crankshaft pulley and a second dog was provided at the rear. It was attached to the end of the shaft from the gearbox to the final drive gears and enabled the driver to hand crank the engine from the rear. The main gearbox needed to be in gear but it was equally important to ensure the high/low lever was in neutral. A three forward speed Ford gearbox and a high/low ratio lever provided 6 forward speeds from 0.75mph to 15mph and two in reverse. The OTA had a worm and wheel final drive and a live hydraulic system was provided by a twin-cylinder piston pump driven by a belt from the engine crankshaft pulley. The steel channel chassis was set at an angle to raise the front of the tractor to accommodate the single front wheel which was steered with a cable. The resultant high ground clearance gave an excellent view when using an underslung tool bar in rowcrops.

A re-designed bonnet and a sheet metal radiator without the large cast iron OTA badge were the most obvious changes on the Mk II tractor introduced a year or so later. Some Mk II tractors, also known as the 5000 series, had an improved transmission system and power take-off.

The 1951 Smithfield Show was chosen for the launch of the four-wheeled OTA Monarch Mk III and, except for a new front axle with a conventional steering linkage and hinged bonnet, it was very similar to the tricycle model. Wheel track settings could be varied between 42 and 60 inches and various implements were made for the mid- and rear-mounted tool frames. Singer Motors bought the manufacturing

235. The OTA was made by Oak Tree Appliances of Coventry and marketed by Slough Estates of Berkeley Street, London.

rights for the tractors from Oak Tree Appliances in 1953. The three-wheeled OTA was soon discontinued but Singer Motors made the Monarch until they were taken over by the Rootes Group in 1956.

PARAMOUNT

Two tractors were coupled together to form the 100hp plus Doe Triple D and it was possible with a do-it-yourself kit to split them into two separate tractors but this was rarely done. On the other hand, it was relatively easy to reverse the procedure when two tractors were coupled together with a Paramount dual tractor kit. Designed by a Berkshire farmer and made by Paramount Engineering at Coventry in 1968 the dual tractor kit could be used to link any two popular models of tractor together with the minimum of expense. Publicity material claimed that when the power of a four-wheel drive tractor was required the Paramount design was 'as simple to use as attaching a trailer and the driver could operate all controls including throttle,

clutch, gear lever, diff-lock and hydraulics while seated on the front tractor'. A ring hitch drawbar was attached to the rear unit after the front axle and steering linkage had been removed but no modifications were necessary on the leading tractor which required a pick-up hitch.

Sales literature explained that the extremely low price of the dual tractor kit and its ability to increase the work output of conventional tractors made it a must for every farm. Better still, the Paramount system did not require capital investment in heavy equipment which could only be used economically and effectively for a very short period of the year. However, farmers were not impressed and it was not a commercial success.

236. Two tractors of the same type were not necessary when using the Paramount Dual-Tractor kit.

PORSCHE

Dr Ferdinand Porsche made a rear-engined tractor with a 2 cylinder power unit in 1938 and following the war years he introduced the Porsche Volksschlepper, or people's tractor, which had a 2 cylinder 40hp Allgaier diesel engine.

The first Allgaier tractors with single-cylinder 18hp and 22hp hopper-cooled diesel engines were made in Germany in 1947. They were very basic machines with an old-fashioned appearance compared with the Ferguson TE 20 and other models of the day. Ferdinand Porsche became involved with Allgaier in the late 1940s and this resulted in a change to air-cooled engines for the German

237. Some German Allgaier models, including the AP 22 with a twin-cylinder air-cooled engine and a 5 forward and reverse gearbox, were made under licence by Porsche in the late 1950s and early 1960s.

238. The side-mounted vee-belt pulley on the Allgaier Porsche was typical of many continental tractors with a permanently attached mid-mounted mower.

tractors made from 1952. The 12hp Allgaier A 111, for example, had a single-cylinder air-cooled engine, 4 forward and reverse gears and power take-off. Short and long wheelbase models were made and its high ground clearance with a narrow waist gave maximum visibility for rowcrop work.

The Allgaier name was dropped in favour of Porsche in 1955 when the A 122, A 133 and A 144 Porsche tractors went into production at the Allgaier factory. The A 122 with a 22hp 2 cylinder air-cooled diesel engine and a 5 forward speed and reverse gearbox was the smallest model in the range. The 33hp A 133 and 44hp A 144 with 3 cylinder and 4 cylinder engines respectively had a fluid flywheel between the crankshaft and conventional single plate clutch similar to that used on Fendt tractors. A 540rpm power take-off was standard on all three models and the A 144 also had a front power shaft which ran at half engine speed.

The A 111 became the P 111 in 1956 and with the engine speed increased to 2,250rpm in 1957 the tractor, now rated at 16hp, was re-named the Porsche Junior L. In the same way the re-named P 122, P 133 and P 144 became the Porsche Standard, Super and Master in 1958.

Porsche tractors were not sold in the UK until 1959 when Eurotrac (Imports) Ltd at Dover were appointed sole distributors. Three models were available: the 33hp

239. The Porsche-Diesel Junior was developed from the 12hp Allgaier A 111.

Porsche Super, which cost £985 in 1962 and had 8 forward and 2 reverse gears, front-, mid- and rear-power take-off shafts and hydraulic linkage; the 22hp Standard, which had live mid- and rear-power take-off shaft and hydraulic linkage; and the 15hp Junior V, with a similar specification, completed the range imported by Eurotrac. However, their involvement with Porsche was short lived as the tractors went out of production in the mid-1960s.

240. The Porsche Super Export first seen in the UK in 1959 had front hydraulic linkage and a forward tilting bonnet for maintenance purposes. The front power take-off shaft was located inside the tubular drawbar.

POWER TAKE-OFF SHAFTS

The power take-off shaft came into use in the late 1920s and many tractors had one by the mid-1930s. There were no real construction standards in the early days either for shaft dimensions or operating speed. British Standard Specifications introduced in 1948 for agricultural tractors specified a 6-spline 1$\frac{3}{8}$ inch diameter shaft running at 536 plus or minus 10rpm. Most manufacturers met these standards but the Ferguson TE 20 series had a 1$\frac{1}{8}$ in diameter shaft. This caused a few problems with the increased range of power- driven implements introduced in the early 1950s but Lawrence Edwards & Co and other companies made adaptors to convert the TE 20 power shaft to the standard size.

Ground speed power take-off with the power shaft running at a speed proportional to the forward speed was introduced in the mid-fifties and the Ferguson FE 35 was one of the first tractors with this facility. The British Standard power take-off speed was changed to 540 plus or minus 10rpm in the 1958. The American Society of Automotive Engineers (SAE) introduced a second standard speed of 1,000rpm through a 21 spline, 1$\frac{3}{4}$ inch diameter shaft in 1958. Although the new standard was ignored for a while in the UK it was eventually adopted as a standard feature on the more powerful tractors sold in Britain.

Power take-off shafts were a major cause of farm accidents over the years. Farm safety legislation introduced in 1956 therefore required the power take-off shaft to be guarded from the tractor to the first fixed bearing on the implement. The guard on the tractor was required to support 250lbs – considerably more than the weight of most tractor drivers!

RANSOMES

Ransomes, Sims & Jefferies of Ipswich, well known for their threshing machines, lawn mowers, ploughs and other farm equipment, have been involved in tractor manufacture from time to time since 1903 when

J.E. Ransome made a 20hp 4 cylinder petrol-engined tractor which he demonstrated with a three furrow plough.

The MG (Market Garden) cultivator was originally conceived as a pedestrian-controlled garden tractor on rubber-jointed tracks made by Roadless Traction but it was never put into production. However, the Ransomes MG 2 garden cultivator, first demonstrated to smallholders in 1936, was a success and the MG was made in its various forms for about thirty years.

The MG 2 had a 6hp Sturmey Archer air-cooled, single-cylinder side-valve engine with a dry sump. Lubricating oil, stored in a separate tank in the crankcase was pumped to the bearings and a second pump returned it through a filter to the tank. A 4:1 reduction gear on the engine output shaft supplied power to a centrifugal clutch which engaged drive to a forward, neutral and reverse gearbox with a top speed of 2mph in both directions. The gearbox had two inward-facing crown wheels and a central

241. The Ransomes MG 2 market garden tractor cost £135 when it was launched in 1936. It could be used with trailed equipment or a range of implements mounted on the hand-lift toolbar. A 400rpm power take-off was an extra £1.10s.

pinion. Direction of travel depended on which crown wheel was engaged with the pinion. The tractor moved off when the engine speed reached 500rpm and it was steered with two hand levers connected to band brakes on the shafts carrying the crown wheels. The centrifugal clutch also served as an overload mechanism for the transmission, working on the principle that the engine speed would drop if the tractor was overloaded and the clutch automatically disengaged the drive. Both of the 6 inch wide tracks were always under some degree of drive which eliminated sliding and slewing when the tractor changed direction. Spacer blocks between the tracks and the chassis were used to obtain three track width settings.

A considerable number of MG 2 crawlers were sold in France for vineyard work which probably explains why early Ransomes sales literature gave specifications and capacities in Imperial and in metric units. It also suggested to potential purchasers that 'the high class baby track-type tractor was so simple that a boy could operate it and when ploughing it could turn so sharply that headlands would be practically non-existent'.

The MG 5 with a 600cc air-cooled petrol engine, still with a dry sump, replaced the MG 2 in 1948. In common with other petrol-engined tractors at the time it was possible to buy a conversion kit for running the engine on paraffin. The MG 5 had the same gearbox and steering system as the MG 2 but power take-off speed was increased to 700rpm. The instruction book pointed out that the MG 5 was designed to do two-horse work at

242. The ITW version of the MG 6 could be supplied with a 7hp air-cooled petrol or diesel engine.

two-horse speed (2mph) but Ransomes acknowledged the advance of mechanisation by increasing the top speed to 2¼mph. Distinguishing features of the MG 5 included a petrol tank located under the seat (it was on the side of the engine on the MG 2) and a metal cover over the engine.

A drawbar and a hand lift tool bar were standard and an optional hydraulic linkage kit for the MG 5 cost £89.15s. The Neville hydraulic lift attachment, designed in Australia, could be installed by the MG owner to provide finger tip control for the tool bar equipment.

Ransomes made a range of mounted and trailed implements for the MG tractor. Tillage equipment included cultivator tines, ridging bodies and hoes for use with the tool bar and also a range of ploughs, disc harrows, sprayers, seeder units, potato lifter and an earth scraper blade.

The Ransomes MG 6 made its debut at the 1953 Smithfield Show. Basically the same as its predecessors but with centrifugal clutch the reduction gears on the petrol or paraffin engine's output shaft were replaced by a 3 forward and 2 reverse gearbox with a top speed of 4mph. A hand-lift tool bar was standard but a newly designed optional hydraulic linkage with a power take-off driven pump added £52 to the price.

Industrial versions of the MG were announced in 1956. The industrial tractor (crawler model) or ITC had the same track design with optional rubber blocks which could be bolted to the track plates to prevent damage when working on hard surfaces. The Industrial Tractor Wheeled (ITW) on pneumatic tyres had heavy roller chains linking both wheels on each side to give a solid four-wheel drive arrangement. The ITW was steered in the same way as the standard MG tractor to give a system similar to that used for skid-steer loaders.

The reign of the little blue crawlers was nearing its end when the MG 40 was introduced in 1960. There was a choice of an 8hp overhead valve two-stroke diesel engine or a side-valve petrol or paraffin engine with an Amal carburettor and Wico magneto. The engines were started by hand and had a wet sump lubrication system with an oil pump and filter. The diesel engine, which used about 3 pints of fuel per hour, had an ignition wick for cold starting. A centrifugal clutch was still used for the MG 40. The transmission consisted of a 3 forward and 3 reverse gearbox, differential, spur gear reduction units and strengthened Roadless rubber-jointed tracks. The track running gear was improved and wider track guards were added in 1962 when Ransomes offered an optional fibreglass bonnet and track guard extensions.

The last Ransomes MG crawler was made in 1966 but during its long production run more than 15,000 motor cultivators, including 3,000 MG 2s, 5,000 MG 5s and MG 6s together with approximately 2,000 MG 40s, were made in Ipswich.

Ransomes, who had sold the agricultural machinery side of their business in 1987, re-entered the tractor market in 1997 with six

243. The de-luxe version of the MG 40 had a hinged fibreglass bonnet. Front wing extensions were fitted to protect the engine and tracks from overhanging branches in fruit orchards.

Japanese Shibaura four-wheel drive compact tractors with Ransomes' green paintwork. The term 'compact' suggests tractors in the 10–30hp bracket but the 3 and 4 cylinder diesel-engined Ransomes compacts ranged from the 18hp CT 318 to the largest 45hp CT 445 which had five more horse power than the New Fordson Major Diesel had under its bonnet when it was launched in 1951! A mechanical or hydrostatic transmission was used on the 18hp, 20hp, and 25hp tractors while the 33hp CT 333 HST had hydrostatic drive with a shuttle-shift transmission. A creep speed box was standard on the 38hp and 45hp models.

Ransomes became Textron Groundcare in 1998 and Iseki tractor distribution was added to the Ipswich operation.

244. Ransomes returned to the tractor market in 1997, after a break of 30 years, with the CT range of compact models from Japan.

RENAULT

Louis Renault established a car manufacturing business with eight men at Billancourt in France in 1898 and made his first tractor in 1919. The 30hp GP crawler, based on the Renault FT17 World War One battle tank, had a 4 cylinder water-cooled petrol engine with the radiator behind the engine and a 3 forward speed and reverse gearbox. Renault built more than 400 GP crawlers in 1919 and 1920 and a big increase in the price of petrol in France resulted in some of these tractors running on gas produced by a rear-mounted methane gas generator. The Renault HO, which appeared in 1921, was a wheeled version of the crawler with a 20hp engine. It had the same gearbox and a rear-mounted pulley which could be set to run in a clockwise or anti-clockwise direction.

The 1926 Renault PE was the French company's first purpose-built wheeled tractor with steel wheels or solid rubber tyres. Early models had the radiator behind the engine which was pleasant for the driver on frosty mornings. The radiator was moved to the front of the engine on the later PE2 version of the tractor. Landmarks in the ten-year production run of about 1,700 Renault PE tractors included the introduction of hydraulic linkage in 1931 and optional electric starting and pneumatic tyres in 1933.

The 50–55hp VI crawler, launched in 1932, was the first Renault tractor with a diesel engine and electric starter, although it was also made with a 40hp petrol engine. The VY 20–35hp diesel wheeled tractor appeared in 1933 but a period of severe economic crisis in France in the 1930s prompted the launch of the much cheaper Renault YL with 8hp and 15hp petrol engines which were made between 1934 and 1938. The 10–20hp AFV tractor made from 1938 to 1942 had an engine which ran on petrol or on alcohol. The AFVH gas-powered version was also made during the war years. Apart from a few prototype versions of the Renault 300 series little else occurred during the remaining years of the war.

245. Renault publicity material informed readers that the 22–30hp R 3042 was more powerful than the previous model but at the same time was just as economical to run.

In an effort to re-build the French tractor industry, the state took over the Renault factory in 1945. The 18–25hp 304 E and the gas-powered 304 H with 4 forward gears and reverse, pneumatic tyres and side-mounted pulley were made at Billancourt until 1948. The letter E indicated that the engine ran on 'essence' – the French for petrol. The R 3040 with a modified 304 engine and optional electric lighting launched in 1947 was the first model with the Renault deep orange paintwork. It was part of a major national effort to re-equip French farms and about 12 R 3040 tractors were made on each working day for the next two years. The prefix letter R was added to Renault tractor model numbers during the period of state ownership when the organisation was known as the RNUR (Régie Nationale des Usines Renault).

The R 3041 introduced in 1948 was a re-styled R 3040 with a bonnet, side panels and radiator grille over the same engine. The R 3041 was made for four years and had a 627rpm power take-off shaft, adjustable wheel track and a cable-operated lift for mounted implements. An optional hydraulic system was added in 1949. The R 3042 with similar styling to the previous model was made between 1949 and 1955. There was a choice of a petrol, paraffin or alcohol engine for the standard and vineyard versions of the tractor with optional hydraulic linkage.

Of the nearly 23,000 R 3042 tractors made, most had a petrol engine and approximately 80 per cent were sold with hydraulic linkage. The R 3042 had a 4 cylinder side-valve engine with coil or magneto ignition and electric starting, 4 forward gears and reverse with a top speed of 13½mph, independent foot brakes and a hand brake. There was an optional side-mounted belt pulley and a 627rpm power take-off shaft on the opposite side of the tractor could be used to drive a side-mounted cutter bar mower. The 552rpm rear power take-off shaft was also used to drive an optional bolt-on hydraulic linkage unit.

Even at this late date Renault sales literature quoted drawbar and belt horse power figures for the R 3042, which was described as a '22–30hp tractor which will run equally well on petrol, alcohol or paraffin'. Buyers were required to 'specify the fuel which will be employed' when ordering a tractor. The R 3042 brochure gave examples of its uses, which included 'the ploughing of 5 acres of medium soil, 10 inches in depth with a double plough in one day'.

The 32hp Renault R 7012 with a 3 cylinder Perkins engine and the 45hp R 7022 with a Hispano-Hercules diesel engine which appeared in 1951 were based on the petrol engined R 3042 tractor. Diesel tractors were about 50 per cent more expensive than petrol tractors in the early 1950s and French farmers were still buying this type of tractor when the R 3046 with an overhead-valve petrol engine replaced the R 3402 in 1954.

It was all change in 1956 when Renault launched the D (diesel) and E (petrol) series tractors. A heavy one-piece cast iron chassis had been used by Renault since 1945 but unitary construction was adopted for the D and E series. Renault opened a London office in the mid-1950s and the D series soon became popular with British farmers. However, fashions had changed in France and there was little demand for the Renault E 30 with a 30hp 4 cylinder water-cooled petrol engine or the improved E 31 which replaced it in 1957. The model numbers used for the D series denoted horse power. The D 22 had an air-cooled twin-cylinder MWM engine while a 3 cylinder water-cooled Perkins was used for the D 30 and the D 35 had a 3 cylinder air-cooled MWM power unit. The transmission was new with a two-stage clutch, a 6 forward speed and reverse gearbox or an optional 12 forward and 2 reverse unit and external drum brakes. The smaller D 16 was added in 1958 to compete with the Massey-Harris Pony and Farmall Cub. It had a twin-cylinder MWM air-cooled engine but was otherwise similar to its big brothers. All of the D series tractors had the same hydraulic system as the earlier R 3042.

Engine speed was increased from 1,700rpm to 2,000rpm in 1960 when the four D series tractors which had added horse power and also improved hydraulics became the Renault N series. The N 73, N 72, N 71 and N 70 model numbers appear to have little meaning – the 20hp N 73 was the smallest and the others had 25hp, 35hp and 40hp diesel engines.

The Renault Super 5 and Super 7 launched in 1962 were the first of a

246. The Renault D 35 had an air-cooled MWM engine.

new generation of the D series tractors. The Super 7 had a 42hp Perkins engine but the Super 5 had a 3 cylinder 35hp Renault water-cooled power unit which was the first diesel engine made by the French company since the late 1930s. Improved styling and more horse power were the main changes on the 46hp Super 7, the 42hp Super 6, the 30hp Super 3 and the 25hp Junior introduced in 1964. Most tractor makers launched new models at frequent intervals during the 1960s in an attempt to improve their sales figures. New colour schemes, changed model numbers and the latest mechanical gimmicks were all used to tempt their farmer customers.

Renault followed the trend with a new white radiator grille and the letter D for the D series was again added to the model number. The Renault Tracto-Control hydraulic system with draft and position control, implement float and optional double-acting spool valves appeared in 1965. A Selene front-wheel drive conversion kit for the Super 5D, Super 6D and Super 7D announced in 1966 was the last of the many changes to the D series which had been in production since 1956.

Renault passed the 50hp mark in 1963 when they launched the 55hp 385 with a 4 cylinder water-cooled Renault or air-cooled MWM engine. It was well advanced for its time with 5 forward gears and reverse, a 540/1,000rpm ground speed power take-off and two engine-mounted hydraulic pumps. One pump supplied oil to the three-point linkage, spool valves and hydraulic disc brakes while the second pump was used for the power steering system. Problems with leaks and burst pipes in the high pressure hydraulic circuit were solved with a model change and improved safety features in 1964. The MWM-engined 385 became the 385 Master 1 and the Renault-engined model was called the 385 Master 2. Both tractors were made until 1969.

247. The Super Series introduced in 1966 was the final version of the Renault D series diesel tractors originally launched ten years earlier. Miss France 1966 is in the driving seat.

Renault tractor production was moved to a new factory at Le Mans in 1967 and the 55hp Renault 86 and 88 with the engines used for the 385 Master tractors were launched in the same year. The MWM engine was used on the 86 and the Renault power unit on the 88, but the new tractors were quite different to the 385 with more angular styling, a twin-range 4 forward and reverse gearbox and the 385 Master hydraulic system was replaced with a less complicated unit.

A few four-wheel drive Renault 456 tractors with a 42hp 3 cylinder MWM engine and similar styling to the 86 and 88 were made between 1968 and 1971. A Selene front-wheel drive unit was used at first but later models had a Zetor front axle with a central drive shaft.

The 30–46hp Renault 53, 55, 56 and 57 diesel tractors and the 45hp petrol-engined 58 replaced the Super D series in 1968 but the days of petrol-engined tractors were coming to an end and the 58 was withdrawn one year later. Renault made their first VF narrow orchard and vineyard tractors in 1968. The four models included the 33hp 50 Vineyard which was only 890mm wide. About 18,000 VF tractors had been made when they were discontinued in 1977.

Renault's tractor operation was given its own identity when it became Renault Motoculture in 1969. The 70hp air-cooled Renault 94 and 80hp water-cooled Renault 96 with MWM engines announced in the same year to meet the growing demand for more power were made until 1973. Apart from a hand clutch lever for the 540/1,000rpm ground speed power take-off they were mechanically similar to the competition with power steering and hydraulic multi-plate disc brakes. The Super Comfort driver's platform was different however, with four rubber mounting blocks to isolate transmission vibration and an optional cab or roll bar.

Renault also met a local demand for medium-powered four-wheel drive tractors in 1972 when the Italian built 34hp, 45hp and 57hp Carraro models were sold in Renault livery as the 321-4, 451-4 and 571-4.

More changes in the early 1970s included an improved Tracto-Control hydraulic system, power steering becoming standard across the range and an optional trailer braking system being added to meet French road vehicle regulations. New models with 51–90hp MWM engines were introduced to meet the demand for still more power and four-wheel drive versions were added in 1971. The prefix '4' indicated that the tractor had either a ZF or a Zetor front axle and the four-wheel drive, 6 cylinder 90hp 4–98 tractor with hydrostatic steering was the most powerful Renault in the early 1970s.

The last Renault tractor with their own make diesel engine was discontinued on the launch of new models at the 1973 French SIMA agricultural show in Paris. Within a couple of years the Renault range included models in the 30–145hp bracket. The model number indicated engine horse power, the figure 4 denoted four-wheel drive and the letter S was used for tractors with a cab. For example, the Renault 651-4 S was a 65hp four-wheel drive tractor with a cab.

The Renault 301, 461, 551, 651 with MWM engines were launched in 1973. The two-wheel drive 301 with a twin-cylinder air-cooled engine and a 6 forward and reverse or 10 forward and 2 reverse gearbox was the only model without hydrostatic steering. The 461, 551 and 651 had 3 or 4 cylinder engines, a 3 range 4 speed gearbox with a shuttle reverser giving 12 gears in forward and reverse and optional Carraro front-wheel drive. The 751/751-4, 851/851-4, 951/951-4 and 1151-4 appeared in 1974 and the 6 cylinder turbocharged 1451-4 completed the range in 1975. The flagship 1451-4 had 15 forward and 6 reverse gears, power steering and safety cab with optional heating and air conditioning on an anti-vibration platform. The Renault

248. The Renault 751S was made between 1973 and 1978.

Automatic Blocamatic progressive diff-lock for the front axle was introduced in 1977 and, with increased horse power for the high range tractors, they were re-numbered the 781, 891, 981 and 1181. Some models were only made for three or four years but the 461, 551 and 651 survived until 1986, the 781 was discontinued in 1987 and the 891/891-4 remained in production until 1989.

Apart from a brief presence in the UK in the late 1950s there had been no official Renault Motoculture sales outlet in Britain since the first Renault wheeled tractor was made in 1921. A significant event for Renault in 1977 was the appointment of their first UK dealer at Thorne near Doncaster and the French company established their own premises in the same area in 1978. Renault Motoculture became Renault Agriculture in 1980 with a separate logo to distinguish tractor dealers from car and truck distributors. The company moved to Shipston-on-Stour in Warwickshire in 1981.

The new 'T' cab, which could be lifted clear of the transmission housing in less than an hour for repairs, was described as 'simply years ahead of its time' when the Renault TX series was launched in 1981. Three models with 103hp, 123hp and 135hp 6 cylinder air-cooled engines had a 12 forward and reverse synchromesh gearbox in three ranges, an optional creeper gearbox and hydraulic dry twin-disc brakes. The re-styled TX series were the first Renault tractors with optional front linkage and the new light orange colour scheme. The medium-powered TS range was launched in 1981 and 84hp and 93hp models were added to the TX series in 1982.

Computers designed to help conserve fuel and achieve maximum productivity were a new feature in the TX and TS cabs from 1983. Renault's Ecocontrol system recorded engine speed and fuel consumption was measured by a sensor in the exhaust manifold. This information was displayed by two needles on the Ecocontrol gauge and the engine ran at maximum efficiency when both needles were in the green zone. A low-line RS cab for tractors up to 93hp was introduced in 1984 for farms with buildings which were too low for the standard TS cab. Renault followed the example of some other tractor makers between 1984 and 1986 when they imported a range of Japanese Mitsubishi compact models which were sold in France.

The Renault LS tractors and the Perkins-engined SP models with an improved hydraulic pump, twin assister rams and new cabs appeared in 1986. Renault also introduced the ACET and TCE electronic systems for their high-powered models in the same year. The ACET system (Aid to Economical Tractor driving) was an improved Ecocontrol unit with a screen to display fuel consumption and indicate the most economical gear ratio and engine speed for the work in hand. TCE (Tractor Control Electronic) was Renault's version of electronic hydraulic linkage control and remote external switches on the rear mudguards were included in the package. The launch of the TX 16 tractors with a 16 forward and reverse transmission and a new range of fruit and vineyard tractors made by Carraro completed a busy year for Renault. The Hydrostable cab introduced in 1987 for tractors from the TX 110 upwards was designed to isolate the driver from harmful vibrations. The new cab had its origins in the Supercomfort driver's platform mounted on four rubber pads first seen in 1969.

The 83hp 90-34M and 90-34T Tracfor models with a standard specification and no optional extras appeared in France in 1988. The 70-34PX and 133-54TX were added in 1991.

Improved electronics led to the launch in 1989 of the Tractoradar system which used a radar sensor to monitor forward speed, calculate wheelslip, distance travelled and work done. The system could also be programmed to automatically reduce the working depth of a mounted implement when wheelslip exceeded a pre-set level.

The 165hp 175-54TZ was launched in 1990 to satisfy the continuing demand for even more horse power but less than 200 were made in a two-year production run. It had a turbocharged 6 cylinder MWM engine, a 24 forward and 8 reverse speed Steyr transmission and ACET computer system. The 24 forward and 8 reverse Tractoshift transmission with three change-under-load speeds engaged with hydraulic clutch packs in each forward gear was a new option for the TZ models from 1991.

Renault launched the 170hp 180-94TZ Multishift and re-introduced the 100hp 6 cylinder 106-54TL lightweight tractor to UK farmers in 1992. The Multi-shift 180-94TZ was the first Renault tractor to have a change-under-load transmission; the 27 forward and reverse speed unit was made by SAME Lamborghini Hurlimann. A 150hp TZ Multi-shift model was added in 1993. Multi-shift tractors did not sell in large numbers but they remained in production until the Ares 700 range was launched in 1997. The two- and four-wheel drive air-cooled 55hp 55-12B/55-14B introduced for the smaller farm in 1992 had a 12 forward and reverse gearbox with a top speed of 17mph.

The gold painted Renault 120-54 and 155-54TZ Nectra with MWM engines appeared in 1994 and the Tractorshift transmission, improved in the same year with clutchless direction changes, was re-named the Tractronic transmission.

The 54–83hp Renault Ceres tractors with sloping bonnets and two cab options were launched in 1993. The MWM engines and back axles came from the previous range but the 10 speed synchromesh gearbox and a reverse shuttle, front-wheel drive arrangement and cabs were new. Optional extras included a creep speed box and the Twinshift change-on-the move transmission with an electro-hydraulic splitter. Renault changed to John Deere engines in 1995 in preparation for new exhaust emission regulations. The Ceres range was also painted green and yellow and marketed by John Deere as the 3000 series.

The Cergos and Ares tractors made

249. The Renault LB agricultural range made by Carraro from 1988 was originally launched in France as a series of fruit tractors. The 52hp and 67hp models were introduced to British farmers in 1993 as the Herdsman range and the 76hp Herdsman was added in 1996.

their debut in 1997. The 75hp, 85hp and 95hp Cergos had a similar transmission system to the Ceres with optional Twinshift and creep speed gearboxes. The 4 cylinder 500 series and the 6 cylinder 600 and 700 series Ares were launched in eight power sizes between 85hp and 165hp. A 16 forward and reverse gearbox was standard on the 85hp, 95hp and 100hp tractors while the more powerful models had a 32 speed transmission. Three fruit tractors, three Ceres models, the 106-54TL and the 155-54TX completed the 1997 Renault range on the UK market.

250. The Renault Ares tractors were launched in 1997.

ROADLESS

Lt. Col. Philip Johnson, who founded Roadless Traction Ltd at Hounslow in Middlesex in 1919, spent World War One developing battle tanks. This experience was used to design half-tracks for commercial vehicles and by the early 1930s Roadless were making a full-track conversion for Fordson tractors. Many other makes of tractor, including Case, Massey-Harris and Marshall, were given the same treatment and the company also developed the rubber-jointed tracks used for small crawlers made by Bristol and Ransomes. Much of World War Two was spent in the production of tracked Fordson and Case tractors for military purposes. Some of them had a wheeled fore-carriage to give extra stability when used with a front-mounted winch or crane.

251. Roadless DG half-tracks were introduced for the E27N Fordson Major in 1945. A skeleton version of the tracks with spade lugs instead of the usual track plates was added in 1949.

With the war nearing its end, Roadless introduced the DG (Driven Girder) half-track for the Fordson Model N in 1944. The large footprint area of the DG track considerably increased tractive efficiency and within a couple of years half-tracks were available for Fordson E27N and other popular tractors. Production continued well into the 1950s with half-track conversions for various tractors including the New Fordson Major Diesel, Field Marshall, Massey-Harris 744D and Nuffield Universal.

252. Roadless made a tricycle-wheeled version of the Fordson Power Major for the American market.

Roadless returned to crawler conversions in 1950 with the Roadless Model E full track based on an E27N Fordson with a paraffin or Perkins P6 diesel engine. It was back to the drawing board in 1951 when the New Fordson Major superseded the E27N. Roadless also designed and built their own prototype crawler which they exhibited at the 1954 Royal Show but it was the Roadless J 17 crawler, based on the New Fordson Major, which went into production at Hounslow later that year. The tractor had an improved rubber-jointed track which was also used for the J 17 based on the Power Major and Super Major.

Crawler sales fell away as demand grew for the more versatile four-wheel drive tractor. Roadless Traction obtained a licence from Selene in Italy to make the Manuel four-wheel drive conversion kit

253. The Manuel-Roadless four-wheel drive Fordson Super Major advertised in 1961 cost £1,230.

for Fordson tractors. The Manuel-Roadless front-wheel drive version of the New Fordson Major was launched in 1956. The Roadless four-wheel drive system with a transfer box sandwiched against the gearbox, a propeller shaft and front axle differential were popular with farmers and Roadless were making four-wheel drive versions of Fordson Major and Dexta tractors well into the 1960s. It was also possible to buy a four-wheel drive conversion kit for existing tractors at a cost of about £500 (plus a £25 fitting charge). Roadless Traction widened their interests in 1963 with the introduction of the four-wheel drive International Harvester B 450 which they made for seven years. The company also made conversion kits for the International Harvester 614 and 634 while Manuel four-wheel drive conversions for Massey Ferguson 35 and 65 tractors were marketed by Robert Eden Ltd of London.

The Roadless Ploughmaster 6/4 with a Ford 6 cylinder industrial engine and Super Major transmission launched in 1963 was the first of many Ploughmaster tractors made over the next 20 years. New Roadless models were inevitably linked to changes made by the Ford Motor Co. The Ploughmaster 65 and 90 announced in 1965 were based on a Ford 5000 skid unit with optional Select-O-Speed. The 6 cylinder Ford engine used for the Roadless 6/4 was re-rated at 90hp for the more powerful Ploughmaster 90 and when a new 6 cylinder Ford power unit was introduced in 1966 this tractor became the Ploughmaster 95. Roadless also moved down the power range in 1966 when they launched the Ploughmaster 46 which was made in small numbers for six years. The Ploughmaster 46 was basically a 46hp Ford 3000 with a Selene four-wheel drive conversion.

The 80hp Ploughmaster 80, introduced in 1967, was a turbocharged version of the Ploughmaster 65 with an assister ram to increase the capacity of the hydraulic linkage. The Ploughmaster 80, which cost £2,165, was not popular and was withdrawn in 1968.

Roadless Traction announced their first equal-size four-wheel drive tractor in 1968. The Roadless 115 with many Ford-sourced components had a white bonnet over its 6 cylinder 115 gross hp Ford industrial engine. The specification included a strengthened Ford gearbox, heavy duty clutch and hydrostatic steering. Prompted by new farm safety regulations Roadless added Duncan safety cabs to their tractors in 1970.

Ford introduced a new and more powerful range of industrial engines in 1971, a year which proved busy at the Hounslow factory. The Roadless 120 and 94T were added to the range and new engines were used on the 115 and the Ploughmaster 95 which became the Roadless 95. The Roadless 120 was a 120 gross hp version of the 115 while the 94T was based on a 94hp Ford 7000 skid unit which had a new front axle with a diff-lock and planetary reduction gears. The Roadless 95 gave way to the 104hp Roadless 105 in 1975 and the new unequal-size wheeled tractor was also equipped with the new planetary front axle.

The introduction of the Ford 600 series in 1975 saw the arrival of the last new Ploughmaster model. The popular Ploughmaster 75 was superseded by the Ploughmaster 78, based on a Ford 6600 skid unit, and the turbocharged 97hp Ford 7600 was used for the Roadless 94T which replaced the Roadless 98 in the same year. The 6 cylinder 104hp Roadless 118, launched in 1976 toreplace the 105, was made on a small scale for about two years.

254. The Ploughmaster 75 replaced the Ploughmaster 65 when the Ford Force 5000 was introduced in 1968.

255. The Roadless 115 was launched in 1968.

Most of the major tractor manufacturers were producing their own four-wheel drive models by the late 1970s and time was running out for Roadless and their competitors. The Ploughmaster 78 and 98 together with the Roadless 118 and 120 were still being made in 1980 when Roadless Traction Ltd moved to Sawbridgeworth in Hertfordshire. The 780 and 980, based on the Ford 6600 and turbocharged 7600 skid units launched that year, were to be the last new models made by the company. They had equal-size wheels and a new design front axle with an improved turning circle. Very few of these tractors were sold so Roadless turned their attention to specialist articulated tractors, including the hydrostatic drive Logmaster for forestry work.

Roadless made one final attempt to improve the situation when Ford launched the 10 series tractors. The two-wheel drive 6/2 launched at the 1981 Smithfield Show with a 6 cylinder 125hp Ford engine, Dual Power 16 forward and 4 reverse transmission and two-speed power take-off was quite a change for Roadless. The Ford 10 series was also used for the more powerful Roadless 78S, 98S, 118S and 120S but most farmers preferred to buy a Ford four-wheel drive tractor.

Roadless Traction were making two- and four-wheel drive Teleshift mechanical handlers with telescopic booms at Sawbridgeworth in 1982 for RWC at Ledbury but Roadless was liquidated in 1983 and the business was bought by L.F. Jewell Ltd. The new owners, who were Ford tractor dealers in Somerset, built a few Jewelltrac 103 and 120 tractors which cost £23,000 and £25,000 respectively and the new Jewelltrac 116 based on the Ford 8210 was sold for industrial purposes.

256. The Roadless 98 K series tractor, made between 1975 and 1982, had a 4 cylinder turbocharged engine and a 16 forward and 4 reverse gearbox.

ROLLO

Scottish engineer and part-time crofter John Rollo designed the Croftmaster tractor which, with components made in different parts of the Scottish highlands, was assembled at Bonnybridge between 1954 and 1960. Engine options included a 3hp or 5hp BSA, or a 5hp Villiers. Later versions of the Rollo with a 9hp Briggs & Stratton engine and parking brakes were more streamlined and had a cushioned seat. The more powerful engines were recommended for heavy work.

The Croftmaster was roller chain driven through a hand-lever operated multi-plate clutch and a 3 forward and reverse gearbox with a top speed of 6mph. A chain drive was used to transmit power from the gearbox to the differential and separate chains took the power to the rear wheels. A pedal-operated expanding shoe brake on the differential shaft was backed up with a hand lever used 'when it was necessary, or advisable, to stop in a hurry'.

257. The Rollo Croftmaster was 'designed by a crofter for crofters'. The 3hp tractor with a hand-pump operated hydraulic linkage cost £315 in 1957. An optional 5hp engine added an extra £13 to the bill.

A tool bar carried on a parallel linkage was raised with a hand-lever operated hydraulic pump supplied with oil from a separate reservoir. The makers claimed that a single furrow plough could be raised well clear of the ground with six to eight strokes of the pump lever. The implement was lowered by opening a tap which released oil from the lift cylinder and returned it to the reservoir.

RUSSELL

258. The Russell 3D self-propelled toolbar.

The 20hp 3D self-propelled tool carrier was introduced by Russells of Kirbymoorside in Yorkshire in the late 1970s. It followed the basic design of the David Brown 2D with a rear-mounted 2 cylinder air-cooled diesel engine with an electric starter. The tractor had hydrostatic motors in the rear wheels which were supplied with oil by a variable displacement pump. The motors were controlled with a single lever which gave an infinitely variable speed of up to 9mph in both directions. Another lever was used to control the hydraulic ram for the mid-mounted tool bar and a third raised and lowered the optional rear wheel mark eradicator tines. The tractor had 48–76 inch wheel track adjustment, disc brakes and a parking brake. Tool bar attachments included cultivator tines, hoe blades and seeder units and the 3D which cost £4,500 in 1979 was still available at a similar price in 1986.

SAME

Francesco Cassani made a diesel-powered tractor with a twin-cylinder water-cooled engine in 1928 and 40hp Cassani tractors with this type of engine were being used by Italian farmers in the mid-1930s. Cassani had also designed and built engines for aircraft, boats and lorries before he established a company called Societa Anonima Motori Endotermici in 1942. The initial letters which form SAME (pronounced Sammy) was the name used in 1948 for a self-propelled, tricycle-wheeled cutter bar mower with a single-cylinder air-cooled petrol engine, driving seat and steering wheel. The mowing machine could also be used with other farm implements or to drive an electricity generator.

The more conventional SAME 4R/20 four-wheeled tractor came next and the four-wheel drive DA 25DT introduced in 1952 was Francesco Cassani's first air-cooled full diesel-engined tractor. Several models were made in the 1950s. They included two- and four-wheel drive versions of the DA 25 and DA 38 (DT was added to indicate four-wheel drive), the 3 cylinder DA 47 Supercassani and the 21hp Sametto orchard tractor. The Sametto had a single-cylinder air-cooled diesel engine, a creep speed gearbox, diff-lock and a four speed power take-off with ground speed and optional four-wheel drive.

The 1958 twin-cylinder SAME 340 was the first model with Cassani's new Automatic Linkage Control system with lower link sensing. Within a couple of years the linkage was also available for the 42hp and 62hp 240 and 360 tractors. Sales literature for the SAME 240 described the automatic linkage control as a system which would ' keep the working depth unchanged of all implements including half-carried types as well as drawn ones which no other device could achieve'. It was also explained that the 240 was comfortable to drive with a windshield, a hydraulic shock absorber for the seat and the new endometer (hourmeter) was an 'absolute novelty, the magic indicator of your tractor'.

259. A twin-cylinder air-cooled engine, 6 forward speeds and reverse, independent and ground speed power take-off and automatic hydraulic linkage control were features of the two- and four-wheel drive SAME 240.

The 82hp 480 with a 4 cylinder air-cooled diesel engine was the most powerful SAME tractor in 1960. Features included hand and foot throttles, a 5 forward and reverse gearbox with a top speed of 15½mph and a power take-off shaft with ground speed. The power shaft turned at 690rpm with the engine set to run at 1,700rpm. Optional extras included four-wheel drive and a belt pulley attachment for the power take-off.

The Italian tractors were not available in Britain until 1964 when Cornish and Lloyds of Bury St Edmunds, Suffolk, imported the four-wheel drive SAME Leone 70 and Centauro to meet East Anglian farmers' need of a tractor with a hydraulic system with the capacity to lift a heavy reversible plough. The 67hp Leone with twin vertical exhaust pipes had an air-cooled V4 direct injection engine, 8 forward and 4 reverse gears and disc brakes and the 55hp Centauro with a V4 diesel engine had a similar gearbox. The Leone 70 with a set of front end weights cost £1,995 in 1968 and the Centauro was £1,755. A.C. Bamlett Ltd at Thirsk in Yorkshire became the sole UK importer for SAME tractors in 1969.

SAME were making around 17,000 tractors a year in the early 1970s and there was further growth in 1972 when Lamborghini joined the SAME group. The Lamborghini tractors kept their separate identity and A.C. Bamlett remained the SAME concessionaire for the UK. The 1974 SAME range included the four-wheel drive 56hp Minitauro 60, the 78hp Saturno 80 and the 98hp Drago. They had 3, 4 and 6 cylinder air-cooled engines with dual clutches and an 8 forward and 4 reverse gearbox. The UK range was extended to five models in the 56–126hp bracket when the Tiger and Buffalo with flat floor cabs appeared at the 1976 Smithfield Show. The 126hp 6 cylinder Buffalo which cost around £15,000 had telescopic ends on the lower lift arms and

260. The windshield on the 480 was a feature of SAME tractors in the late 1950s and early 1960s.

261. The SAME Leone had a central clutch-less drive shaft to the front axle. Some of these tractors had a downswept exhaust system while others had twin vertical exhaust pipes.

dual-speed independent power take-off. The 5 cylinder 100hp Tiger with hydrostatic steering, dual-speed power shaft and a price tag of about £13,000 was advertised as 'the big five with a hundred smooth horses'.

SAME added the Swiss-based Hurlimann company to the group in 1977 and the SAME-Lamborghini-Hurlimann name was adopted in 1978. Sametrac Ltd at Thirsk became the UK distributors of SAME tractors in the same year. The 82hp Leopard 85E (Export) with an air-/oil-cooled engine appeared in 1979. It had a 12 forward and 3 reverse synchromesh gearbox, hydrostatic steering and oil-immersed brakes. The Leopard 85E could also be supplied with a 24 forward and 6 reverse or 20 forward and 5 reverse transmission. SAME (UK) Ltd took over the control of marketing SAME, Lamborghini and Hurlimann tractors in the UK in 1980.

SAME tractors on sale in Britain in the early 1980s included two- and four-wheel drive versions of the Taurus 60, Leopard 85, Jaguar 95, Tiger Six 105 and the Buffalo 130 with lower link sensing and oil-immersed hydraulic brakes. The figures after the model name indicated the approximate horse power of their air-cooled engines. The four-wheel drive Hercules 160 was the largest tractor yet made by SAME. It was introduced to British farmers in 1981 alongside the Centauro 70, Centurion 75 and Trident 130. The turbocharged and intercooled Hercules, which cost £26,545, had an air-conditioned flat floor cab and lower link sensing hydraulics with SAME's Automatic Control Unit (ACU). Other features included separate 540rpm and 1,000rpm power take-off shafts and a diff-lock which remained engaged while travelling in a straight line and automatically disengaged when the tractor changed direction. The two- and four-wheel drive Centauro 70 and Centurion 75 with air-cooled 68hp 4 cylinder engines had a 12 forward and reverse gearbox, lower link sensing and hydraulic brakes. The 125hp four-wheel drive Trident 130 which replaced the Buffalo had a 12 speed gearbox, epicyclic reduction gears on both axles and the very latest cab with air-conditioning, tinted glass and an adjustable steering column.

262. The two- and four-wheel drive turbocharged SAME Leopard 90 with 24 forward gears was launched in 1982.

The turbocharged 88hp Leopard 90 joined the Leopard 85 in 1982 when SAME made more than 25,000 tractors and held sixth place in the manufacturer's league table. The Galaxy and the Laser 110, 130 and 150 models with a new orange, grey and white colour scheme were launched in 1983. The 165hp Galaxy, which replaced the Hercules, and the new 6 cylinder 110hp, 125hp and 145hp Lasers had 24 forward and 12 reverse synchromesh gearboxes, open centre hydraulics with lower link sensing and a fully air-conditioned cab.

New models and the introduction of some Lamborghini features on SAME tractors were the main events in 1984. Tractors over 60hp had pedal-operated hydraulic trailer brakes and oil-immersed front disc brakes became standard on models over 110hp. The 1984 UK price

263. The styling, colour scheme, engine, front axle and load sensing hydraulic linkage were new features on the SAME S 100.

list included the two- and four-wheel drive Condor 55, Minitaurus 60 fruit tractor, Taurus 60, Centauro 70, Centurion 75, Leopard 90 and Jaguar 100. The S 110 and the four-wheel drive S 130, S 150 and S 170 completed the list. The turbocharged 4 cylinder 88hp S 90 and 5 cylinder 98hp S 100 with 24 forward and 12 reverse speeds and open centre, lower link sensing hydraulics were added later in the year.

SAME (UK) Ltd moved to Barby near Rugby in 1986 when, in common with other manufacturers, about 80 per cent of their tractors were sold with four-wheel drive. With the move completed the company became SAME-Lamborghini (UK) Ltd and consequently a range of water-cooled Lamborghini tractors was introduced to British farmers. The main differences between the two makes were their colour schemes and engine cooling systems. 'Air neither freezes or boils' was a SAME advertising slogan used at the time for their air-/oil-cooled engines with an oil spray system to cool the underside of the pistons.

SAME's Synchro-power electro-hydraulic control system replaced the pedals previously used to operate the diff-lock, four-wheel drive and four-speed economy power take-off on their medium-power tractors, including the 60–90hp Explorer II range introduced at the 1988 Smithfield Show. The 'comfortable, climatised

264. The SAME Antares 130 launched in 1990 had an electronic engine governor.

operational station' (cab) on the 6 cylinder Antares 110 and 130 launched in 1990 had the very latest in computerised systems, including an electronic engine speed regulator (governor), radar-operated wheelslip control and a performance monitor.

The 153hp Titan 160 and the Explorer II models with a 12 speed synchromesh reverse shuttle gearbox and low-profile cab for stock farmers appeared in 1991. The Titan 160's electronically controlled powershift transmission, hydraulic linkage and front-wheel drive engagement was also used on the new 160hp Lamborghini Racing and 132hp Hurlimann H-6135 Elite.

The 1992 Fruetto II orchard tractor took electronic controls a stage further: the 75hp 4 cylinder air-/oil-cooled diesel had a computerised engine management system instead of the usual mechanical governor to give more accurate control of engine speed for spraying and similar work. The SAME Solaris 25, 35 and 40 four-wheel drive compact tractors made by Zetor were also sold in Lamborghini livery. The 25hp, 33hp and 40hp Mitsubishi engines had an anti-start security device to deter tractor thieves. The Solaris range had a 12 speed synchromesh gearbox with a reverse shuttle lever on the steering column, load sensing power steering and a 3 speed independent power take-off.

More activity in 1994 saw the introduction of the Titan with a 27 speed electronic powershift transmission and the 110 and 130hp Antares with a 36 speed shuttle transmission. A Mk II electronic engine management system which the driver could use to pre-programme engine speed for working and headland cycles was a new feature on the Antares models. The 80–100hp SAME Silver models with the choice of electronic controls or a more basic control system for stock farms made their debut at the 1994 Smithfield Show. Publicity material explained that the '21st century cab gave easy access to a comfortable working environment and an optional bionic arm would turn the driver into a pilot '.

The SAME-Lamborghini-Hurlimann group acquired Deutz-Fahr in 1995. Watveare Ltd at Westbury in Wiltshire continued to distribute the German tractors in Britain until SAME Deutz-Fahr (UK) established Deutz-Fahr (GB) as a separate company at Barby in 1997. Other developments in that year included the introduction of a hydrostatic transmission for the Solaris, optional automatic APS transmission for the Titan and Antares and an improved transmission for the Silver range.

The Titan 145, 160 and 190 APS automatic transmission continually adjusted tractor speed to suit soil conditions and the Agroshift system on the Antares II enabled the driver to make three clutchless changes in each gear – giving 54 speeds in both directions. The Directronic electro-hydraulic control for the Silver range transmission had two multi-plate hydraulic clutch packs which simplified repetitive shuttle operation. One clutch pack controlled forward travel and the other provided reverse drive through an epicyclic unit. A built-in micro-processor carried out a diagnostic check of the Directronic system every time the driver started the engine. The 60–85hp Golden Range vineyard and compact tractors were launched in 1997 to celebrate 70 years of SAME tractor production. A range of almost sixty new models was introduced by SAME Deutz-Fahr during the next 18 months and the Rubin 120, 135 and 150 were added in time for the 1998 Smithfield Show. The model numbers indicated the horse power of the 6 cylinder liquid-cooled engines. Other features shared with three new Lamborghini Champion models included an oil-immersed multi-disc clutch, an 18 forward and reverse powershift transmission and a cab with a car-like interior.

265. The SAME Silver range was launched at the 1994 Smithfield Show.

SCHLUTER

Small and medium-sized diesel engines were made by Anton Schluter in his Munich factory several years before he built the DZM 14 tractor with a single-cylinder four-stroke engine in 1937. Single- and twin-cylinder 15hp and 25hp models with a 4 forward and reverse gearbox were added in 1938 and a few gas-powered tractors were made during the war period. Serious production did not re-start until 1949 when 1 and 2 cylinder 15hp and 25hp engines were used for the 5 forward speed Schluter DS 15 and DS 25 with 7 forward gears. A 3 cylinder 45hp model with 6 forward speeds and reverse, live power take-off and hydraulics was added in 1959. Engine power had moved into the 24–80hp bracket in the early 1960s with the Schluter 'Big Four' and three Allrad models. The Schluter 'Big Four' consisted of the two- and four-wheel drive S650/S650V and S900/S900V. Mid-1960s sales literature described them as thoroughly modern tractors with high-speed multi-cylinder engines, a 12 speed column gear change, fully independent power take-off and armchair comfort for the driver. The leaflet continued, 'We saw to it that the de-luxe Schluter farmer's seat was not only the finest example of comfortable tractor seats available but that it also formed an elegant part of all Schluter tractors – this is what makes them so special.' The fully upholstered seat with parallel spring suspension and a hydraulic damper was said to help 'ensure a reduction in spinal problems and drivers would feel relaxed and comfortable'. There were levelling boxes on both hydraulic linkage lift rods and power steering so light that the tractor could be 'steered with one finger even on the most difficult terrain'. Sales literature also explained that sophisticated technical extras and modern armchair comfort had been added to the 'Bear Strength' of their tractors and concluded ' Schluter builds tractors for those discerning farmers for whom only the best is good enough.'

Reco-Schlutrac, a subsidiary of Rustons Engineering Co Ltd at Huntingdon, chose the 1978 Power in Action event in Suffolk for the first public demonstration of the 160hp four-wheel drive Schluter Super E 7800TV with unequal-size wheels and a £22,060 price tag. Several models, including 80hp and 95hp two- and

266. Schluter tractors were sold in the UK by Rustons Engineering Co in the late 1960s.

four-wheel drive 'compact' tractors with 'Hydromatic' fluid clutches and a Super-silent cab, were on display at the 1980 and 1981 Smithfield Shows. Described as the 'cost savers' the Schluter range had low speed, long stroke engines 'hand built for longer life' and the cab was tilted with a hydraulic ram for easy servicing. Ruston Engineering's catalogue entry for the 1982 Smithfield Show included 'a range of high quality Schluter tractors from 80 to 240hp'. Hand-built in small production runs, the 240hp Super 2500VL had a hydraulically tilted cab and a hydromatic clutch designed to reduce wear in the transmission system. Schluter tractors were imported until 1984 but very few of them were sold to British farmers.

Schluter introduced a prototype high speed systems tractor in a joint venture with Claas. Called the Euro Trac it made its debut at the 1990 Agritechnica Show in Germany. Eight models of the Euro Trac in the 80–190hp bracket were planned and it was reported in the farming press that fifty were to be available for sale in 1991. The engine was located below and behind the high level centrally mounted cab with reversible controls for bi-directional operation and it could be tilted hydraulically for engine maintenance purposes. The four-wheel drive Euro Trac with equal-size wheels was designed for front- and rear-mounted equipment and provision was made to vary the tractor's weight distribution with a 1.3 tonne metal ballast weight which could be moved backwards and forwards hydraulically. Little more was heard of the Eurotrac.

267. Claas and Schluter introduced the Euro Trac systems tractor in 1990.

SELENE

The Italian Selene SAS company was a pioneer of four-wheel drive conversions for farm tractors. Early examples of these conversions made under the Manuel trade name were imported in the early 1950s for the Ferguson TE 20 by Robert Eden & Co of New Audley Street, London. Drive was taken from a transfer box mounted on power take-off via a propeller shaft to the front axle. Ground speed power take-off was used to drive the front wheels and the power shaft, which was extended through the transfer box, was only available to drive an implement at 540rpm with the front-wheel drive disengaged. A few Ferguson FE 35s and Mk I 65s were supplied by Robert Eden with the ground speed power take-off driven Selene conversion and the same design was still in production when the MF 135, 165 and 175 were launched in 1964.

Meanwhile, an alternative design of front-wheel drive for Fordson tractors had appeared in 1951. A transfer box was sandwiched between the gearbox and the rear axle housing and a propeller shaft transmitted power to the front axle. Selene used this design to convert a few Perkins-engined E27N Fordson Majors to four-wheel drive and then launched a similar unit for the New Fordson Major which Roadless Traction introduced to British farmers in 1955.

Following negotiations with Selene, the first Manuel-Roadless conversion kits were built under licence at Hounslow in 1956, initially for the New Fordson Major and at a later stage for the Power Major, Super Major, Dexta and Super Dexta.

Selene power take-off driven front-wheel drive conversion kits were still available for Massey Ferguson tractors in the early 1960s but not being able to use the power shaft was a serious disadvantage. Robert Eden & Co designed an improved sandwich type transfer box which left the power take-off shaft free for other work. A new company called Four Wheel Traction Ltd, also at New Audley Street in London, was established to manufacture the modified front-wheel drive conversion for Massey Ferguson tractors which made its debut at the 1969 Royal Show.

Selene also made front-wheel drive conversions for other tractors, including the Ford 1000 series tractors made from 1964 at Basildon. Selene SAS were acquired by Schindler in the late 1970s. The new owners had been making front-wheel drive conversions in Switzerland since 1965 and they were sold in the UK by Farm Tractor Drives from 1977 until production ceased in the mid-1980s.

268. This Manuel four-wheel drive conversion for the Ferguson TE 20 was made by Selene SAS of Turin, Italy.

SINGER

Singer Motors bought the manufacturing rights for the four-wheeled OTA Monarch Mk III tractor from Oak Tree Appliances in 1953. Production was moved to Birmingham, England, and Singer took over the marketing of the re-named Singer Monarch Mk III. An improved Monarch Mk IV appeared in 1955, the more obvious changes were a new orange colour scheme and a standard category I three-point linkage which made it possible to use a wide range of implements with the tractor. Singer Motors became part of the Rootes Group in 1956 and after approximately 1,000 Monarch tractors had been built over a period of seven years the last few were made that year.

269. The Singer Monarch, described in sales literature as the tractor that 'sets a new record in economical and efficient working' used approximately half a gallon of fuel per hour.

SKID UNITS

Some manufacturers used a complete tractor or a skid unit to provide the power for self-propelled farm equipment. Tractors supplied without wheels to implement manufacturers and delivered on a wooden pallet or skid became known as skid units. The Howard Dungledozer, used to clean out stock yards and built around a Fordson Standard tractor on Rotaped tracks, was an early example of this idea.

A Farmall M was used for the American International Harvester HM-1 sugar beet harvester made in the mid-1940s and the Shotbolt potato harvester was built around the Nuffield Universal tractor. Claas, Dechentreiter, Ferguson, JF and other companies wrapped combine harvesters around various makes of tractor. It was claimed that the combine unit could be attached or removed in a few hours.

Peter Standen, Catchpole Engineering Co and John Salmon used a tractor skid unit for their one- and two-row self-propelled sugar beet harvesters made in the 1960s and 1970s. The tractor was often provided by the farmer who sometimes took the trouble to take it off the harvester at the end of the season and use it for other work.

270. The Howard Dungledozer was built around a Fordson tractor in the early 1940s. It could load between 12 and 25 tons of manure per hour and the makers suggested higher work rates were possible if 'at least 3 trailers or 6 carts' were available. (Reproduced by permission of Silsoe College Engineering Society, who restored this machine.)

271. The tractor unit on the Standen Crophopper could be removed and used for other work at the end of the hoeing season.

STEIGER

The Steiger tractor took its name from the farmer/inventor who made an articulated tractor on his North Dakota farm in the early 1960s. Within a few years production had moved to Fargo, a city in the state. The Steiger 1250, 1700 and 2200 made in 1966 had General Motors diesel engines, shift-on-the-move transmissions, power steering and a heavy duty drawbar but the standard specification did not include a power take-off and hydraulic linkage.

The four-wheel drive lime green tractors up to 525hp were given big cat names such as Puma, Bearcat, Cougar, Panther, Lion and Tiger with each name devoted to a specific horse power range. Some Steiger models, including the Cougar ST 251, the Panther ST 310 and the Panther ST 350, were sold in the UK in the late 1970s by Offchurch Tractors Ltd of Leamington Spa. They had turbocharged Cummins 250hp, 310hp and 350hp engines respectively, 20 forward and 4 reverse gears, an air-conditioned cab and optional category III hydraulic linkage.

Turbocharged Caterpillar 270hp and 325hp engines provided the power for the mid-1970s Cougar ST 270 and Panther ST 325. The Cougar PT 270, Panther PT 350 and the 225hp Bearcat PT 225 (also with a 6 cylinder Caterpillar engine) had the added advantage of a hydrostatically driven and electronically controlled power take-off. The shaft was protected with an automatic overload shut-down and a 20ft long remote cable was provided for emergency control when the driver wasn't in the cab.

Giant four-wheel drive tractors in the 200–300hp bracket were becoming fashionable in the mid-1970s. The Ford FW 30 introduced to British farmers in 1978 was a 265hp Steiger with a Ford blue colour scheme. The 335hp Steiger was sold in the UK as the Ford FW 60 but the FW 20 and the FW 40 versions of 210hp and 295hp Steigers did not cross the Atlantic.

Steiger Tractor Inc was bought by Case IH in 1986 and from that time the lime green tractors were sold in Case IH livery. The Steiger name re-appeared on the four-wheel drive tractors when the articulated Case IH Steiger 9300 series was introduced to UK farmers in 1996. The rubber-tracked Quadtrac version (plate 44) with an independently suspended track at each corner was added to the Steiger range Case IH tractors in 1997.

272. The articulated Steiger Panther ST 310 made by Steiger Tractor Inc had a turbocharged and after-cooled 6 cylinder Cummins engine. The horn and windshield washer were optional extras!

STEYR

A weapons manufacturing business was established in the Austrian town of Steyr in 1864. Cars, trucks and motor-cycles were added to the product range in the late 1890s and the first tractors were made in 1915. Steyr forged a link with Daimler in Austria and from 1934 they were supplying engines to the Daimler factory in Germany.

Steyr showed little interest in tractor production before 1947 when they became part of the Steyr-Daimler-Puch organisation. Water-cooled four-stroke diesel Steyr truck engines were used for the first post-war Steyr tractors which had a rather old-fashioned rounded appearance. Regular and high-clearance versions of the Steyr 80 Junior had a 15hp single-cylinder engine, a 4 forward speed and reverse gearbox and power take-off. A rear-mounted belt pulley and hydraulic linkage were optional. The Steyr 180 with a 30hp twin-cylinder diesel engine and 5 forward gears and reverse was sold in considerable numbers in Austria and other continental countries. With a top speed of 15mph and leaf spring suspension on the front axle it was considered an ideal tractor for road transport work.

More powerful models had appeared by 1952. They included the 3 cylinder 45hp Steyr 185 with 6 or 9 forward and 2 reverse gears and the 4 cylinder 60hp Steyr 280 with 7 forward and 2 reverse gears. The 185A with a 55hp engine and the 68hp 280A were added in the mid-1950s. The 280A was still in production in 1967.

The Steyr 180, 190, 280 and 290 were made in the early and mid-1960s and special Jubilee versions were made in 1964 to celebrate Steyr's centenary year. Steyr-Daimler-Puch established a depot at Nottingham in 1967 and the Steyr Plus series launched the same year were the first Steyr tractors sold in the UK. There were six basic models which increased to fourteen when four-wheel drive and special versions were taken into account. A water-cooled direct-injection engine with a heater plug in each cylinder for cold starting and a 'frost proof maintenance free radiator with long life filling' were used across the range. The Steyr-Plus 86ST, 430, 540 and 650 had 1, 2, 3 and 4 cylinder engines rated at 18hp, 33hp, 44hp, and 57hp respectively. The 6 cylinder 77hp and 100hp Steyr-Plus 870 and 1090 had a 12 forward and 6 reverse synchromesh gearbox and a two-speed power take-off. The power take-off specifications indicated that at an engine speed of 2,400rpm the shaft ran at 612rpm and 1,067rpm on the 870 and at 673rpm and 1,126rpm on the Steyr 1090. The letter 'a' after the model number denoted four-wheel drive and some of the more powerful Steyr-Plus models, including the 870a and 1090a were available in this format.

273. Live hydraulics with an engine-mounted pump and a 540/1,000 ground speed power take-off were standard features of the 57hp Steyr-Plus 650 introduced in 1967. It was one of the first Steyr tractors sold in the UK.

Sales literature pointed out that the Steyr 'comfort seat left absolutely nothing to be desired and could be adjusted without tools in accordance with the weight of the driver' and the 'hydraulic shock absorber and excellent spring of the seat shielded the body of the driver from unpleasant jolts'.

The 4 cylinder 60hp 760/760a and 6 cylinder 98hp 1100/1100a appeared in the early 1970s. The 1973 Steyr range included six tractors from the 40hp 540 to the new two- and four-wheel drive Steyr 1100/1100a with 12 forward and 6 reverse gears and independent power take-off.

Steyr-Daimler-Puch joined the big tractor league in 1974 when they launched the two- and four-wheel drive Steyr 1200 and the four-wheel drive Steyr 1400a with turbocharged 6 cylinder water-cooled engines and lower link sensing hydraulics. The 155 gross hp 1400a had a 12 forward speed synchro-mesh gearbox with an optional change-under-load transmission which gave a 32 per cent speed reduction in each gear. An optional creep speed box increased the gear range to 36 forward and 16 reverse ratios. Other features included a hydraulically operated diff-lock on both axles and a 1,000rpm power take-off shaft rated at 130hp. The 135hp Steyr 1200/1200a had the same 12 forward and 6 reverse transmission as the 1100/1100a, hydraulic brakes on all driven wheels and live power take-off with ground speed.

The 760 was the only Steyr model listed in the 1976 Green Book; the 66 SAE hp tractor had an 8 speed gearbox with a reversing mechanism to give four speeds in each direction in the field range and four more for road work. The 760 had manual steering, shoe brakes and independent hydraulic linkage.

W. Bridgeman & Son at Newbury in Berkshire were importing Steyr tractors in 1977 and some of them were exhibited at that year's Smithfield Show. The red and white Steyr 545, 760, 980, 1100 and 1400a had 45–140hp water-cooled direct injection engines. The improved 760 had the widest gear range with 16 forward and 8 reverse speeds and the 1400a had the least with a 12 forward and 4 reverse gearbox. The 8000 series, including the four-wheel drive 8100a and 8140a, were imported by Bridgeman & Son in 1978 and 1979 but they changed their allegiance to Hurlimann in 1980 and so the Austrian tractors were no longer available in the UK although Bexwell Tractors at Downham Market in Norfolk, who distributed Steyr tractors in Britain for a while in the mid-1980s, were importing 70–150hp four-wheel drive Steyr tractors with a 16, 18 or 36 forward speed gearbox.

Another chapter in Steyr's history in the UK began in 1989 when Steyr-Daimler-Puch and Marshall Tractors established Marshall-Daimler Ltd at Scunthorpe. The new company introduced the Steyr 8000 range with 64–150hp engines which were sold as the Marshall D series in gold and black livery (plate 188). The 56hp, 64hp and 72hp Marshall S series with low-profile cabs introduced in 1990 were also made by Steyr. However, there was a marked decline in UK tractor sales in the early 1990s and the Marshall-Steyr partnership ended early in 1991.

The Austrian tractors with their familiar red and white paintwork re-appeared later that year when Morris, Corfield & Co at Much Wenlock in Shropshire were appointed Steyr distributors. Three 64–80hp two- and four-wheel drive tractors and four

274. The Steyr 970a had a 70hp turbocharged engine. The tractor could, on request, be supplied with the gear lever on the right-hand side of the seat.

275. The driving seat in the Steyr 9320a could be turned through 180 degrees and a multi-function lever was used to control the infinitely variable forward and reverse hydrostatic transmission, engine speed, and so on.

95–150hp four-wheel drive models were available in time for the 1991 Smithfield Show. Publicity material explained that the comprehensively equipped and technologically advanced tractors lived up to Steyr's 'quality without compromise' motto. The Steyr 900 series launched in 1992 had environmentally friendly engines which could run on rape seed oil and biological oils could be used for the hydraulic system while a catalytic converter was available at extra cost. The five 42–70hp 900 series with 16 forward and 8 reverse gears had a cab low enough to 'fit into the smallest barn'.

The Steyr 9000 series with 78hp, 86hp and 94hp 4 cylinder MWM engines replaced the 8000 series in 1993. Mechanical or optional electronic hydraulic linkage control could be specified and a plastic container incorporated in the system to collect spillages allowed the driver to disconnect the external hydraulic couplings while they were under pressure. Gearbox and hydraulic system oil level sight tubes were a novel feature on the new tractors.

The two- and four-wheel drive Multi-trac range, based on the 9000 series, were introduced in 1994. The M 968, M 975 and M 9083 had 68hp, 75hp and 83hp turbocharged engines under steep sloping bonnets. A shuttle transmission or optional power shift gearbox and an integrated front power take-off and hydraulic linkage were features of the Steyr Multi-trac. The 94hp M 9094 was added later that year. The 320hp 9320a Power Trac, also announced in 1994, was the flagship of the Steyr range. It had a hydrostatic transmission combined with a conventional four speed gearbox and a reversible driving position which made the four-wheel drive tractor equally efficient in both directions.

The Steyr 9100 range was launched in 1996. The 9105a, 9115a, 9125a and 9145a model numbers denoted horse power. These four-wheel drive tractors had push button controls for the 24 forward and reverse speed powershift transmission, hydraulic linkage and hydraulic spool valves. An optional power take-off management system could be used to automatically stop or start the power shaft when raising or lowering the hydraulic linkage.

Case IH acquired Steyr Landmaschintechnic in 1996 but the Austrian tractors were still imported by Morris Corfield and sold through their existing UK dealers. The 94hp, 16 speed Case CS 94 and the 150hp CS 150 with a 40 speed forward and reverse transmission and computerised headland management system launched in 1996 were the first tractors made by Steyr and sold in Case IH livery.

Bonhill Engineering Ltd, at Beverley, near Hull, became Steyr distributors in 1998. This company, previously at Brough, were Fendt tractor importers for the UK but this arrangement came to an end when the German manufacturer was acquired by AGCO, who already owned Massey Ferguson.

STOCKHOLD

H.J. Stockton Ltd of London decided there was still demand in the late 1950s for a relatively basic lightweight tractor similar to the obsolete B.M.B President which had a Morris paraffin engine, a 3 forward and reverse gearbox and optional hydraulic linkage. Apart from the air-cooled 2 cylinder 14hp Petter diesel engine the Stockhold President launched at the 1957 Smithfield Show was similar to the last B.M.B President tractors made in 1956. The basic price of the Stockhold tractor was about £360 with electric starting, lights, power take-off and hydraulic linkage listed as optional extras. Demand did not come up to expectations and very few Stockhold Presidents were sold.

276. The Stockhold President was an improved version of the B.M.B President made at Southport in the early 1950s.

STRAKES

It was common practice in the late 1940s and early 1950s to attach strakes to tractor rear wheels in order to improve wheel grip for heavy cultivation work. A strake on the land side rear wheel was also an advantage when ploughing in difficult conditions. The combined width of a tyre and a strake was too wide to run in the furrow and the increased use of reversible ploughs, and more particularly the advent of improved tractor hydraulic weight transfer systems, led to their demise.

The heavy Opperman 'Quickgrip' strake was bolted to the rear wheel disc and hinged lugs were folded over the tyre to improve wheel grip. Darvill re-tractable strakes made by Stanhay Ltd at Ashford in Kent were easier to use. The spikes were extended beyond the tyre by loosening two lock nuts and driving the tractor forward. The strakes were closed before taking the tractor on the road by reversing this procedure.

Some farmers used chains or tyre girdles on the rear wheels to improve grip in greasy conditions. Griff non-skid tyre chains made by John Griffiths & Sons at Cradley Heath in Staffordshire were wrapped around the tyre in a similar fashion to snow chains on road vehicles. The chains were claimed to give a 'sure, safe grip to all tyres, how ever old and smooth, both in the field and on the road without injuring them'.

277. The lugs on the Opperman Quickgrip wheel strakes had to be folded away before driving on the road. This was not a popular task when the lugs were clogged with hard packed mud.

'Ten minutes to fit and five minutes to detach' was the claim for Ferguson tyre girdles, which could be used on the field or road without any adjustment. The half-round steel section girdles in five hinged parts were secured around the tyre. A special tool was provided to pull the ends of the girdle together and hold them in position while tightening the securing bolts. Spade lugs could be bolted to the cross bars for extra grip. Tyre girdles were designed to creep slightly round the tyre when under load to prevent damage and assist the self-cleaning action of the open-centre tread.

278. Darvill re-tractable strakes, which cost £44.16s.6d per pair in 1953, were available for most makes of tractor.

279. Ferguson tyre girdles could be fitted in a matter of minutes. The tractor was reversed into the girdles which were secured around the tyres with two bolts.

SUTCLIFF

A mini-tractor made partly from recycled Ferguson TE 20 components with a moulded plastic bonnet, wings and transmission cover was introduced in 1995 by Sutcliff Industries of Evesham, Worcestershire. The Sutcliff Mini-Trak had a 3 cylinder 30hp or 4 cylinder 41hp Lister-Petter direct injection diesel engine and a single-plate dry clutch. A 4 forward and reverse gearbox with optional creep speed and disc brakes were installed in a re-conditioned Ferguson TE 20 transmission housing. Independent power take-off, lighting kit and a safety frame or weather cab were optional.

The ST 35 added to the Sutcliff range in 1997 had a 6 forward and 2 reverse Massey Ferguson 35 transmission and a Lister-Petter 30hp or 41hp water-cooled diesel engine. This tractor was also a mix of re-manufactured and new parts, including a suspension seat and new body panels. Production of these tractors was taken over in1998 by the Smallholder Tractor Co, also of Evesham, in 1998. The Smallholder ST 135, based on the MF 135 was added in the same year. There were two models, both with a 4 cylinder direct injection Lister-Petter diesel engine. The standard model rated at 41hp had a diff-lock while the turbocharged 55hp ST 135 T had a diff-lock and power steering.

The Smallholder Tractor range was increased to four models in 1998 with the launch of the four-wheel drive ST28 with a 3 cylinder 28hp Lister Petter engine and a 9 forward and 3 reverse transmission.

280.
An engine-mounted
pump was used for
the Sutcliff
Mini-Trak's live
hydraulic
system.

281.
A 30hp or 41hp
Lister-Petter diesel
engine provided
the power for
the Smallholder
ST 35 made by
the Smallholder
Tractor Co.

TRACTOR VAPORISING OIL

Although tractor vaporising oil or paraffin was cheaper than petrol it was less efficient and unburnt fuel was likely to find its way into the sump and dilute the oil if the engine was not hot enough. Esso Green, Regent Gold and Shellspark were some of the more popular brands of tractor vaporising oil. Shell and BP's Shellspark, coloured purple for easy identification, was claimed to have rapid warm-up properties, improved throttle response and increased tractive effort without engine knock.

It was usual for the engine to have a pre-heating system which used heat from the exhaust to warm the paraffin before it reached the cylinder. Some tractors had an adjustable heat valve in the exhaust manifold which could be used to release exhaust gases direct to the exhaust pipe on hot days or circulate them around the inlet manifold when it was cold.

Several companies, including the Beccles Engineering Co, Fishleigh Ltd and the Loddon Engineering Co, made vaporising oil conversion kits for the Ferguson TEA 20 and other petrol-engined tractors. The Fishleigh vaporiser included a modified carburettor, a small petrol tank and a replacement manifold which pre-heated the paraffin and air mixture before it reached the cylinders. An instruction leaflet reminded the driver to make sure the engine was hot enough before switching to vaporising oil.

War-time restrictions led to a severe shortage of petrol for starting farm tractors so drivers would cover the radiator with an old coat or a corn sack during the winter months to keep the engine warm when they took a break. However, tell-tale signs of white smoke from the exhaust pipe indicated the engine was too cold to run on paraffin and unburnt fuel was finding its way into the sump oil.

282. Vaporising oil engines on the Ferguson 20 and 35 had an aluminium cover over the manifold to pre-heat the fuel before it entered the cylinders.

TRANTOR

A survey of farm tractor use in the early 1970s found that as much as 70 per cent of the work done by so-called 'ploughing tractors' was either of a general nature or consisted of hauling produce and materials around the farm. This prompted Graham Edwards and Stuart Taylor to design and build a prototype two-wheel drive fast haulage

283. High speed haulage of grain from field to store was an ideal test for the prototype 55hp Trantor, a tractor which shared some components with the Land Rover.

284. The Series I Trantor fast tractor had independent front axle suspension and leaf springs with telescopic dampers on the rear axle.

tractor. The 55hp Trantor transport tractor with a Perkins engine was similar in shape and size to a Land Rover with category I hydraulic three-point linkage and power take-off. The vehicle had Land Rover wheels at the front, Unimog wheels at the rear and a passenger seat on both sides of the central driving seat.

The prototype was thoroughly tested and a modified version of the Trantor, now with an 80hp engine, was exhibited at the 1976 Royal Show. More trials were carried out and the production model of the two-wheel drive Series I Trantor was launched at the 1978 Smithfield Show. The first batch of Trantors which cost £13,500 with a safety cab and suspension on all four wheels were made by F. W. McConnel Ltd at Ludlow in Shropshire. They had an 80hp Perkins 4.236 diesel engine, a synchromesh gearbox with a transfer box giving 10 forward and 2 reverse gears with a top speed of 60mph. Four wheel air-over-hydraulic brakes, an air braking system for a trailer and an independently suspended pick-up hitch made the Trantor an ideal machine for high speed road transport. A diff-lock, hydraulic linkage and a two-speed 60hp power take-off shaft meant that apart from deep ploughing it was equally suitable for most field operations. The Trantor was classed as a farm tractor – an added bonus as it qualified for an agricultural road fund licence which cost £8.50 at the time. It could also be used with rebated farm fuel.

The two-wheel drive Series II Mark I Trantor with a turbocharged Leyland engine was launched in 1983. Wheel track width was adjustable in 4 inch steps from 5ft 4in to 6ft 8in and the cab was repositioned to make more space for a de-mountable crop sprayer or fertiliser spreader on the rear load platform. Depending on the type of tyres the Series II was, according to publicity material, 'a high speed or a low ground pressure tractor suitable for all year round spraying and spreading at 12mph and for road haulage at 40mph.'

The 752, 952 and 1252 Trantors rated at 54½hp, 71hp and 92hp with a 10 or 20 speed gearbox and a 12,000 mile or 12 month warranty were being made in 1984. A four-wheel drive 96hp version was added later that year.

The Trantor Hauler with a 6 cylinder 126hp Perkins engine announced in 1985 had an on-line trailer braking system to meet the new road use regulations introduced by the Department of Transport. Most Trantors had a 96hp turbocharged Leyland engine in the mid-1980s but an 80hp Perkins engine was used for a special local authorities version of the tractor. A bogie-unit which enabled the Trantor to tow articulated lorry trailers became available in 1991.

285. The Series II Mk I Trantor made its debut at the 1983 Smithfield Show.

286. The four-wheel drive 126hp Trantor Hauler had an 18.5 ton payload.

The company changed its name to HST (High Speed Tractors) Developments Ltd in 1988 when the design of a new Euro-Trantor was being considered and the first prototype was made in 1996.

Although the Trantor has not made a big impression in the UK several hundred have been sold to British farmers over the years. Production was transferred to India in the mid-1990s where the Trantor was made by Eicher. India and China were seen to be countries with a growing demand for high speed haulage tractors and annual tractor sales in those countries were in excess of 200,000 units by the late 1990s. A new four-wheel drive Trantor 904, also made by Eicher, with an Indian-built 90hp Tata engine, was introduced in 1998.

287. The first four-wheel drive Trantor 904 with a 90hp engine was made in India by Eicher in 1998. It is mainly for sale in India and China.

TRUSTY

Tractors (London) Ltd of Bentley Heath, Hertfordshire, who were making the well-known two-wheeled Trusty garden tractor in the mid-1930s, introduced the four-wheeled Trusty Steed in 1948. The first model, which cost £200, was little more than a ride-on towing tractor with an 8.9hp Douglas engine, centrifugal clutch, 2 forward gears and reverse and a top speed of 8mph. Sales literature explained that it had 'a centrifugal clutch to ensure a silky start at all times and separate drive to each rear wheel gave a very short turning radius' which made it possible for the 'handy and easily controlled little machine to pull a man-sized load and be readily manoeuvrable in a restricted space'.

A more sophisticated Steed introduced in 1950 with adjustable wheel tracks and a mid- or rear-mounted tool bar operated with a spring-assisted hand lever cost £205. The new Steed had a front-mounted 14½hp JAP or a Norton air-cooled engine, a single-plate clutch, 3 forward gears and reverse, independent brakes and power take-off. An engine bonnet was available and the tractor could be supplied with a vertical or horizontal exhaust pipe. A few Trusty Steeds were sold with Roadless half-tracks for working on marginal or hilly ground. About 500 Steeds were built in the 1950s and 1960s and a few more, with occasional improvements, were made before it went out of production in 1978.

The Trusty Tractor Co, still at Bentley Heath, re-introduced the Trusty Steed in 1995. The new four-wheel drive Steed, made in the Czech Republic, had a 33½hp Lombardini 3 cylinder water-cooled diesel engine and a

THE Trusty 'STEED'

The Towing Machine for—

YARDS · FACTORIES · POST OFFICES · RAILWAYS · AERODROMES · BUILDING SITES etc

288. The rear-mounted engine and transmission on the original Trusty Steed were basically the same as those used for the two-wheeled Trusty garden tractor.

hydraulically operated single-plate clutch. Other features of the new Steed included an independent front and rear category I hydraulic system with a separate oil reservoir, hydraulic disc brakes, hydrostatic steering and a de-luxe safety cab with optional air conditioning.

289. A more conventional layout was used for later versions of the Trusty Steed which also had the luxury of a 'waterproof reversible comfort seat'.

290. The four-wheel drive 1995 Trusty Steed with an 8 forward and reverse speed shuttle gearbox was made in the Czech Republic.

TURNER

The
TURNER
All-purpose
DIESEL TRACTOR
"The YEOMAN of England"

The Turner Diesel Tractor has proved its amazing performance under the worst soil conditions. Its tremendous lugging power, derived from the sturdy Turner traction-type Diesel Engine, enables it to operate four furrows as easily as other Diesel Tractors do three—giving ONE-THIRD EXTRA ACREAGE per hour *without* additional fuel cost. And on heavy-duty work the Turner Tractor operates at a fuel cost of only 1/- per hour. Your local Turner Dealer will gladly arrange a demonstration to prove our claim of "*Much* more work at less cost".

for the greatest pull on earth.
on wheels • at lowest fuel cost

291. The Turner was one of the first tractors made in Great Britain with a full diesel engine.

The Turner Manufacturing Co of Wolverhampton, who were involved in the motor vehicle industry in the early 1900s, launched the Turner diesel tractor in 1949 at the Royal Show in Shrewsbury. The tractor became known as the Turner Yeoman of England but this name was not used on early sales literature. The Yeoman of England was described as a '40hp 4 cylinder V-form diesel-engined wheeled tractor designed to be used with trailing or mounted implements'. The Turner had a single-plate dry clutch, 4 forward gears and reverse, spiral bevel differential, spur gear final drive and independent foot brakes. Power take-off, belt pulley, hydraulic linkage and lights were optional equipment. Manufacturers' publicity material in the 1940s and 1950s was often generous in praise of their products and Turners were obviously proud of their tractor. They explained that the Yeoman of England would do 'much more work at less cost per acre and its tremendous lugging power and traction and its economy in operation were some of the many advantages enjoyed by farmers using a Turner diesel tractor'. Potential purchasers were also informed that 'the astonishing lugging power of the Turner diesel engine enabled the tractor to pull four furrows as easily as other tractors could pull three – thus giving one extra acre per hour without additional fuel costs.'

Although an electric starter and a de-compressor were included in the basic price the tractor could be difficult to start in cold weather. Due to this and other reliability problems, the Yeoman of England was not popular and production ceased in 1957.

292. The off-set seat and steering wheel on the 40hp Turner Yeoman of England gave the driver a clear view when working in rowcrops.

UNIMOG

A group of engineers and farmers in southern Germany designed a four-wheel drive fast tractor with equal-size wheels in the mid-1940s. The prototype, built in the style of a military vehicle with a 25hp Mercedes Benz diesel engine and a wide range of forward speeds, underwent field trials in 1946. The tractor, which the designers called the Unimog, had a diff-lock and brakes on both axles, front and rear power take-off shafts, hydraulic linkage, a two-seater steel framed canvas cab and a rear load carrying platform. The name was derived from Universal Motorised Gerat (vehicle) and series production of the Unimog started in 1949 at Göppingen in Württemberg.

The Unimog was used in agriculture, forestry and for municipal applications. More than 600 had been made by 1951 when the Unimog project was sold to Daimler-Benz. Production was transferred to Gaggenau in the same year and the 25hp Unimog 2010 was awarded a silver medal by the German Agricultural Society. Sales literature explained that a variety of implements, including tool bar equipment, front-mounted mower, hay tedder, baler and a crop loader could be used with the Unimog. It was also suggested that a front-mounted binder driven by the power take-off could be 'operated by the driver who was able to watch and control the apparatus from his seat and ... no assistant would be necessary'.

The original steel and canvas cab was replaced with an all-steel version when the U 600 was launched in 1953 and the 82hp Unimog S, specifically designed for off-road operation appeared in 1955. Daimler-Benz claimed the long wheelbase version of the model S Unimog introduced in 1958 was the first farm tractor to have a synchromesh gearbox as standard equipment.

Production passed the 50,000 mark in 1961 and the first 65hp petrol-engined Unimog 406 tractors were made in 1963. An optional Mercedes-Benz direct injection diesel engine was introduced for the 406 in 1964.

213

293. Hoeing rowcrops with an early example of the 25hp Unimog.

The Unimog S was still in production when the Unimog U series which included the U 34, U 40, U 54, U 70 and U 80 was launched in 1966. The U 45, U 66 and U 90 were added in 1968 and the first 100hp Unimog appeared in 1969.

Mercedes-Benz introduced the more sophisticated MB-trac in 1972 and the Unimog range was improved and rationalised to include the U 34, U 52, U 66 and U 84. Two new 82hp and 110hp chassis-type Unimogs with a load platform for mounting a sprayer or fertiliser spreader were launched in the same year.

The U 120/425 with a 120hp engine and an 8 speed gearbox with a top road speed of 50mph launched in 1974 was the most powerful Unimog yet made by

294. Potato planting was another job for the Unimog. The rear load platform carried a large capacity hopper; the planter was attached to the hydraulic linkage and cage wheels reduced soil compaction.

Daimler-Benz. Optional gearboxes with 8 field speeds and/or 8 creep speeds which gave a total of 16 or 24 forward gears were also available. Other features of the U 120 included pneumatically operated diff-locks on both axles and two-speed front and rear power take-off shafts with independent hydraulic clutches. The Unimog reached the 150hp mark in 1975 with the launch of the U 1500 and the 100hp U 1000 was added in 1976.

295. The U 1500 with three implement attachment points and sprung axles was the most powerful Unimog on the British market in the early 1980s.

Long wheelbase models of the Unimog including the U 1300 L and 168hp flagship U 1700 L were added to the Unimog fleet in the late 1970s. By 1980 there were eight Unimogs on the UK market including four specialist agricultural tractors which shared the same basic engine and other components with the MB-trac.

Unimogs marketed by Mercedes-Benz at Milton Keynes in the mid-1980s ranged from the U 600 with a 52hp engine and 12 forward gears to the 150hp U 1500 AG with a standard 16 forward and reverse gearbox. The short wheelbase U 1400 and U 1600 with 136hp and 156hp diesel engines were added in 1988. Seven models were in production in 1990 but the U 1000, U 1200 and U 1700 with 102hp, 125hp and 170hp 6 cylinder engines and a 16 forward and reverse gearbox with a top speed of 47mph were the only ones available in Britain.

Accurate control of front- and rear-mounted implements on tractors with a full suspension system had been a problem until 1990 when the Unimog EHR hydro-tonic system, which constantly monitored working depth or height with ultra-sound sensors provided the solution. The optional Unicomp in-cab computerised engine and performance monitoring system was also introduced in 1990 and, on a practical note, a much larger rear screen improved visibility of rear-mounted implements.

The Terramatic electronic linkage control announced in 1994 improved the Unimog's performance with a plough. The Terramatic system monitored variations in oil pressure on the front or rear hydraulic lift cylinders and used this information to maintain a constant draft and keep the depth as even as possible. The system was also used to monitor the load on the rear platform and keep the spray bar or spreading mechanism at the correct height as the fertiliser hopper or sprayer tank discharged its contents. The Terramatic could be used with the front or rear linkage but not with both of them at the same time. An optional radar sensing unit was available to control the working depth of trailed machines, including sugar beet and potato harvesters.

*296. Four
Unimog AG
agricultural
models
with
87–214hp
engines
were made
in the
mid-1990s.*

Four agricultural Unimogs were available in the UK in 1995. The U 90 AG, U 1400 AG and U 2100 AG launched at the previous year's Royal Show were added to the U 1600 AG first seen by British farmers in 1991. The 87hp U 90 AG had 22 forward and 11 reverse gears and a 5 cylinder water-cooled Mercedes-Benz engine. The other three Unimogs with a 16 forward and reverse transmission had 6 cylinder turbocharged water-cooled engines rated at 136hp, 155hp and 214hp. Other features included front and rear power take-off and live hydraulic linkages, an engine-driven compressor and selectable two- and four-wheel drive. A right-hand steering wheel was optional in the two-seater cab mounted on rubber dampers.

The smaller Unimog UX 100, intended mainly for local authority use, with a 4 cylinder 73hp or a 5 cylinder 120hp engine and hydrostatic transmission appeared in 1997. The driving controls could be moved to either side of the cab to suit the work in hand.

The U Trac 160 launched in 1997 was a new type of agricultural Unimog developed by South Cave Tractors of York. It was based on the Unimog U 1650 with a centrally mounted cab and larger tyres to give increased ground clearance for spraying or spreading fertiliser in rowcrops. The U Trac 160 specification included a 16 forward and reverse gearbox and the option of two- or four-wheel steering. The 1998 Mercedes-Benz Unimog agricultural range included models from the U 90 AG to U 2100 AG with 122–214hp engines and the U 1650 and U 2150 for use with de-mountable sprayers and fertiliser spreaders.

UNIVERSAL

Universal tractors manufactured in Romania by Auto Tractor Braslov were introduced to British farmers in the early 1970s. The tractors were originally developed with Fiat in Italy and Universal Tractors at Mitcham in Surrey were importing the Romanian-built 73hp four-wheel drive Universal 651 M in 1970. It had a 10 speed gearbox, power-assisted steering, Bosch hydraulics, independent power take-off and an alternator charging system. The 651 M cost £1,420 ex Felixstowe docks and an advertisement explained that it was 'a lot of tractor at any price and £600 cheaper than any other comparable tractor on the market.'

landale Universal Tractors at South Cave on Humberside were importing the Romanian-built tractors from 1974 when the range included the Universal U 445/U 445 DT and U 550/U 550 DT two- and four-wheel drive models together with the U 445 SM crawler. The U 445 wheeled tractors had a 45hp Universal engine and a 9 forward and 3 reverse speed gearbox. Features of the 55hp U 550 included a 4 cylinder direct injection water-cooled engine, dual clutch, 8 forward and 2 reverse gears with synchromesh on 3rd/4th and 7th/8th and power-assisted steering. Both tractors were equipped with an independent power take-off, live hydraulics, adjustable wheel track and Duncan safety cab. The four-wheel drive DT models had a conventional transfer box and prop-shaft drive arrangement to the front axle.

Iandale Universal Tractors were still importing the 45–62hp two- and four-wheel drive Universal U 445, U 550 and U 640 tractors in 1980 when prices started at approximately £4,000. Hydrostatic steering was standard on the four-wheel drive 62hp 640 DT and the two-wheel drive model had power-assisted steering. A crawler version of the 640 with power take-off and hydraulic linkage was also available at the time. The U 445, U 550 and U 640 wheeled tractors and two crawlers with 45hp and 69hp engines were being imported by Universal Tractors at South Cave when the 3 cylinder 50hp U 530 was launched in 1981. The latest tractors from Romania were advertised as 'sparkling, highly efficient workhorses with prices from around £4,250'.

297. The Universal U445 SM crawler with a 45hp diesel engine, 6 forward and 2 reverse gears, power take-off and hydraulic linkage, cost £2,020 in 1973.

New SD models with improved specifications and more driver comfort were described as 'a new breed of workhorses from the Universal stable'. They were added to the standard range of two- and four-wheel drive

298. This Universal U445 tractor was built in Romania under licence from Fiat.

tractors in 1982. Features of the 445, 530 and 640 SD models included a semi-flat deck cab, hydrostatic steering, a new Inversor gearbox with a shuttle reverser with 8 speeds in both directions and an assistor ram which increased the lift capacity of the three-point linkage. The importers offered a 2 per cent interest finance plan over twelve months to promote the sale of Universal tractors.

Linx Agriculture at South Cave, who were already marketing Lamborghini tractors, became the Universal tractor distributor for the UK in 1983. The U 850 DT and U 1010 DT were launched in 1984, followed by the U 532/U 532 DT and U 642/U 642 DT which replaced the U 520 and U 640 in 1985. The 101hp U 1010 DT with hydrostatic steering and a two-speed power take-off was the first Universal tractor.with a 100hp engine on the British market.

Linx Agriculture ceased trading in 1986 and Bonhill Ltd, who were importing German grain and root harvesting machinery through their depot at Thetford in Norfolk, were appointed UK distributors for Universal tractors. Bonhill retained their Thetford premises but the Universal tractor business, with a range of 50–100hp wheeled tractors, including high clear and narrow models and two crawlers, remained at South Cave.

Four new Universal 3 series tractors with a more streamlined appearance which brought them close to western European standards were launched in 1988. The two-wheel drive 453, 533, 643 and four-wheel drive (DT) models rated at 45hp, 53hp and 64hp had 12 forward and 3 reverse gears with an optional 8 speed shuttle transmission. The 72hp 723/723 DT had a 16 forward and 4 reverse synchromesh gearbox and inboard wet disc brakes. Other features of the 3 series included a much improved cab with electric wipers, 540/1,000rpm and ground speed power take-off and hydrostatic steering. A radio cassette player and hydraulic trailer braking system were standard on the 643 and 723. The turbocharged 4 cylinder Universal U 853 which cost £13,350 was the cheapest 85hp tractor in Britain when it was introduced in 1990.

Bonhill Engineering were importing the Universal 3 series and a range of Fendt tractors in 1993 but within 12 months Universal Tractors Ltd in North Yorkshire were handling the Romanian tractors. An improved range of three 72–105hp Euroseries 33 models with new flat floor tiltable cabs, fibreglass bonnets and a four-speed power take-off appeared in 1997. The top of the range four-wheel drive 105hp 6 cylinder Universal 1033 DT had a 16 forward and 4 reverse gearbox and the same transmission was used for the 72hp and 733 DT and the 89hp 833 DT.

299. The 70hp Universal 704DT and the 59hp 603DT were imported by Bonhill in the mid-1980s.

300. The 833DT with an 89hp turbocharged engine and a 12 forward and 3 reverse gearbox was one of the new Euroseries 33 Universal tractors launched in 1988.

There was a mix of new and improved models in the 45–73hp Euroseries 3 range launched in 1997. The 45hp 453 and the 53 hp 533 had 3 cylinder engines and an 8 forward and reverse shuttle gearbox while the four-wheel drive models had 12 forward and 3 reverse gears. The same gearbox was used for the 64hp 643/643 DT and the 73hp 703 DT had 16 forward and 4 reverse speeds. Universal Tractor Imports at Ripon in North Yorkshire took over the distribution of the Romanian tractors in the UK in 1997 when Universal Tractors Ltd ceased trading. The 1998 range, still based on former Fiat designs, included seven two- and four-wheel drive tractors, from the 45hp 453 to the 6 cylinder 105hp Universal 1033.

URSUS

The Polish town of Ursus near Warsaw has been connected with the tractor industry since the Ursus Mechanical Works was established in 1893. Internal combustion engines were being made there in 1903 and the first tractors appeared in 1922. Some early Ursus tractors were similar to those made by other companies. For example, the 1922 25hp paraffin-engined Ursus resembled the International Harvester Titan and the 45hp Ursus C 45 semi-diesel launched in 1947 could be mistaken for a Lanz Bulldog.

Ursus were also making military equipment for the Polish government in the early 1930s, along with Junkers aeroplanes, tanks and armoured vehicles for the German army during the war years. The Ursus Mechanical Works was the only tractor factory in Poland in the late 1940s. The product range was gradually extended and by the early 1970s there were factories in five Polish towns with Ursus serving as the headquarters of the Union of Tractor Manufacturers. Arrangements were also made for Zetor and Ursus to share components for their tractors.

The Maulden Engineering Co Ltd at Flitwick in Bedfordshire introduced the Ursus Agripol C-335 and C-350 to British farmers in the mid-1960s. The twin-cylinder 35hp C-335 had 6 forward and 2 reverse gears and the

301. The Ursus Agripol C-350 had 10 forward and 2 reverse gears.

50hp C-350 had a 10 forward and 2 reverse gearbox. Category II hydraulic linkage, diff-lock and electric starting were standard. The 4 cylinder 60hp C-355 with live hydraulic linkage had the same gearbox as the C-350 which it replaced in 1970. Lower link sensing hydraulics were an advanced feature of the two- and four-wheel drive 85hp C-385 and C-385A launched in 1972. Both tractors had 16 forward and 8 reverse speeds, power steering, a two-speed power take-off and an air-conditioned cab.

The C-385, C-355 and C-335 were still being made in 1973 when Ursus tractor production passed the 400,000 mark. Prices at the time included the C-385 for £2,995, the C-355 was £1,690 and the C-335, advertised as 'the best value-for-money tractor on the market today', cost £1,358.

Ursus had an annual production of 70,000 tractors for sale on the world market when the 120hp Ursus C-1201 and the four-wheel drive C-1204 with 6 cylinder water-cooled direct injection engines made their debut at the 1974 Smithfield Show. The C-1204 was the first four-wheel drive Ursus model seen in the UK and both tractors had 8 forward and 4 reverse gears with a torque amplifier which doubled the number of gears in both directions. The torque amplifier could be used on the move to increase or decrease forward speed by about 30 per cent which gave the opposite effect on drawbar pull. The C-1204 had Plowselect hydraulics with an external assister ram, a hydraulic clutch engaged front-wheel drive on the move and the cab was 'a luxury model with noise insulation, air conditioning and a passenger seat'.

Ursus-Bizon (GB) Ltd of Needham Market, Suffolk, imported a four-model range from 1976 which included the Ursus C-1201/1204 and C-385/385A Unified series tractors. They were of similar design with many common parts and a built-in air compressor. The Ursus range imported by Ursus-Bizon in 1978 was reduced to the 85hp and 120hp models which included de-luxe two-wheel drive versions with spring suspension units on the front axle. The four-wheel drive C-1204, which cost just over £12,600, was advertised as 'a big value tractor available through an interest free finance plan'.

The C-385 and C-1201 were still being made when the new 52hp two-wheel drive C-362 was added to the 1980 price list at £5,620. The Ursus range was widened again in 1982 with the launch of the 100hp C-1002/1004 and the 6 cylinder 150hp four-wheel drive C-1604. The C-362 was the only model in the Ursus range without a two-speed power take-off, torque amplifier, power steering and heated cab. Farmers could select standard or SX versions of the 80–150hp Ursus tractor range. Additional features on the SX models included a de-luxe seat, fully adjustable rear wheels, an extra plough lamp and a long/medium wave push button radio.

Five new Ursus tractors in the 60–160hp bracket appeared in 1983. The 80hp, 100hp and 120hp two- and four-wheel drive tractors had a 16 forward and 8 reverse gearbox and the four-wheel drive Ursus 1614 had 12 forward and 6 reverse speeds. Debtrac Ltd, also at Needham Market, were appointed UK distributors for Ursus tractors and other Polish machinery in 1985. The Power-Code variable horse power option was developed in the early 1980s by the Ursus distributor in Holland. It was similar to the Caterpillar VHP system and enabled the driver to select a lower level of engine power when the tractor was used for light work. Debtrac

302. An agreement between Ursus and Zetor led to components beng shared for some tractors made in Czechoslovakia and Romania. The Ursus C-385 and Zetor Crystal were almost identical with the front end made in Czechoslovakia and the back end produced in Poland.

acquired rights to install Power-Code as an option on 80hp, 100hp, 120hp and 146hp Ursus tractors sold in Britain at the time.

303. The Ursus 1201 and four-wheel drive 1204 had a 6 cylinder 120hp engine with a 16 forward and 8 reverse transmission.

Distribution of Ursus tractors in Britain passed into the hands of three farm machinery dealerships in the late 1980s. Eight models were still available and the pre-delivery inspections were carried out at the dealers' premises in Essex, Shropshire and Suffolk.

A new factory was built near the Ursus plant in the mid-1980s to manufacture Perkins engines and Massey Ferguson tractors under licence. The 3 cylinder 2812 and 4 cylinder 3512 and 4512 made in this factory were among the 35–150hp Ursus range imported by BSG Supplies Ltd in 1991. The company was originally based in Ipswich, Suffolk, before later moving to Colchester, Essex. Seven of these tractors, from the 35hp 2812 to the 150hp 1224T, were new models with improved styling and most of them had hydrostatic steering.

304. The Ursus Lightforce de-luxe range launched in 1996 included the 62hp 4512.

Optional hydraulically engaged four-wheel drive was available and the front axle diff-lock was engaged hydraulically via the rear diff-lock.

The political situation in Eastern Europe caused production difficulties and the Ursus factory was forced to close down for a while in 1991. However, the Polish tractors soon re-appeared and there were 18 two- and four-wheel drive models, including the first of the new Lightforce range, and re-styled heavy tractors with a Zetor connection in production by the time of the 1992 Smithfield Show. The two-wheel drive tractors ranged from the 35hp Ursus 335 to the 89hp 1222 and the four-wheel drive models were in the 70–119hp bracket.

The 2 cylinder 335 was mechanically much the same as it was in the mid-1960s and like the 3 cylinder 37hp 2812 and 47hp 3512 tractors it had an 8 forward and 2 reverse gearbox. The 912, 1012 and 1222 rated at 78hp, 100hp and 119hp had 16 forward and 8 reverse speeds but the four-wheel drive tractors only had 4 reverse gears. There were three versions of the Ursus 4512 with an 8 forward and 2 reverse gearbox. The standard 4512 and four-wheel drive 4514 had a 70hp engine and the turbocharged 4514T was rated at 80hp.

The Ursus Mechanical Works celebrated its centenary in 1993 with the launch of a heavyweight range of tractors with a synchromesh gearbox and an adjustable steering column in an improved cab. An independent power take-off and live hydraulic system were features of the 37–90hp Lightforce HD version models introduced in 1996 and the turbocharged Ursus 3512/3514 rated at 62hp were added to the Lightforce range in the same year.

Five Ursus models in the 38–86hp range were being imported from Poland by BSG Supplies in 1997. An 8 forward and 2 reverse gearbox was standard across the range of two- and four-wheel drive models with 3 or 4 cylinder engines.

VALMET

Valmet tractors took their name from Valtion Metallitehtaat, the State Metal Works established in Finland after World War Two. A prototype single-cylinder 12hp tractor was built in 1949 but it did not come up to expectations and Valtion Metallitehtaat designers went back to the drawing board. The company name was shortened to the Valmet Corporation in 1951 and a limited number of 15hp Valmet 15 or Model A tractors with a 4 cylinder side-valve petrol/paraffin engine with magneto ignition were made in 1952. Finland's farmers wanted a more powerful tractor and this requirement was met in 1955 with the launch of the Valmet 20 with a 22hp petrol or 19½hp paraffin engine. Hydraulic linkage was optional at first but later became standard equipment. The Valmet 15 remained in production for a while but the Valmet 20 sold in far greater numbers.

The tractors had become popular in Finland by the mid-1950s by which time the Finnish company was building up export markets in Brazil, China, Spain and Turkey. Valmet were also busy developing their own diesel engine and the 37hp 33D, launched in 1957, had a 3 cylinder direct injection diesel engine, a 6 forward and 2 reverse gearbox and hydraulic linkage. The improved Valmet 359D with the same 37hp engine replaced the 33D in 1959. The new model had an engine-driven hydraulic pump with a separate oil circuit and reservoir and more dials and gauges were added to the instrument panel.

Valmet formed a marketing organisation with Finnish farm machinery manufacturers Fiskars, Rosenlew and Wartsilla in 1960. Brazil had become an important market for Valmet and production facilities were established there in 1961 to build the Valmet 360D tractor which, except for a German MWM (Motoren Werke Mannheim) diesel engine, was identical to the 359D. The more stylish-looking 42hp Valmet 361D which replaced the 360D in 1960 was updated again in 1962 with a diff-lock, hour meter and cushioned seat. The Valmet 361D remained in production until 1965. The 361D was also built under licence in Portugal during the mid- and late 1960s where it was marketed as the F.A.P. (Fabrica de Automoveis Portugues). About 700 of these tractors were made and sold in Portugal, Spain and Portuguese Africa.

The 52 SAE hp Valmet 565 with a 6 forward and 2 reverse semi-synchromesh gearbox, foot throttle and a dual clutch with two equal-size clutch discs and two pedals replaced the 361D in 1964. An improved Valmet 565-II introduced in the following year had the engine-mounted hydraulic pump re-located so that it could be disengaged to reduce the load on the engine when starting from cold. The 4 cylinder 89hp Valmet 900 introduced in 1967 had an 8 forward and 2 reverse synchromesh gearbox, a 540/1,000/ ground speed power take-off, hydrostatic steering and hydraulic dry disc brakes. Yellow and brown paintwork replaced the previous red livery and the instrument panel and gear levers on the right-hand side of the driver's seat in the safety cab would have been equally at home in a motor car. The new yellow colour scheme was used for the Valmet 700 and also for the 500 which replaced the 565-II in 1968. The first two figures of the model number indicated engine horse power rounded to the nearest ten. The 75 SAE hp Valmet 700 was mechanically similar to the Valmet 500 and both models had disc brakes, an improved 8 forward and 2 reverse synchromesh gearbox and wider mudguards.

Announced in 1969, the turbocharged 102hp 4 cylinder Valmet 1100 with a similar specification to the 900 was claimed as the world's first turbocharged tractor. Volvo BM had introduced a tractor with a 6 cylinder turbocharged engine at about the same time but any argument on the matter ceased to be an issue when Valmet and Volvo BM merged ten years later. The Valmet 1100 was also advertised as the first European tractor to have in-cab entertainment (radio) included in the basic price. The first four-wheel drive Valmet tractors were made in 1969 and turbo-charged four-wheel drive versions of the Valmet 900 and 1100 were popular with agricultural contractors in Scandinavia.

The Valtra name, from Valmet tractors, which appeared on farm tractors in the late 1990s, was already being used by Valmet in the early 1970s for a range of industrial tractors and other plant equipment including fork lifts, cranes and loaders.

The Valmet 500 with a new flat floor quiet cab became the 502 in 1971. Similar cabs were used on other Valmet tractors during the next two years and their model numbers were changed to 702, 902 and 1102. The turbocharged 102 SAE hp Valmet 702 S appeared in 1975 and four-wheel drive versions of the 702/702 S and a new 58hp Valmet 602 were launched in 1978.

The 150hp Valmet 1502 bogie tractor introduced in the mid-1970s had six equal-size wheels which were smaller than the usual rear wheels. It was conventionally steered by the front wheels and rubber tracks could

305. The 75hp Valmet 702, which superseded the 700 in 1972, had a hydraulically operated clutch and braking system controlled with suspended pedals in 'the quietest cab yet made'.

be fitted over each pair of rear driving wheels to reduce ground pressure. The 1502 was used industrially but was not successful as a farm tractor.

A new brighter yellow and chocolate brown colour scheme was used for the 02 series from 1978 and for the Valmet 03 series. Quick attach couplers on the hydraulic lift arms and top link were introduced in the same year. The 703 had a synchronised speed splitter while a new 107hp engine was used for the Valmet 1103.

Valmet and Volvo agreed to pool their resources in 1979 and formed a joint company called Scantrac AB. Valmet were making thirteen different tractors at the time, seven had turbocharged engines and six were four-wheel drive models. The Valmet 04 series and the Volvo BM Valmet 05 series Nordic tractors with red and black paintwork and white wheels were launched in 1982. Although the 04 series only carried the Valmet name they were part of the new Volvo BM Valmet Nordic tractor range. The Valmet 49hp 504 and 61hp 604 with a re-styled wedge-shaped bonnet replaced the 02 series and turbocharged engines were used on the two-wheel drive 604 T and four-wheel drive 604 T-4.

The Volvo BM Valmet 05 series were the most powerful tractors in the Nordic range. The 505, 605, 705 and 805 with 65hp, 72hp, 83hp and 94hp engines respectively had a synchromesh gearbox and planetary change-on-the-go Trac-Trol system which provided 16 forward and 8 reverse gears. Four-wheel drive versions of the 605, 705 and 805 were also made.

Volvo BM tractors were sold in Britain by Bamfords of Uttoxeter for a short while in the late 1960s and the Scandinavian tractors re-appeared in 1984 when Nordic Tractors at Thetford in Norfolk introduced the 05 series to British farmers. Prices ranged from £12,500 for the two-wheel drive 505 rising to £25,000 for the four-wheel drive 805. An advertisement which suggested farmers should try these Volvo BM Valmet tractors for themselves carried the slogan 'When you've driven one you'll want to own one – and when you own one you'll want to drive one.'

Improved cabs with optional air conditioning were used on the 05 series when the four-wheel drive 905, 2005-4 and the 2105-4 were launched in 1985. A 105hp naturally aspirated 6 cylinder engine was used on the 905, the 2005-4 had a 140hp turbocharged power unit and the 163hp 2105-4 engine had a turbocharger and intercooler.

When Valmet acquired Volvo BM's share of Scantrac AB in 1985 they were no longer able to use the prestigious Volvo BM name. The two- and four-wheel drive 53hp Valmet 305 and 61hp 405 launched in 1985

306. The 65hp Valmet 505 in a new red and black livery was the smallest of the Nordic 05 series launched in 1982.

were displayed on Nordic Tractors stand at that year's Smithfield Show. In common with the other 05 series the engine and gearbox were mounted well forward to leave space for the fuel tank and reduce the need for front weights. The design also made it possible to split the tractor for repair purposes without removing the cab.

Scantrac UK of Bury St Edmunds, Suffolk, a subsidiary of Scantrac AB Sweden, replaced Nordic Tractors as the Valmet distributor in 1986. They showed great faith in Valmet tractors with the slogan 'Valmet – a legend in it's own lifetime from the land of Gods and Vikings' on advertisements for the 53–163hp Scandinavian 04 and 05 series tractors. Valmet Tractors AB took control of selling the 05 series tractors from a depot in North Yorkshire in 1987. Bamfords International Ltd and the Benson Group at Uttoxeter and later at Knighton in Wales marketed the Finnish tractors between 1989 and 1991 when Valmet Tractors UK was established in Cheshire. The Benson Group, at Knighton, were also making County tractors in the late 1980s.

307. The 16 forward and 8 reverse gears on the Valmet 905-4 were provided by a synchromesh gearbox and a hydraulic quick-shift gear change system.

Improved Power Plus versions of the Valmet 505 to 905 tractors introduced in 1988 had 72–110hp engines, a new front-wheel drive system, more efficient steering, optional Autocontrol electronic hydraulic linkage and a choice of five colour schemes.

The four-wheel drive Mega 8000 series, rated at 120hp, 140hp and 170hp, was launched in 1990. The Mega 8100, 8300 and 8600 had 40kph transmissions with a twin-disc clutch, a 16 speed synchro Trac-Trol quick-shift

308. Valmet offered a choice of colour schemes for their medium-powered tractors from 1988. Black was the predominant colour but purchasers could choose one of five colours for the bonnet and cab.

system and the Valmet Autocontrol II electronic management system. The 1991 Valmet range of 61–170hp tractors included the new two- and four-wheel drive 79–120hp Mezzo range launched at that year's Smithfield Show. Features included a 12 or 24 speed forward and reverse shift-on-the-move gearbox with the optional Hi-Trol fluid drive coupling installed in front of the main dry plate clutch to protect it from excessive wear. The Mezzo E versions had the three-way AutoControl system for the diff-lock, change-on-the-move transmission, power take-off overload mechanism and Agridata which provided full operational information. Advertisements explained that the AutoControl and Agridata systems would allow the driver 'to concentrate on his task with the minimum of stress'.

The 140hp Valmet 8400 with Delta Powershift transmission and the TwinTrac reverse drive system was added to the Mezzo range in 1993. Four new Valmet 55 series tractors with a choice of five colour schemes were introduced in 1992. The 61hp, 67hp, 72hp and 80hp Valmet 355, 455, 555-4 and 665-4 had an 8 forward and 4 reverse synchromesh gearbox or 16 forward and 8 reverse gears with a shuttle reverser on the lower gears and optional AutoControl computerised management system. A 75hp Valmet 565 was also made but it was not widely available.

The 190hp Mega 8800 and the 61–75hp Valmet M 5 range for stock farms were launched in 1994. The M 5 range included the 365-2/365-4 and 465-2/465-4 with 3 cylinder engines and the 4 cylinder 565-4 could have a naturally aspirated or a turbocharged engine. An 8 forward and 4 reverse gearbox was standard but an optional 12 forward and 8 reverse gearbox with very low creep speeds was also available. AutoControl II was standard on the Mega 8800 and the improved AutoControl IV was offered at extra cost. Publicity material explained that AutoControl IV 'changes gear, engages four-wheel drive, monitors wheelslip, engages the diff-lock, monitors engine temperature, adjusts

309. The computerised Autocontrol system was a feature of the Valmet 805.

310. The Valmet 6400 had a wastegate turbocharger, air suspended seat and a wash-wipe facility for the rear screen.

fuelling and everything else a driver needs for day-long efficient operation'.

The Finnish Sisu Machinery Ltd of Runcorn, Cheshire, were distributing Valmet M 5, Mezzo and Mega tractors when the Valmet Sigma Power Mega 8750 was introduced in 1996. It was advertised as a tractor with a split personality and described as a compact and lightweight 160/190hp model which became a real heavyweight when the driver turned up the power. The Sigma Power computer monitored the load at the power take-off and automatically increased the fuel supply when the power shaft absorbed more than 30hp. This additional power was divided between the transmission and power take-off.

Four Valmet Mega 50 tractors in the 110–160hp range replaced the Mega 70 series in 1996. The 160hp Mega 8750 was also made with the 160/190hp Sigma Power system. The two- and four-wheel drive Mezzo 6200 introduced in 1997 with a 4 cylinder 80hp engine was one of the first Valmet tractors to meet the new 1999 engine emission regulations.

Sisu Machinery Ltd sold the Valmet tractor business to Partek of Finland in 1997. Partek then formed Valtra Tractors (UK) Ltd and sixteen Valtra-Valmet models in the 60–190hp bracket were available on the British market in 1998. They included four 60–90hp M 100 tractors, which had replaced the M 5 series, and the Mezzo and Mega range from the 80hp Mezzo 6200 to the 160/190hp Mega 8750 Sigma Power.

VERSATILE

The Hydraulic Engineering Co, founded in Toronto in 1946, used the Versatile brand name for their range of crop sprayers. The Toronto factory was too far from their customers so the company moved to a larger factory at Winnipeg in 1950 and made their first self-propelled grain swathers there in 1954. The company changed its name to the Versatile Manufacturing Co in 1963 and the first Versatile four-wheel drive articulated tractor made its debut in 1966. Versatile were a leading manufacturer of high horse power tractors by the mid-1970s with four models, including the Versatile 900, in a 230–350hp range on sale in North America. The 300hp 900 had a Cummins V-8 diesel engine, a 12 speed gearbox and articulated steering, operated by two hydraulic rams supplied with oil by a 24 gallons per minute gear pump.

The company changed its name to the Versatile Farm Equipment Co in 1977 and this event coincided with the introduction of the revolutionary 55hp four-wheel drive Versatile 150 bi-directional tractor. It worked equally as well going forwards or backwards and the operator always faced the direction of travel but the concept was not completely new as Deutz had made a bi-directional ploughing tractor way back in 1907. However, the Versatile 150 driver did have the added benefit of four-wheel drive, hydraulic linkage and a cab.

A sales agreement with Fiat Trattori of Turin gave Versatile an entry into Europe. The Fiat 44-28 with a 'Constant-Power' 6 cylinder 280hp Cummins engine was selected for the initial introduction to UK farmers at the 1979 Smithfield Show. It was one of four 230–350hp Versatile models in production at the time. The 'Constant-Power' feature gave the 44-28 a constant 280hp from the Cummins engine through a speed range of 1600–2100rpm.

The Versatile Farm Equipment Co continued to meet the North American prairie farmers' demands in the early 1980s for more and more horse power. The 600hp Versatile Model 1080, known as Big Roy, was the flagship of a range of giant tractors from 230hp upwards. The eight-wheel drive articulated Big Roy had four axles and the Cummins engine mounted on high behind the cab virtually covered the rear window. A closed circuit television system installed in the cab enabled the driver to see what was happening behind Big Roy's back.

The 116 gross hp Versatile 276 which superseded the 150 was the first bi-directional tractor with front and rear power-take off and hydraulic linkage. With a front-mounted cutter bar it became a high output self-propelled swather. The Versatile 276 was introduced to British farmers in 1988 by the Ford Motor Co to test farmer reaction to the big centre-pivot steered tractor with a three-range hydrostatic transmission. The Versatile Farm Equipment Co was purchased by Ford New Holland in 1987 after Steiger, who made the Ford FW series tractors, was bought by Tenneco the previous year. The acquisition of Versatile gave Ford New Holland a new source of high-powered tractors and the Versatile 876 in Ford blue livery was introduced to British farmers in 1987.

The 325hp turbocharged Ford Versatile 946 articulated tractor with 12 forward and 2 reverse gears added to the Ford New Holland range in the late 1980s was still listed in 1993. Very high horse power tractors were less popular by the 1990s but the 360hp Versatile 9682 still featured in the 1997 New Holland catalogue.

311. The Versatile 876 was the first Canadian-built giant tractor with a Ford New Holland badge.

VICKERS

Vickers-Armstrong (Tractors) Ltd of Newcastle-upon-Tyne were responsible for the production of the largest British-built crawlers made in the 1950s. Two models with Rolls Royce engines were distributed by Jack Olding & Co at Hatfield in Hertfordshire who had previously marketed Caterpillar tractors in the UK. Vickers crawlers were designed for the construction industry but attempts were also made to sell them to farmers.

The VR 180 Vickers Vigour crawler, made in 1952, had a Rolls Royce 6 cylinder supercharged direct injection diesel engine and a 6 forward and 3 reverse speed gearbox with a torque converter which allowed the driver to change gear on the move. It was steered with a system of servo-actuated multi-disc clutches and manually operated band brakes. The tractor which weighed just under 15 tons developed 181hp at the power take-off when tested by the National Institute of Agricultural Engineering (NIAE) in 1953.

A pre-production model, the smaller 121hp Vickers Vikon, was submitted to the NIAE for testing in 1957. The 4 cylinder four-stroke diesel crawler with clutch and brake steering had a single-plate clutch and a 5 forward and 4 reverse gearbox with a top speed of 5½mph. There were front and rear power take-off shafts and the tractor, including the driver and a full tank of fuel, weighed 11½ tons.

VOLVO BM

The Swedish vehicle manufacturer AB Volvo acquired Bolinder Munktell in 1950. The origins of the Munktell company can be traced back to 1832. The Swedish company was building threshing machines by 1859 and manufactured their first wheeled tractor was made in 1913. This beast weighed a massive

312. The early 1960s Volvo BM Buster 320 had 5 forward gears and reverse.

8 tons, the rear wheels were over 6ft in diameter and the cooling system was able to hold about 90 gallons of water.

The Bolinder brothers started a foundry and engineering and business in Stockholm in 1844 and they were making internal combustion engines by the mid-1890s. The two companies joined forces in the mid-1920s and Bolinder Munktell, abbreviated to BM, made the first BM 10 and BM 21 tractors with two-stroke hot bulb diesel engines in 1929. Some of them were converted to run on wood gas during World War Two.

The Swedish AB VOLVO company, established in 1928, who were also making tractors in the 1940s, bought Bolinder Munktell in 1950 and formed Volvo BM. The BM hot bulb engined models were discontinued in 1952 and BM introduced their first tractor with a full diesel engine in the same year. The new BM 35-36 tractor had a 3 cylinder, 42hp direct injection Bolinder diesel engine.

The BM/T 425 Terrier with a 32hp petrol engine introduced in 1957 was the first of the Volvo BM T series tractors. A 40hp 3 cylinder Perkins diesel engine replaced the carburettor version in 1961 and the Terrier was re-named the BM Buster 320. The 3 cylinder 56hp BM 350 Boxer with 10 forward and 2 reverse gears appeared in 1959 and the 79hp 4 cylinder BM Bison was added in the early 1960s. With engine power increased to 47hp the Buster became the Buster T 400 in the mid-1960s. The 106hp 6 cylinder T 800 replaced the Bison in 1966 and a strengthened Boxer with a 66 SAE hp engine, re-numbered the T 600, appeared two years later. The T 810 and the four-wheel drive T 814 introduced in 1969 were improved versions of the T 800 with a 130hp turbocharged engine.

More new models including the very successful Volvo BM T 650 were launched in the early 1970s. The T 650 was a completely new tractor with an 80 SAE hp 4 cylinder engine, 8 forward and 2 reverse gears and a cab of saloon car quality. The standard gearbox did not have synchromesh but Volvo's change-on-the-move Tract-Tol gearbox was an optional extra at a later stage. The T 500 introduced in 1974 had a Perkins engine and a British-built International Harvester transmission. More models were added and by 1978 Volvo BM were making a comprehensive range of two- and four-wheel drive tractors. Valmet completed their acquisition of Volvo AB in 1979 and formed a new company called Scantrac AB. Plans were already well advanced for the new 04 and 05 series which appeared in 1982 and Nordic Tractors at Thetford introduced the new Volvo BM Valmet tractors to British farmers in 1984. Valmet bought AB Volvo's share of Scantrac AB in 1985 and from that point the Volvo name could no longer be used on farm tractors.

313. Bamfords of Uttoxeter distributed Volvo BM tractors in the UK in the late 1960s. This T 800 is hitched to a Bamford plough.

WHEELS AND TRACKS

314. Fordson Model Ns on spade lug wheels played a vital role in the provision of the nation's food in the 1940s.

The change from steel wheels to self-cleaning open-centre tread pneumatic tyres took the best part of twenty years. Aeroplane type pneumatic tyres without any tread were first used on a farm tractor in 1931 and tyres with specialist agricultural tread patterns were coming into use in the late 1930s. A shortage of rubber in the war years slowed the process and pneumatic tyres were not standard on farm tractors until the late 1940s. Various tread patterns were used before the self-cleaning open-centre tread came into universal use.

A number of companies, including Blue Peter and Vacu-Lug who were both established in the 1950s, specialised in re-treading rear tractor tyres. Farmers using this service were told that their own tyres would be returned to them as good as new. Steel spade lug wheels were still preferred by some farmers for ploughing and other heavy work and it was still possible in the late 1940s to buy a new E27N Fordson Major and other tractors with steel wheels.

E.A. Allman & Co at Chichester were one of several companies making various types of tractor wheel from the late 1940s. Their product range included a complete sets of wheels and tyres to convert a tractor from steel wheels to pneumatic tyres, narrow rowcrop wheels with open centre tread tyres and skeleton steel wheels.

Spade lug and skeleton wheel rims which were bolted to the standard dished wheel centres were included in the 1950 Ferguson TE 20 accessories list. Spade lug wheels had a number of steel lugs bolted on a wide rim and skeleton wheels for rowcrop work had detachable lugs which were bolted alternately to the inside and outside of the rim or on one side for working between close spaced rows. Some farmers bought complete wheels but others saved money by using a rowcrop of skeleton rims after removing the standard rims and tyres.

Increased draw pull could be achieved by using half-tracks made by Roadless Traction (see plate 251 on page 184) and a few other companies. The tracks, which ran on a main sprocket driven by the rear axle shafts and a rear idler wheel, had a much larger footprint area than a tyre and consequently reduced soil compaction. Publicity material suggested that it was possible to fit or remove a set of half-tracks in a few hours but it usually took much longer and few farmers even bothered to try.

Rotaped tracks, introduced in 1946, were an alternative method of converting a wheeled tractor to a half-track. Mainly used for drainage work, the tracks were attached to the rear axles and the driving sprockets were bolted to the rear wheel hubs. The back of the tractor was carried on six track

315. Tyre tread patterns with the lug bars connected at the centre were superseded in the early 1950s by self-cleaning open-centre tread tyres.

rails which were moved around the central driving sprocket by a system of diagonal chains. The tracks were marketed by Geo. Monro Ltd at Waltham Cross, Hertfordshire, in the late 1940s. Advertisements explained that Rotaped tracks which increased pulling power by up to 70 per cent did not clog or slip and the tractor could easily be put back on to its rear wheels when required.

Lighter Rotaped tracks, announced in 1958, could be used with some of the more powerful tractors on the market at the time. Leeford (London) Ltd, the manufacturers, claimed that these tracks were more versatile than the earlier design and could be used at speeds of up to 4.5mph for ploughing and other heavy field work.

Soil compaction had become a cause for concern by the early 1950s

316. Steel rims with detachable spade lugs could be attached to Ferguson TE 20 rear wheel centres for ploughing and other heavy work.

and various types of cage wheel with a greater footprint area were made by several companies. Many farmers attached cage wheels to the tractor wheels to help reduce soil damage when preparing seedbeds while others removed the rear wheels and ran the tractor on cage wheels. The steel tread bars were made either from angle iron or round bar, but most tractor drivers preferred the round bar design as wheels with angle iron tread bars threw up clouds of dust when the land was dry.

Water ballasting of tyres to improve traction by adding weight was developed in the early 1950s. Goodyear introduced their Solution 100 system,

317. Rotaped tracks were used by Rotary Hoes for their trench digger. The tractor also had a 22:1 reduction gearbox and heavy cast iron front wheels.

which, with the aid of a special pump, made it possible to fill the inner tube 100 per cent full with water. Other companies suggested that a smaller amount of water, which could be added without special equipment, would be equally effective in improving traction. The water was protected from frost with calcium chloride. Tyre companies had problems in convincing some farmers that ethylene glycol anti-freeze solution for tractor radiators was not suitable for use in inner tubes.

Hedge cutting machinery manufacturer J. Foster & Co of North Cave, Yorkshire, noted that tractor tyres soon became damaged or worn when hedge cutting or clearing scrub. The company therefore introduced the Sabard sectional steel tyre cover in the 1950s to help overcome the problem. The tyre covers were made in six hinged sections from ⅛ inch thick steel plate and sales literature advised that they could 'be fixed around the tyre in a matter of minutes'.

Most tractor drivers had to use a foot pump to inflate their tractor tyres in the 1940s and 1950s but a few were fortunate enough to have an air compressor in the farm workshop or tractor-powered pump.

318. Catchpole Quick-Fix cage wheels could be fitted in 30 seconds without spanners.

320. Farmfitter's Jumbo power take-off driven pump
had many uses around the farm.

319. Sabard tyre covers were designed to protect
tractor tyres from damage by sharp stumps when
clearing scrub.

321.With one brake applied the other wheel was used to drive the tractor Treadmill made by the Howard Rotavator Co in
the early 1970s.

322. Very wide low ground pressure tyres were introduced in the mid-1970s to help reduce damage to soil structure.

323. These rubber half-tracks which cost about £900 and could be used with worn tyres were made in the early 1990s and were used with most popular tractors.

324. The SRT suspended rubber half-tracks designed by the Silsoe Research Institute could be used at speeds of up to15mph.

The Schrader tyre pump with a length of hose and pressure gauge using one of the engine pistons was an easier way to inflate the tyres. A threaded connector was screwed into a plug hole after removing one of the sparking plugs and the engine was run on the remaining cylinders while the selected piston inflated the tyres.

Small power take-off driven air compressors suitable for inflating tyres or paint spraying were also used in the early 1950s. Lawrence Edwards & Co made a 100psi capacity power take-off driven pump with 18ft of hose and a tyre pressure gauge which could be fitted to the power shaft in a matter of seconds. The Edwards pump advertised at £12.10s 'put an end to back breaking tyre pumping and could inflate a full set of four Fordson Dexta or Ferguson tyres in under six minutes'.

Farmfitters Ltd of Gerrards Cross in Buckinghamshire made the Jumbo power take-off driven pump which could be used to inflate tyres or pump liquids. The makers suggested that with suitable accessories the Jumbo pump could be used to spray fruit trees, spread liquid manure, transfer fuel from a barrel to the tractor tank, pump up tyres and blow dust and dirt from the engine radiator.

Soil compaction caused by the increasing weight of farm tractors was becoming a serious problem in the mid-1970s. Oversize tyres were some help but the much wider terra tyres with a larger footprint area were even better. The large ground contact area provided by crawlers and half-tracks was the best way to reduce soil damage but these tractors were painfully slow. Rubber half-tracks wrapped round the rear wheel and a smaller wheel in front of it were used in the days of the Ferguson 20 and this idea was revived in the late 1980s.

Kitco rubber half-tracks, which appeared in the early 1990s, were suitable for most makes of tractor and they could be fitted by two people in less than an hour. The tracks worked well in most conditions but there

325. The rubber-tracked 65E to 95E Claas Challengers with 310–410hp engines were launched in 1998.

was a risk of them coming off when reversing the tractor or making sharp turns on very dry land.

The Silsoe Research Institute built a rubber half-track conversion which they demonstrated at various field events in 1990. Test results indicated a 25 per cent increase in performance compared with a standard two-wheel drive tractor. The Silsoe (SRT) suspended rubber track was positively driven by a sprocket bolted to the rear wheel hub and a compensating system maintained constant track tension. A parallel link air-spring suspension system was claimed to give a comfortable ride. The tracks were exhibited at the 1991 Smithfield Show by Richard Stocks Ltd of Wisbech, Cambridgeshire, but they were not a commercial success.

Rubber-tracked crawlers were developed by Caterpillar in America and the first Challenger tractors were seen in Britain in 1989. The Track Marshall TM 200, also with rubber tracks, appeared in 1990 and John Deere introduced their rubber-tracked 8000 T series in 1997.

WINGET

Slater & England Ltd at Gloucester, who were well known for their Winget concrete mixing equipment, acquired Muir-Hill in 1959. The company, which was part of the Winget-Gloucester Group, introduced the Winget small tractor with a Lister diesel engine in the mid-1960s. It had a diff-lock, hydraulic linkage and adjustable wheel track. Winget became part of the Babcock and Wilcox Group in 1968.

326. The Winget tractor was, according to a 1967 advertisement, 'easy to handle and easy to buy'.

ZETOR

Tractors were being made in Czechoslovakia by Skoda, Praga and Wikov in the years between the two world wars. The Praga motor plough turned five furrows at a time and had the same 40–50hp petrol engine used for the Praga Grand motor car. Wikov tractors had separate carburettors for petrol and paraffin and belts were used to transmit power to the driving wheels.

A factory was opened at Brno in 1942 to produce aircraft parts and V2 rockets but it was bombed in 1944. The state-owned Zbrojovka Works took possession of the mostly destroyed factory premises and the first 2 cylinder water-cooled 26hp Zetor 25, made in November 1945, went into quantity production in March 1996. The Zetor 15 was added in 1949 but it was decided to develop the Zetor 25 and the smaller model was only made for a year. About 8,500 Zetor 25 tractors had been built by 1950 when production was moved to the nearby Works of Precise Engineering which became the Zetor works in 1952.

Zetor was the only tractor manufacturer in Czechoslovakia in 1960 and almost 160,000 model 25 tractors had been made at Brno when the new Unified Range I Zetor 3011 and 4011 were launched in 1962 with the 2011 added in 1963. Czechoslovakian tractors imported through Sheerness in Kent in 1965 between 1966 and 1969 were among the first Eastern European models sold in Britain. They were initially marketed by the Pride & Clarke Motor Cylcle Co and early models were supplied with a full tool kit and supply of spare parts! Within a year the Motokov Foreign Trade Corporation, through Skoda (GB) Ltd, were marketing the Unified Range I Zetor models in the UK. The London-based import company was advertising the Zetor 2011, 3011 and 4011 for £585, £650 and £795 respectively in 1967. The 3013 narrow version of the 3011 cost £670 and the four-wheel drive 3045 £779. The tractors had 2, 3 and 4 cylinder direct injection diesel engines rated at 23.5,

327. Optional equipment for the Zetor 3011 included an air compressor with a tyre inflator, front power take-off and a seat for a co-driver.

328. The Zetor Crystal 8011 had 8 forward and 2 reverse gears, a two-speed power take-off and a luxury safety cab.

32½ and 47 SAE hp, dual clutch, 10 forward and 2 reverse gears, diff-lock, expanding shoe brakes, live power take-off and category II Zetormatic hydraulics with draft control. Zetor 3011 sales literature explained that the design of the tractor incorporated everything which could be achieved at the time 'to afford the driver appropriate comfort, facilitate control and ensure the highest possible efficiency'. Instruments were 'neatly arranged in the driver's visual field' and a spring suspension seat could be adjusted with three positions available 'for drivers of different stature'. Variants of the Unified Range I (UR I) tractors included the 2023 crawler, the four-wheel drive 3045 and 4045 and the half-track 3016 and 4016 with slatted rubber belts running round the rear tyres and central rubber-tyred bogie wheel.

329. A balancer unit was added to dampen engine vibration on the 100hp 4 cylinder Zetor 10145 which, like the other tractors in the Crystal range, was re-styled in 1985.

The 5511 with new styling was added to the Brno range in 1966; it was the first Zetor model with front suspension springs on the stub axles which could be locked when required. The earlier models were improved and re-styled as the 2511, 3511 and 4511 in 1967. The 80hp Zetor Crystal 8011 and four-wheel drive 8045 introduced in 1972 shared many parts with the Ursus C-385. Both tractors were the result of a joint Czechoslovakian and Polish design and production programme with the engines made by Zetor and the back ends by Ursus. The Crystal was the first of a group of more powerful Zetor tractors: the two- and four-wheel drive 12011/12045 rated at 120hp appeared in 1974 and the high horse power range was completed in 1983 with the launch of the 100hp 10011/45 and the 16045 with a 6 cylinder 160hp engine.

The two-wheel drive Zetor 4712, 5711 and 6711 seven series with 45hp, 56hp and 65hp engines was also introduced in 1972. Zetor could not use a 4711 model number as it was the registered trademark of a perfume manufacturer. Variants of the seven series included the 4718, 5718 and 6718 with a safety cab, the four-wheel drive 5745 and 6745 without a cab also the 5748 and 6748 with cabs. The high horse power Zetor Crystal tractors were still in production in 1978 when the seven series was replaced by the nine series 4911, 5911/5945 and 6911/6945 with a safety cab included in the standard specification. There were tractors in the 50–160hp bracket when the improved 5011, 6011 and 7011 Zetor ten series was launched in 1980. The more powerful four-wheel drive tractors from the 8045 had torque multipliers and turbochargers were standard on the 12045 and 16045. The ten series cost from £4,293 to £16,480 plus carriage from Kings Lynn, power steering, trailer air brakes and a quiet cab with radio were included in the price. Press advertising suggested that farmers buying a new ten series tractor on easy terms would benefit from a painless low interest rate purchase, improved engines, reduced diesel costs and bare minimum maintenance costs.

The new Zetor 5245 four-wheel drive version of the 50hp 3 cylinder water-cooled 5211 was launched at the 1984 Smithfield Show. The existing Zetor Crystal and Unified 1 ranges were re-styled and modified with an increased capacity hydraulic system and an improved cab with a fully adjustable seat. The addition of the 5245 gave Zetor six two- and four-wheel drive UR I tractors in the 50–120hp range on the UK market. The new model had a dual clutch, 10 forward and 4 reverse gears with synchromesh on the 4th to 5th ratio and two-speed power take-off. This specification meant that the 5245 was comparable with its more expensive competitors but Zetor were still using power-assisted steering system and drum brakes.

The improved 60hp 6211 and four-wheel drive 6245 had the same gearbox as the 5245, a self-adjusting clutch, an independent 540/1000 power take-off with an air-operated clutch and hydraulic drum brakes. The front wheels were driven by a central shaft running from a transfer box to the front axle and drive could be engaged and disengaged on the move. The 6211 and 6245 were given an optional power boost when a British Holset turbocharger introduced in 1986 as a factory-fitted extra raised power output from 60hp to 75hp. There were still six two- and four-wheel drive Zetor tractors with 46–112hp engines on the UK market in 1986. The Unified series had 10 forward speeds and 2 reverse and the Crystal models had 16 forward and 8 reverse gears. The Zetor range had grown to 18 models by 1989 with tractors in approximate 10hp steps from the 50hp two-wheel drive 5211 to the four-wheel drive Zetor 14145 with a 6 cylinder 140hp engine.

The Zetor 9520/9540 introduced in 1990 was the first of a new range of turbocharged tractors made in Czechoslovakia. The 90hp four-wheel drive tractor had an air compressor to operate the electro-pneumatically engaged diff-lock and trailer braking system. An air line for inflating tyres was provided in the tool box and the air system could also be used for small power tools and paint spraying.

More new tractors were launched in 1992 and within a year there were 10 different models in the three Unified ranges with 50–140hp power units. The 3 cylinder 50hp two- and four- wheel drive 3320/3340 were the smallest of the UR I series with 60hp, 70hp and 84hp 4 cylinder models completing the group. Features of the

330. A clean water container for hand washing was provided in the Zetor 9540 cab.

331. The 84hp Zetor Super Turbo 7341 was the most powerful model in the UR I Super range launched in 1998.

UR I models included a 10 forward and 2 reverse synchromesh gearbox, an engine mounted hydraulic system pump, hydrostatic steering and multi-plate dry disc brakes. The two- and four-wheel drive UR II series consisted of 80hp and 90hp 4 cylinder models and the 6 cylinder four-wheel drive 11245, 12245 and 14245T rated at 105hp, 120hp and 140hp with 16 forward and 8 reverse gears. The 90hp turbocharged 9520/9540 was the only model in the UR III range. Zetor prices in 1993 ranged from £11,050 for the 3320 to £33,180 for the flagship 140hp 14245.

An agreement made with John Deere in 1993 gave the American company distribution rights for the 40–85hp Zetor models, using a green and yellow colour scheme and running deer badge. The supply of diesel engines made at Brno for other John Deere equipment was also included in the deal. A 'no frills' 6340E economy version of the 6340 with a standard cab, hydrostatic steering and a compressor was added in 1994. To avoid confusion the 6340 became the 7340.

The new UR I Super range with a restyled cab and bonnet was launched in 1998. The 4 cylinder 60hp, 70hp and 84hp tractor model numbers were changed from 4320/4340 to 4321/4341 and so on, and the 75hp 6340 E became the 6431 ECON. Hydraulic lift capacity was increased and transmission options included a 10 forward and 2 reverse manual change or a 10 forward and reverse shuttle gearbox.

Zetor tractors were still being distributed by the tractor and agricultural machinery division of Motokov UK at Kings Lynn in 1998. Models available included the UR III series with a choice of gearboxes, wet disc brakes and an air compressor. The two- and four-wheel drive 7520/40, 8520/40 and 9520/40 had 4 cylinder engines rated at 70hp, 80hp and 90hp. The flagship 1054 four-wheel drive model had a turbocharged and inter-cooled 105hp engine and the 70hp 7540E economy model had a no frills specification and a price to match. In common with badge engineering elsewhere in the farm tractor industry most of the Zetor models made at Brno were also sold in certain parts of the world as John Deere tractors.

The 4 cylinder 80–105hp Zetor Forterra UR 3 series with a completely re-designed cab and interior layout was introduced to farmers at the 1998 Smithfield Show. A new 110hp 6 cylinder UR 3 Forterra 11641 with a SAME Deutz-Fahr engine, a 24 forward and 18 reverse speed powershift transmission and elc hydraulics went into production in Czechoslovakia at the same time but this tractor was not available in the UK.

GLOSSARY

Badge engineering Equipment made by one company with another's badge and colour scheme.

Category I, II and III linkage Standard measurement specifications for the hydraulic three-point linkages. Category I is the smallest used for farm tractors (e.g. Ferguson TE 20).

Centrifugal clutch Two or three spring-loaded shoes with friction linings rotate with the crankshaft inside a hub on the output shaft. When engine speed reaches a certain level the shoes are thrown outwards centrifugally to grip the hub which is attached to a shaft connected to the gearbox.

Closed centre hydraulics The pump only provides sufficient oil to carry out the required functions; at other times it maintains circuit pressure but reduces oil flow to save power.

Clutch and brake steering Used for crawler tractors. The tracks are driven separately through a clutch unit with an integral brake and direction of travel is changed by using a lever to partly or fully disengage the drive to one track. A sharp turn is achieved with further movement of the lever which also applies a brake.

Cone clutch Rotating male and female cones operated with a pedal to engage or disengage drive from the engine to the gearbox. (e.g. Field Marshall tractors)

Controlled differential steering An alternative steering system for crawlers using a special design of epicyclic gearing and a brake for each track. When the brake is applied to one track it slows down and the speed of the opposite track is increased.

Donkey engine Petrol engine used to start a diesel engine.

Dual clutch Two separately controlled clutch discs are attached to the engine flywheel, the pedal is pushed part way down to disengage drive to the gearbox and fully down to stop the power take-off shaft.

Gasoline American term for petrol.

Hydrostatic steering A hydraulically operated steering system with no mechanical linkage between the steering wheel and the front wheels.

Independent pto clutch A separate clutch unit, usually operated hydraulically by lever and not linked to the main transmission clutch.

Inter-cooler This reduces the temperature of the air compressed by a turbocharger en route to the cylinders. The cooled air will be more dense and increase the effectiveness of the turbocharger. Water or air, depending on engine design, is used as a coolant.

Kerosene American term for petrol.

Live hydraulic system This remains in operation after the transmission clutch has been used to disengage drive to the wheels. The hydraulic pump may be mounted on and driven by the engine or it can be housed in the transmission system and controlled with an independent clutch or a dual clutch.

Live power take-off The power take-off shaft continues turning when the drive to the transmission is disengaged. It is controlled by an independent or a dual clutch

Lower link sensing Changes in draft detected through the lower links are relayed to the draft control valve to raise or lower the implement.

Open centre hydraulics The pump provides a constant flow of oil but pressure is varied according to need.

Orchard tractor Narrower than a standard model and often equipped with guards to deflect tree branches away from the tractor.

Overhead-valve engine The valves are located in the cylinder head above the pistons.

PAVT rear wheels Power adjusted variable track. Engine is used to vary wheel track width after releasing a mechanism locking the wheel centre to the rim.

Plow An American term for furrow – tractors were rated as a one-plow, two plow, etc. model until the late 1940s. ('Bottom' is an alternative American term for plow.)

Pony engine An American term for donkey engine.

Power-assisted steering A mechanical linkage is used with a hydraulic ram to reduce the effort required from the driver.

Regular tractor An American term used for a basic specification tractor, equivalent to a standard model in Britain.

Side-valve engine An engine with the valves at one side of the cylinder block.

Rowcrop tractor Generally a small tractor with adjustable wheel track to suit different row widths. American rowcrop models usually have a single or twin-vee front wheels. In recent years some high horse power American tractors have been classed as rowcrop tractors.

Styled tractor Tractors built mainly since the mid-1930s with a sheet metal bonnet, radiator grille and mud-guards or wings are described as styled.

Systems tractor Has front and rear implement attachment points and sometimes a load carrying platform. Most can be operated in either direction and have root harvesters and other large machines attached around them.

Tool carrier A three- or four-wheeled frame, normally with rear mounted engine and transmission at the rear. Implements are mounted on the frame. Some models also have a load carrying platform on the frame.

Turbocharger This is a blower fan driven by exhaust gases which runs at speeds of approximately 80,000rpm to force extra air into the engine cylinders and increase power output. The air is compressed, making it more dense but also increasing its temperature.

Unitary construction A tractor assembled by joining the engine to the transmission without the use of a supporting frame.

Unstyled tractor Generally made before the 1930s, tractors with no covering over the radiator, steering column and engine and were known as unstyled tractors.

Vineyard tractor Narrower than an orchard tractor it is sometimes less than 3ft wide.

Wastegate turbocharger A turbocharger which operates normally at the lower end of the engine speed range but reduces the speed of the turbocharger impellor at high engine speeds.

INDEX